Inventing: How The Masters Did It is a book that should be of genuine interest to everyone. The histories of the six master inventors covered in depth in the book are fascinating and exciting stories of the struggles, failures and successes of six human beings whose inventions have had a major impact on the lives of all of us. The book gives a most enlightening insight into the real-life operations of the process of invention and innovation. It should be required reading especially for those who are seriously concerned about today's problems and the need to invent solutions for these problems, and particularly for those who would propose that this be accomplished by Governmental action." — Edward J. Brenner

Executive Director
Association for the Advancement
of Invention & Innovation
Former Commissioner, U.S. Patent
Office

"An inventor in his own right, Dr. Vanderbilt is highly qualified to evaluate the methods used by eminent inventors of the past, and to suggest how such know-how can be utilized by present-day and future inventors." — Per K. Frolich

Past President, American Chemical
Society
Former Chief Scientist of the U.S.
Army Chemical Corps

INVENTING:

HOW THE MASTERS DID IT

Byron M. Vanderbilt

Moore Publishing Company
Durham, North Carolina

Library of Congress Catalog Card Number: 74-14959

ISBN 0-87716-054-6

CONTENTS

FOREWORD

"Nothing new under the sun" is an oft-quoted expression that suggests the fact that an invention is rarely wholly new. It follows that each inventor assimilates one or more ideas and builds upon experience.

"Necessity is the mother of invention" is only half true because the necessity is not always realized until the invention has been marketed. Of course, it remains true that need provides a strong inventive impulse.

The inventive mind can be fascinating. It is not limited to human cerebration nor is it equated to intellect. Indeed, apes invent but their inventions are dead-end. They do not contribute to a body of knowledge from which their successors may borrow and to which they may add. Such an on-going contribution is necessary for progression.

Romans played with steam-propelled toys long before Fulton changed novelty into industrial reality.

Bone and stone tools and weapons were used long after copper was discovered. It remained for Asiatics only 5000 years ago to usher in the Bronze Age.

Early in the Bronze Age the wheel was invented but practical vehicles were still far from being a fact.

Explosives were known to ancient Chinese, however, little practical use was made of them until much later in military and industrial uses in the nineteenth century.

As means of communication enabled one inventor to transmit his knowledge to another, inventions and experiences rapidly accumulated. The great explosion of ideas during the Renaissance began the ever increasing change in our lives. Much credit must be given to inventors of the Middle Ages, however, both for innovation and continuation of ideas. Just as the Wright Brothers followed Langley, Leonardo da Vinci surely followed unknown contributors.

At any rate, the infusion of new thoughts added impetus to rapidly communicated experiences and led to the Industrial Revolution which changed the world forever.

In this book, Dr. Vanderbilt picks up on some of the greatest inventors, describes their inventions and investigates the mentality that led to their greatness. It would be presumptuous for me to paraphrase his text; rather I endorse it, and praise its purpose.

Much of its purpose is to acquaint the reader with inventors. Especially should young people make this acquaintance, because youth is nothing without invention and innovation.

As a physician and surgeon I never cease to be amazed at the innovation that lies around every corner, often overlooked until pointed out by some creative mind. Such an idea may not be new under the sun and may or may not be born of necessity, but it does enhance the lot of mankind and make the world a better place.

On a personal note, inventions have improved my life in a way unsuspected a few months ago. They brought author and publisher together for the mutual purpose of inventing this book. Knowing Dr. Vanderbilt as an inventor and author is second only to knowing him as a friend.

Eugene V. Grace, M. D.
Publisher

From Frances Miller's *Thomas A. Edison*.

Throngs pay last respects to Edison.

Edison's body lay in state for two days in the Edison Laboratory at West Orange, New Jersey. Throngs passed by the open casket day and night, first two abreast and later four as it became obvious that all who had stood in waiting lines for hours could not be admitted. The first hour of the first day was reserved for Edison laboratory and factory personnel.

PREFACE

The underlying thesis upon which this book has been written is that a study of the backgrounds and research methods of great inventors can yield valuable information. Certainly in other fields of endeavor, contemporaries benefit from the methods used by their predecessors. In like manner shouldn't scientific and engineering research and development personnel, teachers, and students benefit from an intimate knowledge of the lives of the great inventors of the past? Other writers have employed this approach in varying degrees in studying how various inventions were made. However, the dimensions of the inventor's background, personal characteristics, and research methods have not been emphasized sufficiently in such studies.

The six inventors selected for this study did most of their work prior to World War I, which is a good chronological landmark indicating when the lone inventor largely gave way to directed and team research and development. All continued to invent even after success had been achieved from one or more outstanding inventions. All were Americans except Nobel and he was an internationalist. Thus, the six lived and worked in nearly analogous environments.

The first six chapters are biographical. Chapter 7 deals with backgrounds, characteristics, and methods of research which were largely common with our eminent inventors. The United States patent system has often been cited as the primary reason for the burst of technical innovation which took place in this country during the nineteenth century. How did the subject inventors fare with the Patent Office and the courts? This question is answered in Chapter 8. Chapter 9 describes briefly other inventors who have used successfully the methods summarized in Chapter 7. Finally, conclusions drawn from the six case histories are compared to those ascribed to psychologists and others dealing with the subject of creativity.

The biographical chapters should be a broader interest than only for those interested in invention. In spite of the fact that technology has often been a greater factor in shaping our nation's future than have acts of statesmen and the military, the history of technology is seriously neglected in our schools and libraries. Whereas in 1931 Emil Ludwig described Edison as the greatest American of the century (*American Magazine*, December 1931), few contemporary inventors are known to the public. Whereby those high in government or the military, corporation officers, university officials, and the like can use their respective offices to propel themselves into prominence, an inventor must create his greatness entirely on his own.

In writing the six biographies I have relied largely on published literature. Although an attempt has been made to read all significant books written about these great inventors, primary publications in periodicals and patents of the six have been utilized where pertinent.

I wish to acknowledge the cooperation and generous assistance of the library staffs of the University of North Carolina, Chapel Hill. Use of the various libraries at Duke University and the United States Patent Office, as well as gracious help from many people located there, is also gratefully acknowledged. Information, copies of photographs, and allowance of quotations from publications by numerous authors, publishers, and companies are sincerely appreciated. To my wife, Elizabeth, who has withstood many inconveniences as I pursued information for this book, I extend many thanks. Very special recognition and gratitude are due Carolyn Doughty of Chapel Hill who has not only handled the stenographic work relating to this treatise but has offered many helpful editorial suggestions as well.

Byron M. Vanderbilt

June 1974

Chapel Hill, North Carolina

Chapter 1

Charles Goodyear

New England, the six most northeasterly states of the United States, was the most prosperous part of pre-Civil War America. The Puritan leaders had been university-trained men, and universal education became a tradition in that area. The Industrial Revolution came to New England in the early 19th century and soon "Yankee notions" were being peddled in the middle and southern states. The cold Labrador current made the New England coastline the best fishing area of the eastern seaboard. The whaling fleet operating out of these ports spurred ship building; this resulted in the development of the clipper ships, the fastest sailing ships afloat in the 1840's. The New England environment nourished greatness as evidenced by such inventors as Eli Whitney and Elias Howe, and statesmen, as Daniel Webster and the Adams family.

In 1800 in the state of Connecticut two babies were born who were destined to have profound effects on their country and the world. One was John Brown, the abolitionist leader; the other was Charles Goodyear, who invented the vulcanization of rubber. Both were alike in that each felt the Lord had delegated him to accomplish a certain mission in life. Beyond this the two were totally different. Whereas Brown used violence in attempting to gain his objectives, Goodyear sought his goals by hard work and personal deprivation. However, every school child knows of John Brown. As to Goodyear, if anyone knows the name at all, it is likely associated with that of a leading tire manufacturer.*

Charles Goodyear, the Connecticut Yankee, was the eldest child of six of Amasa Goodyear of New Haven. The father was a manufacturer who specialized in products not previously made in the young nation. In 1805 the family moved to Naugatuck, Connecticut in order to utilize the water power there. Amasa manufactured buttons, utensils, farm equipment, and clocks. He was the first to manufacture pearl buttons in the United States and he patented and made spring steel hay and manure forks to replace those made of wrought iron. He developed also an improved scythe.

Charles received an average elementary and secondary school education based on the standards of the day which were relatively high in Connecticut due, in part, to the proximity of Yale College. At the age of 12 he attended a nearby private school and, although one of the youngest pupils, he was one of the best. The Goodyear children also had tutors from time to time. The boy played little, preferring to use his free time for reading. Charles did not attend college. In the early 1800's such training was primarily for ministers, lawyers, and doctors. Although Charles at one time considered the ministry, being the eldest he was expected to take part in his father's business. This he did at an early age. At age 17 he went to Philadelphia to serve a four-year apprenticeship with a large importer of hardware. In 1821 he returned to Naugatuck and his father's firm became A. Goodyear and Son, manufacturer and marketer of steel forks and other articles

*The Goodyear Tire and Rubber Company was founded by Frank A. Seiberling in Akron, Ohio in August 1898. Although the company was named after Charles Goodyear, none of the Goodyear family was connected with the new company.

for the farm trade. The business flourished and the father was said to respect his son's judgment in their business affairs.

In 1826 the family business was expanded to include another son, Robert, and renamed A. Goodyear and Sons. To utilize Charles' experience from his apprenticeship, and to increase outlets for their manufactured products, the elder son returned to Philadelphia to open the first store in United States for marketing domestic hardware. He was now married and the father of two children. Charles did not like working with machinery and found the retail business more to his liking. He continued a partnership interest in A. Goodyear and Sons. In 1830 the family business suffered severe losses due to an over-extension of credit and the national financial crash of that year. Subsequent liquidation resulted in the Goodyears losing all of their physical assets plus the patent rights to manufacture steel forks.

The Goodyears were unable to satisfy all their debts and in 1834 Charles was thrown into debtors' prison where he remained for three months. During the next 10 years he was to spend frequent stays in such quarters. Prison life allowed him long hours for reflection. He decided that his best opportunities lay in the field of invention. This was to his liking and establishing a new business was next to impossible since unsatisfied creditors would seize any physical assets which he might assemble. Already Goodyear had obtained four patents which dealt with such diverse subjects as buttons, a valve for drawing molasses, an air pump, and boats built upon closed metal tubes. Manufacture of some small articles in the home provided a bare existence. His wife assisted in spite of her many babies. Of the five children which followed the first two, four died before reaching four years of age.

Columbus, in describing one of his voyages to the New World, referred to "bouncing balls used by Haitian natives." Archeological investigations of Mayan culture have confirmed that rubber balls were used at least as early as the 11th century. In 1735 members of the French Academy of Sciences obtained samples of rubber from natives of the Amazon valley and reported on the origin of this elastic material. The natives called it, cahutchu, derived from caa, meaning wood, and o-chu, meaning tears. In French the name is still caoutchouc, and in German, kautschuk. The famous English scientist Joseph Priestley observed that when this natural gum material was rubbed over pencil markings and such, they were erased; hence he named it rubber. With the advent of many rubber-like substances prepared synthetically, this broad class of materials is now known scientifically as elastomers. However, the term *rubber* continues to be used broadly for both natural and synthetic rubbery materials. The American Society for Testing Materials defines rubber as "a natural or synthetic material that can be, or is already, vulcanized to a state in which it has high extensibility and forcible, quick retraction."

Natural rubber is obtained as a white milky liquid, called latex, from certain types of plants when the surface is cut. It originated in the tropical jungles of South America and Africa. Latex contains 30-50% rubber dispersed as fine particles in the aqueous medium. Based on total solids, the hydrocarbon rubber constitutes 92-94%, with the other 6-8% consisting of resins, proteins, and other complex bodies. The nonhydrocarbon materials keep the rubber dispersed and protect it against degradation by air, sunlight, and the like.

Rubber became an article of commerce in the United States about 1823. The first sale of rubber articles were

4

rubber shoes imported to Boston from Brazil. Although crude and clumsy, since there was no competitive material so waterproof, the shoes sold for three to five dollars a pair. The manufacture of rubber bottles and shoes by the natives of Para, a northern state of Brazil which includes the mouth of the Amazon, had become a thriving business. Rubber latex was collected and used the same day for preparing such articles. The latter operation, usually carried out by the wife and daughters of a family, consisted of applying a series of latex coatings onto clay or wooden forms held on the end of sticks. After each successive coating the article was held for about one-half minute over a smoky fire of wasson palm nuts. The heat from the fire precipitated the rubber from its latex and evaporated most of the moisture. The ingredients of the smoky flames also had a mild curing effect on the rubber since articles so prepared were not tacky. Preparation of a shoe required about 25 coats. After standing for four or five days, the clay forms were removed by crushing and washing. Wooden forms, with a precoating of clay to allow slippage of the finished article, were usually used when making shoes. The Indians received 10-15 cents per pair of shoes exported from Para.

With crude rubber selling for about 5 cents per pound and rubber shoes bringing several dollars per pair, it was not surprising that enterprising Yankees were attracted to this new business. Since rubber was exported as smoked articles or as crude lumps located in the Amazon valley, the New Englander had to dissolve the rubber in a solvent in order to employ it as a liquid coating. Turpentine was the solvent used. In 1832 the Roxbury India* Rubber

*Rubber was called India rubber by Priestley to identify it as coming from the East Indies, the source of the wild rubber imported into England at that time. In the United States it was originally called Indian rubber. The common name became India Rubber, and the India part of the terminology was not dropped until about the turn of the century.

Company was set up in Roxbury, a village adjacent to Boston. Cloth was coated with rubber solution and used in the manufacture of shoes, life preservers, coats, caps, and wagon covers.

Edwin Chaffee, one of the partners of this first American rubber company, was an ingenious mechanical inventor. He was the first to use carbon black in rubber, having compounded rubber with lampblack in an attempt to replace patent leather. He built not only a machine for coating cloth with rubber solution but also developed what are known today as the rubber mill and the calender. A mastication machine had been previously invented by Thomas Hancock, the Englishman who is credited with having started in 1820 the first rubber factory in the world. Hancock's machine consisted of a hollow cylinder with studded teeth in which a spiked tooth roller turned. Both Hancock's machine and Chaffee's roller mill were not only used to soften the rubber by mastication but also to mix therein compounding ingredients such as clays, metal oxides, pigments, tars, oils, etc. However, it was Chaffee's mill, consisting of two horizontal rolls running in close contact at unequal speeds, that carried the day. One big advantage over Hancock's machine was that the rolls of the rubber mill could be heated with steam or cooled with water, thus controlling as desired the temperature of the rubber being mixed. As today's calender, Chaffee's machine was with the three rolls placed one above the other.

The apparent success of the Roxbury Company caused others to undertake rubber manufacturing. Stock issues were eagerly bought by speculators who visioned big profits. Whereas rubber-coated fabrics had been reasonably successful in the mild British climate, their use during the hot summers and cold winters in the New England-New York area was a different story. Rubber-coated apparel became rigid and hard when exposed in the winter and soft and sticky in the summer. The public soon had their fill of such materials and company after company in the rubber trade failed. Not a single American rubber company survived the rubber panic including the Roxbury Company. However, rubber shoes, bottles, and crude toys continued to be imported from Brazil where the Indian method of smoking successive thin layers of rubber deposited from latex resulted in products which were much less tacky under warm conditions than rubber articles made by his supposedly more intelligent brethren in factories.

It is not surprising that Charles Goodyear, the man who had resolved that invention would be his life's work, should be attracted to the new material, rubber. Paramount in his interest was the fact that here was the only material capable of making air-tight and water-tight compartments which could serve as life preservers in water. His first work in the rubber field dealt with life preservers and when he died in 1860, his main experimental equipment for rubber research in his home was a large water tank for testing such equipment.

In 1834 Goodyear purchased a life preserver from the salesroom of the Roxbury India Paper Company in New York City. Back in Philadelphia he decided that he could improve on the valve which Roxbury was using for inflating the preserver, and he returned to New York hoping to sell his improvement. Instead of a sale, Goodyear received a mournful story from the store manager that the whole rubber industry was on the brink of disaster unless some means could be found for decreasing the sticky nature of rubber at summer temperatures. He was told that the Roxbury Company had to bury $30,000 worth of rubber shoes because of their tackiness and foul odor.

Goodyear was astonished that the manufacture of rubber goods was in such a sorry state. Returning to Philadelphia he had an opportunity to brood more on the subject; he was lodged in debtors' prison. Goodyear, knowing little or nothing about the properties of rubber except what he had learned from his contact in New York, thought that tackiness was the only difficulty to overcome. He resolved to do this with dry powders which he would incorporate into the rubber.

Luckily the cost of materials for carrying out research on rubber was low. Turpentine was used to soften the rubber so it could be mixed with other materials and processed into shapes. Goodyear's only laboratory for the next year was the family kitchen; his only source of power, his hands. He cut the crude rubber into small pieces, kneaded them with turpentine, mixed in compounding ingredients as desired, and then sheeted the mixture out on a marble slab using his wife's rolling pin. Since a young man, Goodyear had been plagued with periodic severe indigestion pains. It is likely that working in an atmosphere containing turpentine vapors and handling rubber which contained the solvent added to the discomforts of his dyspepsia, as the disease was known in those days. One can be thankful that he did not have available coal tar naphtha, a highly aromatic and more toxic rubber solvent, which was becoming available to rubber manufacturers in England about that time.

After mixing rubber with a number of finely divided powders, Goodyear concluded that magnesia (magnesium oxide) was best for removing the tackiness. He was able to adhere such a mixture softened with turpentine to glazed, closely woven cotton fabric by pressing them together with an iron roller. With the financial backing of Ralph B. Steele, a former boyhood companion, Goodyear, his wife, and occasional extra labor produced a few hundred pairs of rubber shoes during the winter of 1835-36. The work shop was a small cottage which also served as the family residence after their move to New Haven. The shoes were stored to allow further testing before being put on the market, but on the advent of warm weather they became a mass of sticky gum.

Goodyear now reasoned that the tackiness of the rubber may have been due to the nonvolatile portion of the turpentine solvent. The basis of this reasoning was that shoes produced by the Brazilian Indians using latex were not nearly as tacky as those using turpentine solutions. Furthermore it was known that the nonvolatile content of turpentine increases with age. Goodyear was able to locate several drums of rubber tree "sap" which had been exported from Para in drums. Although he found the latex largely coagulated on receipt, he was able to prepare a few shoes from it as he had done with turpentine solutions. He found them equally tacky. Thus he concluded correctly that the tackiness of rubber is an inherent property.

Goodyear publicized his "improved process" for manufacturing rubber articles and when failure resulted, he not only lost the support of Mr. Steele, but that of his friends. Feeling there was no further chance of local support in New Haven, Goodyear sold most of the furniture which the family possessed, placed his wife and children in a cheap dwelling in the country, and went to New York City seeking further support. There he was provided a room by J. W. Sexton where he lived and continued his experiments. A drug firm, Silas Carle and Nephew, supplied him with small quantitites of chemicals. We do not know what arrangements Goodyear had with his early supporters, but no doubt they were to share in any successful developments.

Goodyear now found that if he boiled his rubber-magnesia compound in lime water (solution of calcium hydroxide), it appeared " to have the effect of tanning"*, thus making the rubber surface less tacky and with less tendency to flow. However he soon found that the tanning effect was lost if goods so treated were washed with a weak acid, even vinegar. He then tried unsuccessfully mixing quicklime with the rubber instead of using magnesia. Also he tried to decrease the surface tack by coating with metals. In one case where he had applied an imperfect bronze coating, he removed the bronze by means of nitric acid. The rubber specimen became discolored and was discarded. "In reflecting on this circumstance some days afterwards, it occurred to the writer (Goodyear) that he had not sufficiently examined the unusual appearance of the article." On locating and examining the rubber specimen, he found it nontacky and leatherlike.

This chance observation led to the first major step forward in Goodyear's search to improve the qualities of rubber. Although not an adequate answer, it was of utmost importance in that he had obtained his best results by a *chemical* method rather than by mixing in large quantities of inert compounding ingredients.** Goodyear knew that animal skins were converted by vegetable tanning agents from their putrescible state to stable, stronger, more abrasion-resistant leathers. He knew that animal fats could be converted by lye to soap. He knew that acids attacked and dissolved some metals. He knew quicklime attacked his hands whereas magnesia did not. Although no chemist and admittedly so, Goodyear had contacts with Yale and its famous Professor Benjamin Silliman, one of the few academic scientists in America interested in applied

---

*Any quotation, unless otherwise stated, is from Goodyear's book *Gum-Elastic* (1).

**In case of Goodyear's rubber compounds containing magnesia, as high as an equal weight of magnesia per weight of rubber had been used.

chemistry (2). From supplemental reading and discussions with Silliman, Goodyear no doubt learned that science knew little about rubber except that by analysis it had been shown that it contained about 90% combined carbon, the remaining 10% being largely hydrogen. The analysts at that time had missed the 7% or so of nonrubber in natural rubber and that these proteins and other nonhydrocarbons were responsible for rubber "spoiling" and developing a foul odor. Goodyear, and apparently others, were not surprised that rubber deteriorated with age since it was a plant product.

The lowly South American Indians had done better with rubber than had the scientists. However, the white man could not adopt the technology developed through the centuries in the case of rubber as he had done in the case of tanning skins to leather since at that time, there was no successful means of shipping rubber latex long distances. Thus Goodyear logically concluded that the best approach in finding how to make rubber more suitable for personal and industrial uses was to experiment and experiment, observe results closely, and pray that the answer would come. Also he concluded that he, a nonscientist, was as qualified as anyone else to do this.

Following his observation of the effect of aqueous nitric acid on rubber, Goodyear developed the use of gaseous nitric acid, which of course contained some nitrogen dioxide. An abandoned rubber factory on Staten Island was obtained for operations. However, the financial depression beginning in the spring of 1836 caused him to lose the financial support that he had. Late that summer he obtained a small loan from a friend and visited the officials of the Roxbury rubber factory which was now idle. Goodyear was allowed to use the equipment there and some rubber shoes were made using an improved method of fabrication and the acid gas curing process. Two licenses to use the acid process were sold. The few thousand dollars obtained allowed Goodyear to have his aged parents, who were in dire financial straits, join his household at Boston. However differences arose between Goodyear and the Roxbury manager, resulting in the inventor leaving the Roxbury works in 1838. Subsequently he was able to move his operations to the Eagle Rubber Company at Woburn, a town about 10 miles northeast of Boston. The Eagle Company was largely shut down at that time but continued to make a few rubber articles.

The owner-manager at the Eagle works was Nathaniel Hayward, an illiterate man who couldn't even sign his name. The original company had failed in April 1838 and Hayward, as one of the stockholders, took over the plant. Hayward signed a contract to work for Goodyear for $800 per year and turned the Eagle factory over to him to use. He agreed also to impart to Goodyear all the knowledge he knew relating to rubber.

Goodyear learned for the first time that Hayward followed the practice of filtering the turpentine which he used through a bed of sulfur. Sulfur has an appreciable solubility in hydrocarbons. At times Hayward had dusted sulfur over the surface of his rubber-coated fabrics and exposed them to direct sunlight. He explained later that he got the idea of exposing white rubber goods to the fumes of sulfur "to make them whiter, taking the hint from having seen straw bonnets bleached in this manner." Hayward had the ingredients for vulcanization but failed to recognize that in the sulfur treatment of the rubber surface followed by exposure to sun rays, it was the heat from the sun, and not some magic solarization effect, which caused some curing of the surface by the sulfur.

Goodyear knew nothing about what sulfur might do to

rubber, but at that stage he tried everything which showed any promise. When he took charge of the Woburn factory, he ordered that every batch of rubber mixed should contain several parts of sulfur and should also be subjected to his acid gas curing process. Hayward had only used traces of sulfur in rubber compounds, and he warned Goodyear that the higher proportion in personal apparel could lead to skin irritation and objectionable odor.

On Goodyear's insistence Hayward applied for a patent on his rubber-sulfur combination. The patent was applied for on November 23, 1838 and granted February 24, 1839.* Claims included use of sulfur in turpentine solutions of rubber, incorporation of sulfur into the rubber by means of a mixing mill, and spreading sulfur on the surface followed by Goodyear's acid process. In the patent it is stated that the sulfur causes the gum "to dry more perfectly." Hayward appointed Goodyear as his agent to obtain the patent and assigned it to him for one hundred dollars when granted plus certain future payments.

After Goodyear took over the Woburn factory, the two men began turning out a variety of rubber goods including life preservers, beds, coats, carriage cloths — and mailbags, a 1,500 order from the U. S. Post Office Department. Goodyear considered this recognition by the Government as the final step in his rise on the ladder of success. Unfortunately he publicized his apparent good luck in the newspapers.

In filling the mail bag order Goodyear went all out to use thick layers of rubber mixed with a variety of pigments in order to give them a leather-like appearance. The mail bags were hung in the factory for a few weeks for seasoning and inspection. Inspection was easy; in a short

*See Reference (6).

time the rubber was so soft it was dripping from the handles of the bags. Most of the several thousand life preservers which had been sold were returned for credit. It was now apparent that even with several parts of sulfur mixed into the rubber, the acid gas treatment would penetrate only very thin layers of rubber, and that certain pigments accelerated the softening and deterioration of rubber. Goodyear's period of relative prosperity had been short. All of his private holdings were confiscated and sold to meet his debts.

Goodyear had now spent about four years trying to overcome the poor properties of rubber so that its unique properties of waterproofing, a barrier for gases, and elasticity could be utilized. The people of the Boston area wanted nothing more to do with rubber or people working with it. Millions of dollars had been lost since the first American rubber factory began operations in 1832 and not a single factory was in successful operation in 1838. Goodyear's friends and even his faithful wife now urged him to give up his fruitless search and undertake a respectful enterprise. However, Goodyear could not stop his pursuit to tame rubber. It was that inner urge which most inventors have that will not admit defeat, as well as, in Goodyear's case, the firm conviction that the Lord expected him to improve the properties of rubber so that His people could use it to protect themselves from diseases caused by exposure to dampness and from loss of life due to drowning.

Goodyear proceeded to shut down his operations at the Woburn factory. He had to dismiss Hayward and all other paid personnel. The family turned to making a few small articles for which there was still some demand. Goodyear continued his experiments using primarily the family kitchen for his laboratory. In January 1839 the long-sought "accidental experiment", which Goodyear felt would come if he persisted long enough, happened. Following is Goodyear's own story on how one of the most important inventions in history was achieved and his explanation on why it happened to him. (1)

The inventor now applied himself alone, with unabated ardor and diligence, to detect the cause of his misfortune, and, if possible, to retrieve the lost reputation of his invention; and, as had happened on former occasions, he had hardly time enough to realize the extent of his embarrassment, before he became intently engaged with another experiment, and his mind buoyant with new hopes and expectations; which, as it afterwards proved, were to be, for this time at least, more than realized.

While on one of the visits above alluded to, at the factory at Woburn, and at the dwelling where he stopped whenever he visited the manufactory at Woburn, the inventor made some experiments to ascertain the effect of heat upon the same compound that had decomposed in the mail-bags and other articles. He was surprised to find that the specimen, being carelessly brought in contact with a hot stove, charred like leather. He endeavored to call the attention of his brother, as well as some other individuals who were present, and who were acquainted with the manufacture of gum-elastic, to this effect, as remarkable, and unlike any before known, since gum-elastic always melted when exposed to a high degree of heat. The occurrence did not at the time appear to them to be worthy of notice; it was considered as one of the frequent appeals that he was in the habit of making, in behalf of some new experiment.

He however directly inferred that if the process of charring could be stopped at the right point, it might divest the gum of its native adhesiveness throughout, which would make it better than the native gum. Upon further trial with heat, he was further convinced of the correctness of this inference by finding that India rubber could not be melted in boiling sulphur at any heat ever so great, but always charred.

He made another trial of heating a similar fabric, before an open fire. The same effect, that of charring the gum, followed; but there were further and very satisfactory indications of ultimate success, in producing the desired result, as upon the edge of the charred portions of the fabric, there appeared a line, or border, that was not charred, but perfectly cured.

He now removed with his family to Lynn, in order that he might have access to the steam power of Messrs. Baldwin & Haskins, for the purpose of trying experiments in vulcanizing by steam.

A few weeks after, he removed from Lynn to Woburn, where he now pursued his inquiries and experiments for some months quite alone, until the desired result was obtained. On ascertaining to a certainty that he had found the object of his search, and much more, and that the new substance was proof against cold, and the solvents of native gum, he felt himself amply repaid for the past, and quite indifferent as to the trials of the future.

The facts have been stated precisely as they occurred in reference to the discovery of the acid gas, as well as the vulcanizing process. The incidents attending the discovery of both have a strong resemblance, so much so, they may be considered parallel cases. It being now known that the results of the vulcanizing process are produced by means, and in a manner, which would not have been anticipated from any reasoning on the subject, and that they have not yet been satisfactorily accounted for, it has been sometimes asked how the inventor came to make the discovery. The answer has already been given. It may be added, that he was many years seeking to accomplish this object, and that he allowed nothing to escape his notice that related to the subject. Like the falling of an apple, it was suggestive of an important fact to one whose mind was previously prepared to draw an inference from any occurrence which might favor the object of his research. While the inventor admits that these discoveries were not the result of *scientific* chemical investigations, he is not willing to admit that they were the result of what is commonly termed accident; he claims them to be the result of the closest application and observation.

The discoloring and charring of the specimens proved nothing, and discovered nothing of value, but quite the contrary; for in the first instance, as stated of the acid gas improvement, the specimen acted upon was thrown away as worthless, and left for some time; in the latter instance, the specimen that was charred was in like manner disregarded by others.

It may, therefore, be considered as one of those cases where the leading of the Creator providentially aids his creatures by what are termed accidents, to attain those things which are not attainable by the powers of reasoning he has conferred on them.

There has been some question as to the location where "the specimen, being carelessly brought in contact with a hot stove, charred like leather." The popular version was that it was in the family kitchen. Barker points out that it could not have been in the family kitchen or the Woburn factory but rather "the dwelling where he stopped whenever he visited the manufactory" (3). Goodyear lived 10 or more miles from the Eagle factory and when working there usually boarded at the home of Elizabeth Emerson. This lady apparently ran a boarding house since members of the Eagle India Rubber Company stayed there from time to time and used her living room as sort of a hotel lobby to congregate. It is known that Goodyear did experiments in the good lady's home. She later testified in court that, "He put his rubber in oven of my stove, heated rubber on a fire shovel, and nailed specimens on outside of my house."

Goodyear found that his heated rubber-sulfur compound was not only nontacky when hot but remained flexible when exposed to the January subfreezing weather. It was insoluble in solvents which would dissolve the raw rubber. He called his new product by such names as heated gum, fireproof gum, and metallic gum-elastic. The last was a corollary relative to the change of some metals by heat; for example, the production of steel from pig iron containing the proper proportion of carbon. Goodyear had been searching for a chemical cure of rubber since he had discovered the effect of nitric acid on rubber. He used, no doubt, the manufacture of leather as sort of a prototype and expected to get his rubber cure, as in tanning, at room temperature. This he did with nitric acid and expected to do the same with sulfur.

Even if Goodyear had been a highly trained chemist of his day, he would have known little more about the chemical reactions of rubber than he did. We know now that the natural rubber molecule is made up of a series of isoprene units, C_5H_8, attached one to another as if by polymerization. It may be represented graphically as:

$$-(CH_2-\overset{\overset{\displaystyle CH_3}{|}}{C}=CH-CH_2-)_x$$

We also know that the reason rubber can be vulcanized is due to its unsaturation, *i.e.*, the presence of double bonds. The nature of chemical bonds of organic compounds was a complete unknown in 1840. It was not until 1858 that Kekulé determined that carbon was "tetratomic" and had four "affinity units". The concepts of organic chemistry then moved forward rapidly. In 1864 Crum Brown wrote the structural formula of ethylene with a double bond, and in the same year Lothar Meyer described ethylene as being "unsaturated".

The exact mechanism by means of which sulfur converts natural rubber and synthetic elastomers to crosslinked compounds is still unknown. There is one or more sulfur atoms in each crosslink. A simple way to visualize the chemistry of vulcanization is that sulfur atoms become attached to some of the carbons attached by double bonds and these sulfur atoms further combine with similar carbon atoms of one or more other rubber molecules. Since the valence of sulfur in carbon-sulfur compounds is usually two or four, a sulfur atom is capable of reacting with two or more rubber molecules. This is a simplified version of vulcanization, but the end result is the same as more sophisticated mechanisms. It was not until the 20th century that Baekeland, Staudinger, and others showed that decreasing the solubility of polymers by so-called curing was a chemical crosslinking of long polymer chains (4).

One would think that Goodyear's discovery of vulcanization would have ended his long struggle. Instead it marked the beginning of five of the bitterest years of his life. Wolf describes these next few years dramatically (5):

> During the next few years, before he was able to prove himself right, Goodyear was to encounter adversity that would have turned the heart of Job, crushed any but fanatic or fool. The whole history of invention contains not another story such as his. He starved and suffered, experimented alternately in jail cell and sickbed, sold his children's schoolbooks to buy food, was constantly ridiculed and called crazy. A neighbor's testimony tells of a family going into the fields to glean fuel; a family with no money for bread, the children digging half grown potatoes for the sake of something to eat; of the inventor's two-year-old son dying and being hauled to his grave in a wagon, his poverty-stricken father trudging behind the sad procession.
>
> The indifference which Goodyear encountered is easily understood. The great losses which the entire community had suffered in rubber manufacture, the length of time he had spent in what appeared to be fruitless efforts to accomplish anything with the gum, the recent mailbag disaster, and the inventor's utter destitution were hardly calculated to convince anyone that the new discovery was any more valuable than the previous ones.

Goodyear at first credited his vulcanization as being due primarily to the heating step and felt that there were likely other materials as well as sulfur which would do the trick. He undertook a series of experiments in which he mixed and heated rubber with about every chemical he could put his hands on. He carried out the mixing by hand and heated the various composites on a tin plate by means of a candle. Surprisingly he found sulfur unique for curing rubber. We know now that selenium and certain organic peroxides are curing agents for rubber, but the former is too toxic for such a use and peroxides have many shortcomings for this purpose. Goodyear studied also sulfur in combination with other chemicals. In the presence of certain metal oxides and salts, the sulfur reacted with the rubber more rapidly and more completely. White lead, a basic lead carbonate then available as a pigment for paints, proved to be the best of the "accelerators" tried. Today it is common practice to use one or more accelerators, usually organic sulfur compounds, when vulcanizing rubber.

Goodyear made the important observation that sulfur did not react with rubber until heated to 270°F or higher. This allowed mixing of rubber compounds containing high proportions of fillers with sulfur in the 200-250°F range at which temperatures the rubber is soft and more processable. This so-called high scorch temperature of sulfur-curing systems has been a very important factor in rubber manufacturers being able to process large batches of rubber and mold it into intricate shapes.

Goodyear had no means of maintaining uniform temperatures so results were hard to duplicate. Also he had no equipment for making large samples which he thought were essential to convince others of his invention. He continued his experiments the best he could using hot coals from the family fireplace, his wife's kitchen oven, furnaces in the local factories which he begged to use in off-working hours, as well as the tempering oven at the village blacksmith. In the course of these experiments he determined the optimum proportion of sulfur to be about 3% based on the rubber and the best cure conditions to be 3-5 hours at 280-300°F.

Goodyear decided finally that he did not have the equipment to make large samples and thought he would try to sell his invention using small samples. He decided also that the Boston area was too prejudiced against rubber for him to make any headway and resolved to go to New York. He was able to borrow fifty dollars from his former tutor, William DeForest, who had only recently married his widowed sister, Harriet. In New York Goodyear contacted William and Emory Rider, merchants, who were sufficiently impressed by his invention to supply him money to support his family and to continue his experiments. The Rider brothers supplied Goodyear with about $30,000.

Hayward was reemployed at $50 per month and new methods for carrying out the vulcanization were studied at Woburn. Heating was carried out in dry air, in steam, in water under pressure, in molten lead, and liquid sulfur. Much trouble with fires was encountered in furnaces. At last a method was developed for making shoes by filling the crudely shaped shoes with sand and heating them on metal racks in a hot air oven. By 1841 Goodyear had succeeded in vulcanizing rubber-coated fabric by passing continuous sheets of it over rolls in an oven.

The inventor pursued his goal of making various vulcanized rubber articles in a consistent manner in the factory during the day and experimented in the kitchen at night. He invented "shirred" rubber fabrics by cementing cloth to stretched vulcanized rubber. These subsequently found wide use in suspenders. DeForest, a woolen manufacturer, became interested in the shirred product and began to help finance Goodyear's work in 1841.

On December 6, 1841 Goodyear had a justice of the peace in New Haven draw up a caveat* dealing with his sulfur curing of rubber which was submitted to the U.S. Patent Office. He did not apply for the corresponding patent until 1843. The delay was due to his belief that he did not have sufficient funds in 1841 to prepare adequate samples to demonstrate the utility of his invention and to file foreign patents. At that time foreign patents had to be filed simultaneously with their U.S. counterpart. The delay in filing his patent proved to be a serious error.

Goodyear's big problem was the formation of blisters at the surface of rubber articles when vulcanized. Although he relentlessly continued his heating experiments in 1842-43, most resulted in failures. Nonetheless, from such experiments came knowledge. He learned that his sulfur and white lead had to be bone dry and the former free of acid. His coated goods had to be free of turpentine and temperatures during cure had to be increased slowly and uniformly. Looking back on Goodyear's experience, it is remarkable that he mastered blister-free vulcanization as well as he did. With few exceptions today all rubber articles are vulcanized in metal molds under high pressure or in steam autoclaves under pressure. These pressure techniques force gases from the rubber before it hardens, thus avoiding blisters, and contact with metal or steam serves to provide uniform temperature control.

By the summer of 1844 things were beginning to look up for Goodyear. Even so, that year he spent a time in

*A caveat was a general disclosure of an invention which was as yet incomplete, but might serve later as a conception date for a subsequent patent application. Caveats were discontinued by the Patent Office in 1910.

debtors' prison in Springfield where in cooperation with his brothers Nelson and Henry he was trying to start a rubber factory. On June 15, 1844 Goodyear was granted a patent on his vulcanization process (6). Thus, five and one-half years after his actual discovery of vulcanization, he could finally start to profit from his invention. His first licensee was the Naugatuck India Rubber Company of Naugatuck, Connecticut. One would think that he would have arranged his license so that the licensee produce at maximum capacity, thereby rendering higher income to himself. Instead he saddled it with an agreement to carry out development work on any new product which he might develop — often a good way to lose money.

Once Goodyear's patent on vulcanization had been issued, he had the choice of entering a monopolitic manufacturing career or licensing his process to others. His patent was one of the most basic ever issued. His vulcanization process was essential in making any material which contained rubber; there was no alternative. Goodyear had had experience in manufacturing in his early partnership with his father. He was aware that capital could be raised for the manufacture of rubber articles as evidenced by the early venture of the Roxbury Rubber Company and others. He was also aware of the usual financial plight of inventors who attempted to live on royalties from their patents. Nevertheless he chose to continue the life of research and development. In 1851 Goodyear commented on his decision to license and not manufacture (7):

> Previous to the discovery of the vulcanizing process before described, and for several years after the writer began his experiments, he entertained the idea of carrying on the business, and of establishing

a reputation for himself as a manufacturer of gum elastic.

Subsequent to the discovery, however, upon making a survey of what remained to be done to perfect the prominent fabrics, and extend the application of the discovery, the extent of which he did not, even then, fully understand, he abandoned the idea of all practical operations as a regular manufacturer, and has since that time confined himself, with a fixed purpose, to perfecting a series of improvements, embracing the various processes, and so far as possible, all the important fabrics and the most important applications of them, so as to form a connected system of inventions, and to render their application as practicable and perfect as the nature of the substance would permit.

. . . It would be the wish of the writer to pursue the calling of a manufacturer of gum-elastic, as a means by which he might hope to establish a better reputation for the manufacture than others will be likely to establish for it, did not circumstances conspire to prevent this; but he must content himself to leave the manufacture to be pursued by others, hoping to obtain such compensation from them as will enable him to devote the remainder of his life, (so far as feeble health and a constitution broken by too close application to the labors of experimenting will permit) to making application of this substance to the useful purposes and inventions, which would otherwise probably escape the notice and attention of others, as the original discovery might have done had it been sought after with less enthusiasm by the writer. The granting of licenses to others has been attended with much harm, as well as many advantages, in bringing the manufacture into notice. A great number of establishments, with means to operate, have accomplished much more in a practical way, within the time, than one individual with limited means could have done; but on the other hand there was danger that the reputation of the invention would suffer from so many persons, unacquainted with the manufacture, being engaged in bringing it forward.

Although Goodyear had 20 licensees by 1851, there were many manufacturers of rubber products who did not license. As usual when an important invention is made, remote references in the literature are dug up in an attempt to show that he who brought the invention to successful utilization did nothing new but simply used the results of others. In 1791 in a British publication there was a statement that Dr. Peter Bergius of Stockholm had converted rubber to an "elastic horn-like substance" by "an intense degree of heat". Although no mention was made of sulfur, the critics now contended that Bergius must have used sulfur in his rubber! In 1832 Dr. Friederich Lüdersdorff of Germany had heated turpentine with sulfur before using it to dissolve rubber. Van Geuns, a Hollander, from 1828-42 made up for the medical profession various rubber articles containing amber powder and boiled linseed oil. Although amber is yellow, it is a fossil resin — not sulfur. Such flimsy references were used by vocal critics against Goodyear. Some infringers figured it was cheaper to buy advertisements in the press than to pay royalty. The following is one which appeared in the November 6, 1850 issue of the *N. Y. Commercial Advertiser* (8):

26

LATEST DISCOVERY IN RUBBER – NEW RECEIPT – Get patent 'honestly if you can, but get it.' If other people make discoveries which renders your patent obsolete, useless, throw it up – take out another covering everybody's discovery – not necessary that you should be inventor, but swear strong – pay five, ten, even twenty thousand dollars to agents to get a re-issue; commence a dozen suits to annoy your neighbors. If defeated, try again, and again. If, in an interlocutory motion, your opponent is refused by the Judge get some name under which to publish, and boldly assert that your patent is sustained by the Court. Truth is not necessary under this new system, boldly assert that you have heavy suits, no matter if twelve or fifteen of the most eminent legal advisors in the country pronounce your re-issued patent a fraud, wholly illegal – no matter, you publish in newspapers that a decision is in your favor. It will also tend to soften the blow of a thorough Waterloo Jury Trial, verdict and judgment against you. If any of the deluded operators refuse to pay any further to the conspiracy fund, for carrying on the game before the public sue them – keep capitalists out of the business, and you will make a fortune, retire, and be perfectly respectable.

A single world of caution: don't fail to make the world believe your man is a great genius; use his name, but keep him always out of sight.
Nov. 4. HORACE H. DAY,
Manufacturer of India Rubber, 23 Courtlandt St.

It is not surprising that others had mixed sulfur with rubber prior to Goodyear. The commonest and cheapest chemicals carried by pharmacists were lime, magnesia, talc, and sulfur. In those days sulfur was well known to most, particularly children, because of the popular sulfur-molasses spring tonic! Of course, Nathaniel Hayward's work with sulfur at the Eagle Rubber Comapny led to Goodyear's interest with the chemical. Actually Hayward's work should have had little or no impact on Goodyear's patent position since Goodyear induced Hayward to file his patent and bought it from him. However later, infringers of Goodyear's patent attempted to get Hayward to claim that he was the real father of vulcanization. Luckily in 1841 Goodyear had Hayward sign the following affidavit:

Boston, 3d April, 1841.

To all whom it may concern.

I hereby certify that, to the best of my knowledge and belief, Charles Goodyear is the true and original inventor of fireproof India rubber, and of other improvements caused by the use of large quantities of sulphur and lead, and of heating the same, and by that and other methods of removing the offensive smell; and I am certain that the same has been accomplished by him at a great expense of time and money.

NATHANIEL HAYWARD

Ten years later Hayward testified that the document was authentic and that he had signed it willingly.

Although Goodyear sued some companies and individuals, prosecution of infringers often required more money than he had. Like Edison in the years following his development of the electric light, Goodyear preferred to spend his time and money on research and development rather than in the courtroom. Horace Day of Jersey City, the above-cited advertizer, was one of the most conscienceless infringers. Although he had a license to make shirred goods, he made no royalty payments and made other rubber goods without the pretense of a license. When Day decided to enter the highly successful rubber boot and shoe market, he did not have the meek Goodyear to contend with, but rather the Shoe Association. This trade group consisted of four companies which had exclusive rights to make boots and shoes under license from Goodyear. Suit was brought against Day under Goodyear's name but was backed by the Shoe Association. Apparently Day welcomed the suit since he, with the cooperation of a number of other corporations and individuals, expected to prove U. S. 3,633 illegal. In 1849 Goodyear had sought and been granted a re-issue of his patent broadening the claims in accordance with disclosures in his caveat of 1841. In the patent application Goodyear had restricted the third ingredient in addition to rubber and sulfur to white lead and other oxides and salts of lead (6). In the caveat the third ingredient was defined as white lead or "oxides of metals generally and pigments". Day maintained that the re-issued patent contained information which had not been available to Goodyear when filing either the caveat or patent application.

The trial took place in Trenton, New Jersey in April 1852. Day and his associates retained Rufus Choate, a U.S. Senator from Massachusetts, as chief counsel. He was considered the greatest trial lawyer of his time. The Shoe Associates retained Daniel Webster, then Secretary of State under Fillmore. It would appear highly unusual for men in such public offices to take part in a civil case for fees. It was even then. Probably because Webster was a godlike creature known to be in ill health and heavily in debt, there was no public outcry in his taking the case. He received a payment of $10,000 with the understanding that he would receive an additional $5,000 if he won the decision.

Webster spent only a week in Trenton, allowing himself two days for reviewing the hundreds of pages of deposition which his assistant counsel had assembled. In the final arguments Choate spent five hours attempting to prove that Goodyear was not the first to invent vulcanization and pictured Day as a martyr suffering from ill treatment by Goodyear and his associates. When it came time for Webster to make the closing statement for Goodyear, the courtroom was packed and there was an overflow of hundreds in the street. This was Webster's last appearance in any courtroom; in six months he was dead. He was a sick man at the time and although the eyes of the 70-year-old glowed as he emphasized the high points of his plea, he could not thunder as he had done in the past in the U. S. Senate. The gaunt, bent, white-haired figure of Goodyear sitting at the counsel table added to the drama. Webster's speech was a great one and it was recorded in full for posterity. The high points of it include the following (9):

We have reached that point in this discussion where the great question of the case rises up before us. . . .That question is, the truth or falsity of the claim made by Charles Goodyear to the invention of the process of vulcanizing India Rubber. Did he make such an invention? Is he who sits here before us the man known now, and to be known forever, while the history of art remains, as the individual who introduced, to the knowledge of his country, and to the knowledge of the whole civilized world, this extraordinary phenomenon?. . . .Is Charles Goodyear the discoverer of this invention of vulcanized rubber? Is he the first man upon whose mind the idea ever flashed, or to whose intelligence the fact ever was disclosed, that by carrying heat to a certain height it would cease to render plastic the India Rubber, and begin to harden and metallize it? Is there a man in the world who found out that fact before Charles Goodyear? Who is he? Where is he? On what continent does he live? Who has heard of him? What books treat of him? What man among all the men on earth has seen him, known him, or named him? Yet it is certain that this discovery has been made. It is certain that it exists. It is certain that it is now a matter of common knowledge all over the civilized world. It is certain that this curious result has grown into knowledge by somebody's discovery and invention. And who is that somebody? . . . .We want to know the name, and the habitation, and the location of the man upon the face of this globe, who invented vulcanized rubber, if it be not he who now sits before us . . . .

I ask again if there is anybody else than Goodyear who made this invention, who is he? Is the discovery so plain that it might have come about by accident? It is likely to work important changes in the arts everywhere. It introduces quite a new material into the manufacture of the arts, that material being nothing else than elastic metal. It is hard like metal, and as elastic as pure original gum elastic. Why that is as great and momentous a phenomenon occurring to men in the progress of their knowledge, as it would be for a man to show that iron and gold could remain iron and gold, and yet become elastic like India Rubber. It would be just such another result. Now, this fact cannot be kept out of sight; somebody has made this invention. That is certain. Who is he? Mr. Hancock has been referred to. But he expressly acknowledges Goodyear to be the first inventor.

Pointing to the bent and white-haired Goodyear, Webster wrung involuntary applause from the crowd when he declaimed: 'I say that there is not in the world a human being that can stand up, and say that it is his invention, except the man who is sitting at that table.'

The decision of the Great India Rubber Case, as it was called then and now, was a complete victory for Webster and his clients. The presiding judges, Grier and Dickerson, went out of their way in their verdict to praise Goodyear and lambaste Day and his like. Among other things their decision included the following:

. . . And yet when genius and patient perseverance have at length succeeded, in spite of sneers and scoffs, in perfecting some valuable invention or discovery, how seldom it is followed by reward! Envy robs him of the honor, while speculators, swindlers, and pirates, rob him of the profits. Every unsuccessful experimenter who did, or did not, come very near making the discovery, now claims it. Every one who can invent an improvement, or vary its form, claims a right to pirate the original discovery. We need not summon

Morse, or Blanchard, or Woodworth, to prove that this is the usual history of every great discovery or invention.

The present case adds another chapter to this long and uniform history. Every man who has made experiments with India Rubber, sulphur, lead, or any other substance; who has heated them in a stove or furnace; who has annoyed his family and his neighbors with sulphurous gas; who has set up a rubber factory and failed; who has made India Rubber goods that no one would buy, or if bought, were returned as worthless; in fine, all who had ceased their experiments and endeavors, because they had not discovered that such qualities could be given to that substance, are now paraded forth as the inventors and discoverers of vulcanized India Rubber.

Although Day was ordered by the court to pay royalties due, he escaped most of the payments by transferring his property in New Jersey to others. However, the favorable decision did effectively frighten off most other would-be infringers in the United States.

One reason why Goodyear had waited until 1843 to file his basic application on vulcanization was that he could file then applications simultaneously in England and France, at that time the two leading industrial nations of the world. As it turned out, he got patent protection in neither. In December 1841 Goodyear gave small samples of vulcanized rubber to Stephen Moulton, a young Englishman visiting in the United States. Goodyear engaged Moulton to act as his agent with the Macintosh Company. This company refused to negotiate until they knew more about the process so Moulton returned to America. However, the samples which he had brought to England fell into the hands of Thomas Hancock, England's leading rubber manufacturer. Hancock realized at once that they were remarkable in that they did not become sticky when heated nor hard when cooled. Although Hancock wrote later that the samples "afforded no clue to the mode" of how they were made, he did notice that they had "a dirty, yellowish grey colour" and "a slight smell of sulfur". Hancock carried out an intensive series of experiments using sulfur in rubber and filed a patent in England on November 21, 1843, a few weeks before Goodyear filed there. The result was that Goodyear was denied a patent in England. In 1855 the Hancock patent was sustained by an English court although the defense acknowledged that Goodyear's samples led Hancock to his invention. In France Goodyear was granted a patent, corresponding to U. S. 3,633, on April 16, 1844. Later it was sustained in court against a previous ruling that it was void because Goodyear had sent a few samples of vulcanized rubber shoes to France prior to filing his patent there. However, in 1855 the patent was declared void in that, as required by French law, the invention had not been placed in public use within two years after patenting. Goodyear thought his actions in France did constitute reduction to manufacture within two years. The court ruled no and the patent was dedicated to the French Government.

In late 1852 with his sweeping patent victory in the United Stated behind him, Goodyear with his wife and five children sailed for Europe. The purpose of taking all of the children was, at least in part, to assist potential licensees in setting up rubber operations in Europe. In spite of the patent positions in both England and France, Goodyear hoped by legal action, know-how, and subsequent auxiliary patents to obtain licensees abroad. He had exhibited at the

Charles Goodyear, from a portrait by G.P.A. Healy in 1855 on a hard rubber panel

The first Mrs. Charles Goodyear from a portrait by G.P.A. Healy

industrial fair in London in 1851, spending $30,000 in an attempt to show that he, not Macintosh-Hancock, knew more about vulcanized rubber. Although Goodyear stayed in London from late 1852 to November 1854, he was unsuccessful in getting any business started there. His gracious wife Clarissa died in England in March 1853, the mother of nine children. Goodyear remarried in May 1854.

Goodyear and family moved on to Paris in November 1854 with the objective of setting up an elaborate exhibit at the world fair to open there the following spring. This he did to the tune of about $50,000, using largely credit based on notes received from potential French licensees. Goodyear's Vulcanite Court at the Paris fair was very well received, winning one of the gold medals awarded. He received also the Cross of the Legion of Honor. He was in a debtors' prison in Paris when he received the latter. The three French companies which were to operate under his license had failed due to lack of proper equipment and the annulment of Goodyear's French patent. The security which he had used in borrowing money in France was now worthless.

The year of 1855 was one of disaster for Goodyear. He was arrested for debts and spent 16 days in Clichy Prison in Paris, he lost the patent suit in England to Thomas Hancock, and the court in France annulled his patent there. He returned to England in early 1856 and there was held in the sheriff's office for several days while French creditors sought his further arrest. He became chronically ill and for nine weeks his recovery was in grave doubt. In April he was moved to Bath, England where the fight to regain his health continued. In May 1858, approximately two years later, the family sailed for the United States.

Goodyear's six years in Europe had not only been a financial disaster, but his long absence resulted in a deteriorating situation in America as well. Unknown to him his trusted attorney had been "dipping into the till" of royalty income. His basic patent was to expire in June and although an extension had been applied for*, this was being fought by Horace Day and others. The practice of Goodyear requiring all licensees to stamp "Goodyear's Patent" on all rubber articles sold gave the public the erroneous idea that he was involved in all such manufacturing and making huge profits. Day and his colleagues were joined by the Macintosh Company and Thomas Hancock in fighting the application for extension. Once the patent had expired the British could export to the States vulcanized rubber goods which were, of course, not made under the Goodyear license.

In an account of receipts and expenditures relative to his patent listed in the application for extension, Goodyear showed a net profit of about $33,000 for the 14 years. The Hon. Joseph Holt, Commissioner of Patents, refused to consider any arguments relative to the validity of the patent but stated that the only consideration was if the patentee had received adequate remuneration for his contribution to the country, and if he had been diligent in introducing his invention to public use. Holt granted the seven-year extension and in so doing took it upon himself to comment in a dramatic manner on the abuses endured by Goodyear:

. . .Has the inventor been remunerated?. . .
It is extremely difficult to estimate in the coin of dollars and cents the worth of eighteen years of

---

*At that time the life of a patent in the United States was 14 years. The patentee could apply for a seven-year extension if he could prove that he would not receive adequate compensation during the 14-year period.

36

the prime of human life — especially so, when that life is one of lofty genius, of indomitable enterprise, and of stainless virtures . . . .He is now seen tottering toward that grave which must soon open in his path . . . .No inventor probably has ever been so harassed, so trampled upon, so plundered by that sordid and licentious class of infringers known as 'pirates' . . . .In the very front rank of this predatory band stands one who sustains in this case the double and most convenient character of contestant and witness . . . .

At the close of all his toils and sacrifices, and of the humiliations he has been called on to endure, this public-spirited inventor, whose life has been worn away in advancing the best interests of mankind, is found to be still poor, oppressed with debt, and with the winter of age creeping upon his shattered constitution . . . .He now begs that he may be allowed to enjoy for a few years longer that precarious protection which our most feeble and imperfect laws extend; and, were the appeal denied, I feel that I should be false to the generous spirit of the patent laws . . . .The patent will, therefore, be extended for seven years from the 15th June, 1858.

After obtaining the extension of his patent, Goodyear's fortunes greatly improved. He was able to collect royalties more readily and his annual income reached about $30,000. For the first time he hired a private secretary, Rev. A. S. Hunt. In order that he be nearer his business contacts, in late 1858 Goodyear and his family moved to New York. Then in 1859 he purchased a home in Washington, D. C. Goodyear felt that the army and navy were not using rubber goods as much as they should and he wished to improve his contacts with them. This move may have helped to educate the military in the use of rubber blankets, ponchos, boots, shoes, pontoons, and the like. During the Civil War the North bought about 27 million dollars worth of such rubber articles.

At his home on I Street between 17th and 18th NW, Goodyear set up a laboratory-workshop which contained a large tank for testing life-saving equipment. Although the urge was there, his health was so poor he could do but little. On May 30, 1860 the father, considered too ill to go by rail, left by boat with his personal physician to visit his daughter Cynthia who was extremely ill in New Haven. On reaching New York he learned that Cynthia was dead. He was unable to attend her funeral and he followed her to the grave a few weeks later. This man, who was honored in 1939 on the centennial anniversary of the discovery of rubber vulcanization as one of the nation's great, received the following obituary notice in the *New York Times*:

GOODYEAR — In this City on Sunday, July 1, at the Fifth-av. hotel, of gout, Charles Goodyear, aged 59 years. The friends of the deceased are invited to be present, without further notice, at his funeral, which will take place, at the residence of his son, Charles Goodyear, Jr., New Haven, Conn. on July 3, at 2 o'clock.

Charles Goodyear had more than his fair share of personal tragedies. He lost six of his 12 children in their early childhood. Two of the three children of his second wife died before they were little more than one year of age and the third was only two months old when his father died. He failed to reach the deathbed of his 32-year old daughter when he himself was stricken. His faithful wife

Clarissa died in 1853 in London far away from relatives and friends after only a few years of relative affluency with her family. In 1841 Charles' father Amasa Goodyear moved with his youngest son Amasa, Jr. and family to Florida to grow citrus fruit for the northern market. During the same year in a six-week period, Amasa, his son, and granddaughter died of yellow fever.

Charles himself suffered most of his life from acute indigestion and, as he became older, supposedly from gout. Barker suggests that Goodyear died of lead poisoning and not gout (10). Symptoms of the two diseases are quite similar. Gout has been known as the rich man's disease. Goodyear hardly met that qualification. For years he had worked with white lead as a major ingredient in rubber compounds. In these experiments in the family home and in the combination workshop-home, all took part in the work. The white lead dust was no doubt inhaled by Goodyear and to some degree by all members of the family. Since he used some of the same equipment in his experiments as did his wife when preparing food, the family may have become contaminated with lead by ingestion as well as by inhalation. Barker (10) feels that Goodyear acquired lead poisoning because of mixing rubber containing white lead by means of his fingers. Inorganic lead compounds are not absorbed through the skin, but it is certainly true that such intimate contact with white lead for years in poorly ventilated quarters made him a prime target for lead poisoning. Certainly it adds to the tragedy of Goodyear's personal life if the lead compounds which he used in his studies to conquer rubber caused much of his physical suffering and hastened not only his own death but possibly those of certain members of his family. This is no doubt a distinct possibility.

Goodyear's dire financial straits from about 1835 to

1844 not only caused hardship on himself and family but also greatly increased the time of invention to utilization. If he had had the facilities and assistants with which Edison was always able to associate himself with, he could have decreased the development period of his vulcanization process from about five years to one or so. Goodyear knew he had the answer and what had to be done to successfully demonstrate it. He lacked suitable equipment and help to carry out the closely controlled experiments necessary to determine optimum proportions of ingredients and cure conditions. The big loss from his slow progress in the development stage was that of patent positions in England and France.

After 1844 we can be less sympathetic with Goodyear's financial problems. His income became very substantial. He took his debts very lightly, even those to his friends. When he was spending money recklessly on exhibits in England and France, he still owed deForest $46,000 which he had borrowed 10 years before. Goodyear was in a way a self-made martyr. In his book *Gum-Elastic* he goes into detail in describing his personal problems and his suffering and that of those dependent upon him. He felt that he and only he could develop the uses of vulcanized rubber to their full potential and if in the process of doing so he usurped money from others, that was a lesser sin than if he fell down on the job the Almighty had delegated him to do.

In 1864 Charles Goodyear, Jr., an executor of his father's estate, petitioned the Government for a second seven-year extension of his father's vulcanization patent. In the petition it was maintained that Charles Goodyear, Sr. left countless debts and a family without adequate means of support. The petition was refused by the Commissioner of Patents. This would appear to have been the proper action. One must remember that the nation was in the throbs of a tragic civil war and millions were being spent on rubber goods for the Union Army. Theoretically royalty payments increased such costs. In 1861 Congress had modified the patent laws in that the life of a patent was increased from 14 to 17 years and the possibility of extending the length of time of coverage eliminated. Although Goodyear's patent was not affected by the new law, the fact remained that this patent was to be in effect for 21 years. Although the inventor had never entered into rubber manufacturing operations, many of the Goodyear clan did on a profitable basis. Goodyear had other patents, some of which were bringing in royalty income. Regli, who goes into Goodyear's personal life more than other biographers (11), states that Charles Goodyear's legacy was adequate to pay his debts and provide funds for dependent members of the family. Charles, Jr., who patented a shoe-sewing machine, was aided in promoting his invention by money left by his father. William Henry Goodyear, the third child of the second Mrs. Goodyear, has stated that although his father's estate was somewhat involved at the time of his death due to foreign litigations, "it must have been ultimately worth, after all royalties were paid in, some two hundred and fifty thousand dollars" (12). Charles Goodyear did not receive just compensation for the new industry which he created; he did not, however, die a poor man.

The world is indeed fortunate that there was a persistent Goodyear who believed that by a combination of chance and keen observation he would learn how to convert that amazing elastic material, rubber, from a useless to a useful material. It was not until about the turn of the past century that chemists had enough information about high polymers, a class of materials of which natural rubber is one, that a scientist might have systematically studied how to chemically crosslink rubber. Once rubber vulcanization was a fact, it took industry about 25 years to develop sufficient demand for the raw material that certain forward-looking people realized that wild rubber from Brazil could not meet future demands. It took the British another 25 years to develop a domestic supply. If Goodyear had not discovered vulcanization, it is likely that the beginning of the "bicycle age" in the 1890's, and that of the automobile shortly later, would have been postponed for decades. As we learned during World War II, vulcanized rubber tires are an absolute necessity for vehicles going faster than a few miles per hour.

Goodyear's invention was not only opportune, but it is also amazing that 130 years later scientists and engineers have found nothing as good as sulfur vulcanization for converting natural and most synthetic rubbers from low-strength gums to strong, tough, high-abrasion resistant materials. Equally amazing is the fact that in the vulcanization process that unique property of rubber, elasticity, is not only preserved, but is enhanced.

One studying the life of Goodyear might conclude that he was a bizarre person and became famous in spite of his many inadequacies. The truth would appear to be that although he showed poor judgment in many instances, he did have the earmarks of an educated man and in many respects those of a good scientist. One must remember that he worked during the mid-19th century when industrial research was unknown and organic chemistry, the field in which rubber falls, was practically non-existent in America.

Goodyear's book of two volumes (1), published first in 1853 and again in 1855 by Yale College, is not only well written, but many features of it are presented in a masterly manner. It is not just a rubber technician's book; Goodyear discussed rubber technology, his philosophy of invention, the Patent Office, his relationship with licensees and competitors. The book has surprisingly clear and accurate discussions of rubber processes and end uses which are quite meaningful even today. Until recently the rubber industry has been noted for its secretiveness relating to compounding recipes and overall process operations. Goodyear's book was certainly a milestone in the publication of rubber technology and one of the few until recent times. One wonders when he found time to write it!

Based on the facts that Goodyear was a friend and had discussions with Professor Silliman of Yale and that Yale College published his book, one can conclude that Goodyear was accepted by the academic community. He got along famously with Webster at the Trenton trial. He must have been a charming and persuasive individual to get what assistance he did in the 1835-44 period when any venture in rubber manufacture was considered idiotic. Also Goodyear must have had a way with women. At the age of 54, a semi-invalid with a dependent family and in debt, he wooed and married Fanny Wardell of London, a lass of 20 years. She stood by him during 1855-58 when he was in and out of debtors' prison and extremely ill. This second Mrs. Goodyear described later their last winter in England as "one of deep trial, constant sickness, acute bodily and mental distress, and great pecuniary inconvenience and anxiety. The history of that period can never be told."

In writing about Charles Goodyear I have abstained from the dramatic. However, it appears appropriate to end the chapter about this remarkable man with a quotation from Barker's *Charles Goodyear* (13):

As the great inventors of the past, those benefactors of mankind, take their place in our modern judgment of their achievements, a small, sickly, bright-eyed individual, on crutches, hesitantly shuffles to the very front row. He is Charles Goodyear — Discoverer of Vulcanization.

Chapter 2

Alexander Graham Bell

To the general public, the name Bell should connote the inventor of the telephone. Certainly the various Bell Telephone Companies got the "Bell" of their names from Alexander Graham Bell. However, an electric bell is a part of every telephone. This, plus the practice of every Bell Telephone Company of including a picture of a bell as a part of its trademark name, tends to lead to the assumption that the Bell Telephone Companies are so named because of the use of this device. Thus Bell, the inventor, has been pushed aside in favor of this noisemaker! To further complicate the situation, one finds that the name of the parent company of the Bell system is American Telephone and Telegraph Company. Thus it would appear reasonable to assume that the telegraph companies, which preceded commercial telephony by four decades, pioneered the telephone. Actually they had nothing to do with the original invention and when the Bell telphone patents were offered to the Western Union Telegraph Company for one hundred thousand dollars, the offer was turned down by their president, William Orton, with the comment, "What use could this company make of an electrical toy?" All this is very confusing.

Had it not been for the famous American physicist, Joseph Henry, we would likely not be faced with this confusion of telephone company names. While on a trip to the Patent Office in 1875 relating to his patent applications on harmonic telegraphy, Bell called on Henry, who at that time was Secretary of the Smithsonian Institution. Bell sought the advice of this noted man, who was an acknowledged authority in the field of electricity, relative to certain qualitative indications that he had observed that speech could be transmitted by a varying electrical current. Bell informed Henry that he was considering publishing his results so that possibly others would pursue and perfect the process, inasmuch as he himself was not qualified to do so having little or no knowledge of electricity. Henry's laconic answer was, "Get it." This bit of advice resulted in a teacher of speech inventing the telephone whereas scientists experienced in the field of electricity had tried and failed.

The second son of Alexander Melville Bell was born in Edinburgh, Scotland on March 3, 1847. He was given the same name as his grandfather, Alexander. At the age of 11, Alexander the Third apparently decided that it was confusing to have so many Alexanders in the same family. The individualistic youth gave himself the middle name of Graham and encouraged others to so address him. However, his parents continued to call him Aleck.

The grandfather was an early authority on phonetics and speech therapy. The father followed a similar vocation and was professor of elocution at Edinburgh University from 1843-65 and at the University of London from 1865-70. Alexander Melville wrote many books and became world famous because of his analysis of how various sounds are produced by the speech organs. The *Encyclopedia Britannica* devotes approximately the same space to Alexander Melville Bell as that to his son, Alexander Graham.

46

Graham grew up in a home environment of high educational standards. His father loved to quote Shakespeare by the hour, and his mother was a portrait painter and a musician. He was taught at home until 10 years of age and then attended private and public schools until 14. Subsequently he attended lectures of interest in Edinburgh and London. He received extensive piano lessons and at one time considered seriously to devoting his life to music. Melville Bell encouraged his sons' interest in speech. He was contemptuous of speech with an accent. Graham grew up to speak pure English; he could not be identified either as an Englishman or a Scotsman by his speech.

Following his formal education, Graham spent a year with his grandfather in London. The seventy-one-year-old Alexander was still giving lessons in speech and the grandson was allowed to sit in on some of them. The grandfather's extensive library fascinated the youth, and he read all he could find on acoustics. By the time of his return to Edinburgh, Graham had resolved to be a teacher. By the age of 16 he obtained a position as tutor of both music and elocution at nearby Elgin. Shortly he became a resident master at the Weston House Academy there. Thus, Graham was a well-educated youth even based on British standards (which at that time were well above those of United States).

At the age of 18 Graham began research on how the various vowel sounds are produced by the mouth cavities. He found soon that Helmholtz of Germany had included data on such work in his famous book, *On the Sensations of Tone as a Physiological Basis for the Theory of Music*. At that time the book was available only in German. Bell, who could read no German, attempted to learn what Helmholtz did by studying the sketches in the book and erroneously concluded that Helmholtz had sent vowel sounds by telegraph! If vowel sounds could be sent by electricity, he reasoned, why not consonants as well and hence speech. Thus, because of the lack of linguistic training, Bell had stumbled on the conception of the telephone.

In 1867 Graham gave up his Elgin post and took one nearer London at Somersetshire College in Bath. One year later he became his father's assistant at London University. When the father went to Boston that fall to give a series of lectures, the son took over the elder's classes and private lessons. Both Bells were now important people in the field of elocution which at that time was of considerable interest in England with the public reading of Shakespeare and Dickens providing entertainment.

Tragedy struck the family of Alexander Melville Bell beginning in 1867 when the youngest son, Edward Charles, died of pulmonary tuberculosis. At that time the disease was called consumption. The medical profession knew little about it except that it tended to attack the young, particularly those living in cities. Also doctors had the erroneous idea that the disease was hereditary. The parents considered moving to Canada where a family friend, Reverend Thomas Henderson, was living in retirement in Paris, a small town on the Grand River in Ontario. The remaining two sons were against the move. The elder, Melville James, was teaching at Edinburgh University and was now married. Early in 1870 Melville James became sick and Graham went to Edinburgh to relieve him of his duties. However, in May 1870 the older brother died at the age of 25, also from consumption.

While substituting for his father during his stay in America and relieving his brother, Graham had overworked himself. His pallid appearance and frequent exhaustion indicated symptoms of the dreaded consumption. The family physician recommended the only possible cure known at that time — move to a healthier climate. Ontario's southern peninsula was then "Arizona" for Britons. At fifty-one, Melville Bell abandoned his London career and moved to a rural, developing country where he could never hope to regain the professional status he then had.

The three Bells and Melville James' widow, who had not only lost her husband but shortly before their baby boy, arrived in Quebec on August 1, 1870. They continued on to Paris, Ontario and spent a few days there with Reverend Henderson while searching for a suitable home. A comfortable house on several acres on the edge of Brantford was purchased. It was then, and still is, known as Tutelo Heights. Brantford, then a thriving city of 13,000, is only 21 miles west of Hamilton, one of the chief cities of Canada.

In the autumn of 1870, Graham did light work around the house and grounds but spent considerable time lounging in a hammock swung between tall birch trees at the edge of the Heights overlooking the Grand River. During the winter he continued to convalesce and by spring was a new man. Alexander Melville had gone to Boston the previous fall to fulfill his lecture engagements arranged before migrating to Canada. When invited to continue lectures there the following spring, he declined since he had accepted a professorship of elocution at Queen's College, Kingston, Ontario. He suggested that his son be considered for the Boston position. In early 1871 Graham was notified that the Boston School Board had alloted five hundred dollars for such lectures; he was invited to deliver these at the Boston School for the Deaf and the Clarke Institute for Deaf-mutes in Northampton. The former subsequently became the Horace Mann School.

Graham began his duties in the Boston area the first week of April. Boston was then the literary and scientific center of the United States. Graham's lectures were well received. Spending two months in the United States, he lectured at Hartford as well as at Boston and Northampton. In the summer of 1871 at Tutelo Heights, bright days and cool nights further improved his health. In September of that year he opened a private school in Boston for teaching the deaf. Although he initially had only four pupils, his success with a congenitally deaf pupil, plus some publications, had by the fall of 1872 established Bell as a local authority on teaching the deaf.

During his first Canadian winter, Graham resumed some of his old experiments with tuning forks based on the work of Helmholtz. While still in England Bell had begun to use a simple telegraphic setup to study the sympathetic vibration of tuning forks. The work was continued at Tutelo Heights using a piano as well as tuning forks as the sources of uniform vibrations. Bell was very much impressed by the fact that he could employ one tuning fork to interrupt an electric current and utlize that electric current to vibrate another one. This led to his concept that by employing different frequencies of vibrations in connection with sending telegraphic signals, more than one message could be sent simultaneously.

The idea of sending more than one message at the same time over a single telegraph line was not new. The duplex scheme, permitting simultaneous transmission in opposite directions between two stations, was first proposed in 1853. This is possible by an arrangement whereby the receiver at a given station is unaffected by the sending current from its own station but responds to the operation of the distant transmitter. Bell's approach was different; he sought to send two or more separate and distinct messages over the line in the same direction. Once he had established his residence in Boston in the fall of 1872, he proceeded to teach during the day and work on what he now called his harmonic telegraph at night. The transmitting instrument, which he built himself, consisted of a tuning fork, the prongs of which were placed between the poles of an electromagnet. A wire from one of the prongs completed an electric circuit by dipping into mercury. Upon causing the fork to vibrate, the wire attached to the prong was alternately lifted out of the mercury and then pushed into it again. The circuit was thus broken and closed with each vibration of the fork, and the intermittent action of the electromagnet on the prongs of the fork caused it to remain in continuous vibration. The circuit was connected to a like fork with magnet through a telegraph key. When the circuit was closed by pressing the key, the receiving tuning fork would be caused to vibrate. If there were several forks of different frequencies at the receiving end, only that having the same pitch as the transmitting fork would vibrate.

Bell proposed to have a number of transmitting forks in a given circuit with receiving forks of like pitches. Each transmitting fork would be provided with a sending key. Thus theoretically as many messages could be sent simultaneously as there were like pairs of tuning forks at the transmitting and receiving stations.

A. Graham appeared to have forgotten about his health problem which had brought the Bells to Brantford. When he closed his private school for the summer and returned to Brantford for his vacation, his mother was appalled by his pale and emaciated appearance. However, this time it was only a matter of overwork plus poor eating and sleeping habits. His mother's anxious care resulted in a quick recovery and the son returned to Boston in October 1873 ready to resume his dual role of teacher-inventor. This time Bell stayed at the home of Mrs. Sanders in Salem, the grandmother of one of Bell's private pupils. The child lived with his grandmother and Bell gave the lad private lessons each evening on his return from Boston. Salem is a distance of 14 miles from Boston which meant approximately an hour's journey each morning and night by train. Bell was now Professor of Vocal Physiology at the School of Oratory of Boston University and had a room in one of the university buildings for his private teaching.

With such a full schedule, Bell was forced to carry on the work of his harmonic telegraph largely at night. But carry on he did. Mrs. Sanders had kindly turned over the entire third floor of the roomy clapboarded New England house to him for his experiments. Wires ran down the stairways to his basement shop. By November 1873 Bell had abandoned the tuning fork approach and turned to steel reeds instead to get sympathetic vibrations. Soon this led to the use of multiple reeds in a construction as that of the harp. His reed apparatus required more sophisticated workmanship and early in 1874 Bell placed an order for a piece of apparatus with Charles Williams who had a shop in Boston. The workman who got the drawing was Thomas A. Watson. This began the relationship which led to the famous first words by telephone of, "Mr. Watson, come here, I want you".

The harp-type arrangement of reeds led Bell closer to the concept of transmitting speech rather than simple musical vibrations. He calculated that it would take a harp arrangement of 4,000 to 5,000 individual reeds to transmit the human voice, assuming, of course, that a mechanism could be worked out whereby corresponding reeds could be brought to sympathetic vibration at the receiving end. Bell realized that if the electrical transmission of speech was to be a success, rather than have a multitude of reeds each with its rate of vibration, it would be necessary to develop a reed or equivalent which would vibrate as did the air during the production of a sound.

In spite of his heavy work load of teaching and work on harmonic telegraphy, Bell continued to look for a method by which his deaf pupils could "see speech". The deaf child does not learn to speak because he cannot hear and thus imitate. Bell decided to investigate Leon Scott's phonautograph and learned that one was available at the nearby Massachusetts Institute of Technology. In 1837 Scott, a Frenchman, built a recording device in which a pig's bristle attached to the center of a diaphragm of thin, stretched sheepskin, traced vibratory patterns upon lampblack-coated paper wrapped around a revolving cylinder. The bristle stylus left a visual record of the sound waves whch struck the diaphragm. Bell spent days speaking and singing into the apparatus. He finally concluded that the phonautograph had a vibration frequency of its own and did not give basic recordings. However, Bell's work with the membrane of the phonautograph gave him the idea of making a model of the human ear in an attempt to get more accurate tracings of speech vibrations. He consulted Dr. Clarence J. Blake, an aural surgeon at Harvard, who suggested that he use the real thing; *i.e.*, take a human ear and get tracings from it. Blake obtained such a specimen from the Harvard Medical School and Bell took it to Brantford the summer of 1874 for experimentation.

Bell moistened the ear with glycerin to increase its flexibility, attached a blade of dried grass to the membrane, and then attempted to use the "apparatus" much as he had done with the phonautograph. The sliver of grass was vibrated in various manners as he shouted vowels at different pitches against the membrane. Bell was amazed that a membrane as small and delicate as that of the ear could transmit vibrations to the relatively massive inner bones of the ear. He knew, of course, that the ear membrane could transmit all kinds of tone qualities, overtones, pitches, etc. He knew also that if a piece of iron was vibrated in close proximity to a magnet wrapped with insulated wire, it would generate an undulatory current, that is, one which rose and fell in waves. Thus he would convert sound waves to corresponding electric sine waves, and then convert the electric waves back to sound waves! The basic idea of the telephone was conceived on the banks of the Grand River near Brantford, Ontario in the summer of 1874.

Hermann Von Helmholtz, the versatile German philosopher and man of science, laid the basis for the science of telephony. He explained the mechanism of the inner bones of the ear as acting in sympathetic vibrations with the ear membrane. His work on selectively transmitting the vibrations of a tuning fork to one of like pitch at a distance via an electric current led to Bell's work on harmonic telegraphy. Helmholtz's work apparently inspired the following prediction in 1854 of Charles Bourseul, a Frenchman:

> Suppose that a man speaks near a movable disc, sufficiently flexible to lose none of the vibrations of the voice; that this disc alternately makes and breaks the connection from a battery; you may have at a distance another disc which will simultaneously execute the same vibrations.

Following the path outlined by Bourseul, Philip Reis, a German inventor, constructed what he called a telephone in 1861. Reis mounted a flexible diaphragm over an opening in a wooden box, with a thin piece of platinum attached to the inner center of the diaphragm. A brass spring, mounted near the membrane, connected to an electromagnet through a battery. Sounds against the flexible diaphragm caused it to contact the spring intermittently causing the electromagnet to be activated and de-activated. This produced some sound as had been observed by C. G. Page of Salem, Massachusetts in 1837 when he suddenly magnetized or demagnetized a rod of iron. However, Reis failed to realize that what little success he had was due to the fact that over a very narrow vibration range, he got a continuous undulatory current. Instead his conception of the working of his apparatus was that "each sound vibration effects an opening and a closing of the circuit".

When Bell returned to the Boston area in the fall of 1874, he did not take steps to test immediately his concept on how speech could be transmitted electrically. After all his first requirement was to make a living. His school opened to a large enrollment and his lectures at Boston University were well attended. Bell was getting a statewide reputation for his work of educating the deaf and had several outside lecture engagements scheduled. Furthermore his financial backer, Thomas Sanders, a leather merchant of Haverhill, Massachusetts, who paid for materials for Bell's experiments but nothing for his personal expenses, was only interested in bringing the harmonic telegraph to commercial utilization. Thirdly, although Bell felt that his prospective magneto-type speaking telegraph was of great theoretical interest, he thought it likely that the reproduced sound would be too faint to have commercial possibilities

55

for sending messages.

By December 1874 Bell was spending fewer evenings in Mrs. Sanders' attic in Salem and more time in the loft of Williams' shop in Boston. Young Watson had now been assigned regularly to the making of Bell's apparatuses. The two became friends and Bell, the teacher, described to the young electrician in some detail what he was trying to do. Watson, who also lived in Salem, would often stay late to assist Bell with his experiments, the two catching the midnight train for home.

In February 1875 Bell filed a patent application on his multiple telegraph. He was now being backed by Gardiner Greene Hubbard, a wealthy lawyer of Boston, as well as by Sanders. The three had a formal agreement in that Sanders and Hubbard would each pay half of the expenses of Bell's telegraphic inventions, all profits to be shared equally by the three. Mr. Hubbard got William Orton, president of Western Union Telegraph Company, to look over Bell's equipment. This resulted in an invitation for Bell to come to New York and test his apparatus on their commercial lines. This was the big chance the inventor had been hoping for. He gave up his teaching with the hope of resuming it in April. The experiments went reasonably well at Western Union but many adjustments and improvements were obviously needed.

Bell's patent application on the harmonic telegraph was declared in interference with an application of Elisha Gray of Chicago. Helmholtz's work on transmitting sympathetic vibrations from tuning forks had been translated into English and it was not surprising that others had used the harmonic approach to multiple telegraphy. However, Bell won the interference with Gray and his patent was issued in April 1875 (1). Problems relating to reducing the harmonic telegraph to practical use continued to harass the

56

young inventor. It appeared to be too complicated for a practicing telegraph operator to handle. No offer came from Western Union. Unknown to Bell or his backers, Thomas Edison, in the late summer of 1874, had perfected his quadruplex for sending four telegraph messages simultaneously on a single line. Since Edison was at that time under contract to Western Union, it is unlikely that this company had any serious interest in Bell's development unless it proved highly superior to that of Edison. The latter, an ex-telegraph operator, had developed a method of multiple telegraphy which was easily operable and found wide commercialization.

By May 1875 Bell was broke. His parents loaned him money to file foreign patents on his harmonic telegraph. With no private pupils except the young son of Thomas Sanders, Bell was in real need of the essentials of life. Fortunately he was able to get Boston University to advance the next year's fees for his lectures there. Also he was now working on his autograph telegraph, a device whereby he hoped to record telegraphic messages in the form of handwriting at a very rapid rate. Bell failed to bring either of these telegraphic inventions to fruition. However, electric oscillations corresponding to various harmonic vibrations are widely used in telephony today in connection with push button dialing, long distance automatic connections, and data transmission between computers.

On the afternoon of June 2 Bell and Watson were experimenting with a three-component harmonic telegraphic apparatus in the two attic rooms, 60 feet apart, over Williams' shop. They were now using tuning springs rather than tuning forks or fixed reeds for sending the vibrations of various pitches. During the course of the work, one of the transmitting springs stuck to its electromagnet. While plucking it to get its release, Watson heard a shout from Bell in the receiving room. Bell's sensitive ear had heard the sound caused by Watson's attempt to release the spring. The contact had not been broken and they were getting the effect of a continuous but varying electric current. Bell's trained ear detected "timbre" as well as pitch in the musical sounds. He now realized that he had underestimated the magnitude of the magneto effect caused by changing the lines of magnetic force in a field containing a closed circuit.

Before the night was over, Bell had designed the first of many experimental telephonic apparatuses which were tested during the summer of 1875. Parchment paper was first used for membranes. The tests resulted in sounds being heard but actual words could not be identified. However in a few days the gleeful Bell was able to report to his backers that he had transmitted sound by wire using no battery in the circuit. Bell, of course, used the then well-known principle of converse electromagnetism; that is, if the intensity of a magnetic field enclosed by a conductor is changed, a current of electricity will flow in the conductor. A diagramatic sketch of Bell's simplest telephone is as follows:

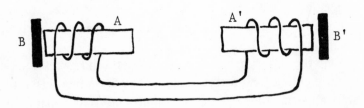

The two permanent or electromagnets, A and A', are mounted in fixed positions, each wrapped in a coil of insulated wire. The soft iron diaphragms, mounted to allow free vibration close to the magnetic poles, are shown by B and B'. If B is vibrated by sound waves striking it, the magnetic field, in which lies the coil, changes resulting in a flow of current through the wire circuit causing diaphragm B' to be more or less attracted depending on the direction and magnitude of the current. These feeble electric impulses reproduce the spoken word faithfully at the receiving end but because of low generation of electric current in such a system, it required one with a loud voice as that of Bell at the transmitting end and one with a delicate ear at the receiving end to hear the speech accurately. However, Bell's strictly magneto telephone convinced him without the least doubt that continuous current was the route to the transmission of speech and with proper transmitter, receiver, and circuit, speech could be transmitted over long distances.

In spite of Bell's accidental discovery and subsequent confirming experiments that speech transmitted by a continuous current could be highly audible, his financial backers insisted that he successfully complete work on his multiple and autographic telegraphs before pursuing the visionary telephone. Hubbard was particularly dogmatic about it. This was very distressing to Bell who wished to please Mr. Hubbard to the utmost since he sought his daughter's hand in marriage. Mabel Hubbard had been completely deaf since the age of five because of a severe attack of scarlet fever. She was sent to Germany during her early teens to improve her ability to understand speech by lip reading. She had returned to Boston about the time Bell began teaching there. Her father approached Bell for advice as to further education for his child, and soon Bell became a friend and a frequent guest of the family. Now Bell, age 28, wished to marry his part-time pupil.

By the fall of 1875 Bell was in poor health and mentally

depressed. His family, those of his fiancée, and most of his friends were distressed because of his obsession with the idea of talking by electricity. His father was very concerned because of his son's neglect of his professional work. Mr. Hubbard seems to have told Bell that unless he gave up this nonsense of the telephone and perfected his method of multiple telegraphy, he could not marry his daughter. In early September Bell became ill and returned to Brantford for rest.

The tranquil environment at Tutelo Heights brought quick recovery. Also Bell was not entirely idle; he began composing the patent specification for the speaking telegraph. Bell's fierce spirit reasserted itself and he resolved to complete the telephone come what may. Since Sanders had already advanced a great deal of money and Hubbard was cold on the telephone, Bell resolved to look for other financial support. His agreement with Sanders and Hubbard covered only his United States patents.* Thus, he hoped to get financial help on the basis of sharing potential income from his foreign patents. Bell was still a British citizen which meant that he must file in Britain first if he hoped to get patent coverage there.

Bell approached a neighbor in the Brantford area, Honorable George Brown, a Canadian senator and editor of the *Toronto Globe*. Brown raised prize shorthorns on his 1,000-acre farm near Brantford. Brown evidenced great interest in Bell's telephone experiments and agreed to loan him money so he could repay the lecture fees advanced by Boston University and hence be able to spend a

---

*Both Sanders and Hubbard in 1876, when the telephone was an assured success, graciously maintained that it was outside their original agreement with Bell. However, both participated in the commercialization of the telephone and benefited financially therefrom.

considerable part of his time on the telephone. Bell returned to Boston in high spirits. However, no word and no money came from Brown. By early October Bell had to give up work on the telephone and return to teaching. He not only gave his lectures at Boston University but resumed his teaching of private pupils which included a class of normal school teachers. After all, Alexander Graham Bell was in love, and the family of Gardiner Greene Hubbard, who lived in an elegant home in Cambridge, did not appreciate frayed shirt cuffs and threadbare suits.

Time passed. In spite of his heavy teaching load, by October Bell had his patent application completed. Still no word came from George Brown. Although Hubbard and Sanders were not optimistic about the telephone, they knew it was new and certainly justified the cost of patent coverage. However, Bell insisted that he must file in England first and would consult with Brown again during the Christmas holidays while at Brantford.

Bell's matrimonial hopes took a sudden change for the better. Mrs. Hubbard became an ally of the infatuated young man, and although parental consent for immediate marriage was not forthcoming, the couple became officially engaged on Mabel's 18th birthday, November 25, 1875. At once she became a real help to Bell, assisting with his paper work and getting her ardent suitor to follow more healthful eating and sleeping habits.

During his Christmas vacation, Bell called on George Brown at his Toronto office. After some delay an agreement was signed whereby Brown and his brother Gordon would each pay Bell 25 dollars per month for a maximum of six months and they would handle and pay the fees of filing Bell's basic telephone patent in foreign countries. For this they would receive a half-interest in all such patents filed. If this agreement had been consummated, it would have been a close second for value received to that when the Dutch bought Manhattan Island from the Indians. Actually the Browns made only one monthly payment to Bell. George Brown sailed for England on January 25, 1876 on other business but with a copy of Bell's patent application which he had promised to file in the British Patent Office immediately on his arrival in London. Actually he returned in late spring with the patent specification still in the bottom of his trunk. Apparently Brown felt that the talk of transmitting speech by electricity was so much humbug and his reputation might be severely damaged if he became associated with it. Brown's dealing with Bell is certainly one of the most incredible episodes in the history of invention.

Hubbard was exasperated at the delay on filing Bell's telephone patent application in United States. It had been written since the previous October but held up until a corresponding case could be filed in England. After Brown sailed, Hubbard sent a signed copy of the patent application to his attorney in Washington with instruction to file it immediately on word from Brown that the case had been filed in Britain. No cable came from Brown even after a fortnight. After three weeks of waiting, Hubbard determined to wait no longer. Without saying anything to Bell, he communicated with his Washington attorney and the application was filed February 14, 1876. Hubbard's move was fortunate. A few hours later on the 14th Elisha Gray filed a caveat in the U. S. Patent Office which covered his idea on a speaking telegraph. A caveat is not a patent application, but if Gray had beaten Bell to the Patent Office, it would have likely complicated the issuance of Bell's patent. Actually the patent application moved rapidly through the office and was granted March 7, 1876 almost as it had been written. (2).

62

Bell had progressed experimentally little beyond the magneto telephone when his patent application was written. However, his experiments were now directed towards having a battery in a circuit with a varied resistance. His first successful experiment, in which entire sentences were understood, employed a battery with the wire attached to the transmitter diaphragm penetrating into dilute acid in a metal cup. Aqueous acids are electric conductors but poor ones as compared to metals. The depth of the wire in the acid, and consequently the resistance of the circuit, varied as the wire moved up and down as the diaphragm vibrated. On the night of March 10, 1876, tests were being carried out at Exeter Place, Boston, where Bell now had two attic rooms, a bedroom and work room, separated by a hallway and two doors. Watson was stationed in the bedroom with a reed receiver and Bell in the shop using a dilute acid transmitter with a platinum wire dipping down from the diaphragm at the base of a speaking-tube mouthpiece. Bell leaned over the transmitter and shouted, "Mr. Watson — come here — I want to see you." The excited Watson soon appeared and was able to repeat the message exactly. This demonstration indicated that a varied resistant transmitter was the proper route although one containing liquid acid was hardly a practical device. It is of interest to note that the first historic message by telephone was after Bell's basic telephone patent had been issued.

Bell now moved ahead with the telephone with enthusiastic backing by Sanders. The harmonic telegraph was largely abandoned. Bell was his own teacher. It would appear that he still did not appreciate how effectively a diaphragm can respond to sound waves or how small the iron attached to a nonmetallic membrane might be and still adequately increase and decrease the electric current passing through the magnetic field. He first felt that the iron disc attached to the membrane must be so large that it needed mechanical support such as a hinge. It was not until Bell went to an attachment so small that no support was required that he made substantial progress to an effective and practical telephone. In the course of a paper presented before the Academy of Arts and Sciences on May 10, 1876, Bell described the following telephonic apparatus:

Two single pole electromagnets, each having a resistance of 10 ohms, were arranged upon a circuit with a battery of five carbon elements. The total resistance of the circuit, exclusive of the battery, was 25 ohms. A drumhead of goldbeater's skin*, seven centimeters in diameter, was placed in front of each electromagnet, and a circular piece of clock-spring, one centimeter in diameter, was glued to the middle of each membrane.

This design was one of the telephone setups shown at the Philadelphia Centennial Exhibition. Sunday, June 25, 1876 was a notable day in the history of the telephone. Bell continued to be burdened by his classes during May and June of 1876. Mabel Hubbard had urged Bell to exhibit his multiple telegraph and telephone at the Centennial. Patents had now issued on both and the problem was now to create public interest, not secrecy. He was, however, unwilling to do so, mindful of needed improvements in the telephone. When at last in April he consented to the exhibit, it was too late to enter them in the technical section where they belonged. Mr. Hubbard was in charge of the educational section of the

---

*The prepared outside membrane of the large intestine of an ox. It took its name from the fact that it was used between leaves of the metal when beating it.

Massachusetts entry at the Exhibition, and Bell had entered an exhibit of Visible Speech charts there. Hubbard assured him that even though the date had expired for new entries, it would be a simple matter to add his apparatus to his earlier exhibit. Bell considered this unethical and not until the wrath of the entire Hubbard household was brought to bear upon him did he relent. Thus at the last minute Bell's telegraphic and telephonic apparatuses were sandwiched in with the Visible Speech charts in an obscure corner of the Massachusetts educational exhibit.

Bell's annual examinations of his speech classes began Monday, June 26. A few days before, a wire was received from Mr. Hubbard at Philadelphia that the Centennial judges would reach the section containing Bell's exhibits on Sunday the 25th. Bell was beside himself. He maintained that he had to remain in Boston to look after his pupils. After much persuasion by Mabel and her mother, he left for Philadelphia on Saturday accompanied by William Hubbard, a young nephew of Gardiner Hubbard. History records no reason why the faithful Watson was not taken along to assist in the presentation to the judges. Bell had resolved that come what may, he was returning to Boston Sunday night to begin his examinations on the 26th.

Sunday was a hot and humid day. Just before the committee reached Bell's exhibit, they had decided they had had enough for one day. Fortunately the Emperor of Brazil, who was visiting the States and that morning was accompanying the group of judges, recognized Bell and began a conversation with him. The two had met a few weeks previously relative to their common interest in the education of the deaf. Bell now informed the Emperor of his great disappointment that the committee was not going to get to his exhibit that day since he was forced to leave that evening for Boston. "Ah!" said Dom Pedro, "Then we must have a look at it now." The weary judges could do nothing else but follow their famous guest.

Bell had decided to concentrate on the telephone. He now went to the transmitter which was on the other side of the building, about 500 feet from the receiver. He began reciting Hamlet and members of the committee and visitor took turns at the receiver. Sir William Thomson, later Lord Kelvin, headed up the committee. Everything went excellently. In his recommendation to the Award Committee relative to Bell's exhibit Sir William said in part:

> I need scarcely say I was astonished and delighted as were others, including some other judges of our group, who witnessed the experiments and verified with their own ears the electric transmission of speech. This, perhaps the greatest marvel hitherto achieved by the electric telegraph, has been obtained by appliances of quite a homespun and rudimentary character. With somewhat more advanced plans and more powerful apparatus we may confidently expect that Mr. Bell will give us the means of making voice and spoken words audible through the electric wire to an ear hundreds of miles distant.

Before the judges left the exhibit area they asked that the apparatus be moved to the Judges' Hall the following Monday for further tests. Bell agreed reluctantly since it meant leaving the apparatus in the hands of the inexperienced William Hubbard. The second test worked out very well also, with Sir William bringing Lady Thomson to listen and speak over the apparatus. Since Thomson wanted to see more of Bell's magic before he returned to England, he visited Bell in Boston in early July. Atlantic and Pacific Telegraph Company provided their facilities in the Equitable Building and conversation was exchanged between two rooms. Bell presented the instruments which were used that day to Sir William before he sailed.

When Bell went home for his summer vacation in late July he took an assortment of telephone equipment with him. After some preliminary work at Tutelo Heights, he decided he was ready for a test over a distance. Arrangements were made with the manager of the Brantford office of the Dominion Telegraph Company to use the wires between his office and their Paris office. The transmitter was set up in Brantford and the receiver in Paris with a spare wire to telegraph between the two stations the results from the receiving end to Brantford. The two towns were eight miles apart and the battery supplying current in the circuit was in Toronto, some 68 miles away. Graham was able to recognize his father's voice as well as that of his uncle, both of whom were at the Brantford station. Many townspeople gathered at the station in Paris and were allowed to listen in. The test continued for about three hours even though Bell had rented the line for only one hour.

In honor of this first successful test on a commercial telegraph line and his son's successes at the Centennial Exhibition, on August 4 Melville Bell held a public reception at the family home. They wished to demonstrate the telephone to the guests, but the nearest telegraph line was one-quarter mile away. The telegraph company again cooperated and Graham strung stove pipe wire fastened to fence posts to hook up with the telegraph line. This test included about 10 miles of wire and voices originating in Brantford were distinctly heard in Tutelo Heights. In these tests Bell exhibited true showmanship by using a transmitter which had a triple mouthpiece so that three people could sing into the instrument at the same time.

When Bell returned to Boston in early September, there was a lively interest in the telephone both on the part of the public and scientific groups. Several of the eastern papers had reported on the Brantford tests and on September 9 the *Scientific American* had an article on these tests. However, no one except Bell seemed to think that the telephone would ever compete with the Morse telegraph. The potential use of the telephone was considered that of sending messages as by telegraph and critics contended that the spoken word would be much more liable to error than the dots and dashes of the telegraph.

Thomas Watson had now been induced by Hubbard to give up his job at Williams' shop and spend full time assisting Bell. He was given a one-tenth interest in the Bell patents plus nine dollars a week, which was about half of what he was making at the shop. Beginning about October 1, the two began a period of intensive work on the telephone. They studied diaphragms of all sizes including one of boiler-plate iron, three feet in diameter and one inch thick! By trial and error they progressed. On October 9 they carried a two-way conversation over a distance of two miles, the first reciprocal conversation by telephone. By December successful tests were carried out over 143 miles of wire, from Boston to Conway, New Hampshire.

It was now 1877 and not one cent had yet been made from the telephone. Bell was still supporting himself by teaching and Sanders was bearing about 90% of all experimental costs, with Hubbard the remaining 10%. Bell's patents were offered to Western Union for one hundred thousand dollars. This would include three on the multiple telegraph and two on the telephone (3). Western Union had correctly decided that Bell's harmonic telegraph was inferior to Edison's quadruplex* which they were rapidly developing; but they completely missed the boat on the telephone. In refusing the offer of Bell and his backers, Western Union's Orton has been credited with that infamous remark, "What use could this company make of an electrical toy?" A few years later Orton would have been glad to pay millions for these same patents. Soon Western Union was to move from the colossus of American communications to a very secondary role.

Beginning in February 1877, Bell was invited by various organizations to present popular lectures and demonstrations dealing with the telephone. The professor, as he was called in those days, was a masterful speaker and stage manager. At 25 cents a head, and most gatherings were attended by several hundred, Bell's pecuniary status rapidly improved. Among others, three performances were given in Boston and three in New York. With this sudden wealth and a likelihood of establishing the telephone in England, he pressed his suit at the Hubbard household. The couple was married on July 11, 1877 and following a visit at Tutelo Heights, they sailed for England.

In early April 1877 the first commercial telephone began operation. It was a private line between Charles Williams' shop in Boston to his home in Somerville, a distance of about three miles. Watson strung the line. There was a formal opening and news reporters were invited. The *Boston Globe* commented as follows the next morning:

Perfecting the Telephone
Professor A. Graham Bell, the inventor of the telephone, had the pleasure of assisting yesterday at the opening of the first regular telephonic line in

*Chapter 3.

69

the world — a private line between the place of business of a gentleman in this city and his residence in Somerville. The instruments worked admirably, and the enterprising gentleman is very much pleased with his private telephonic wire between town and home. The practical value of Professor Bell's invention is being newly proved every day.

Bell's patents were assigned to the Bell Patent Association, the formal organization set up by Bell and his two financial backers, Thomas Sanders and Gardiner Hubbard. On July 9, 1877 this association was succeeded by the Bell Telephone Company. This company became the National Bell Telephone Company in 1879, and then the American Bell Telephone Company, organized March 20, 1880. Theodore N. Vail became general manager of the Bell Company in 1878. This company and successors established the practice of leasing telephones instead of selling them.

Shortly after Bell's lectures were given in New York in May 1877, William Orton, president of the Western Union Telegraph Company, had second thoughts about Bell's development. He summoned his chief engineer, William L. Pope, and directed him to look into the art and patent situation of this new device. Pope set up a group which searched the world literature and issued patents. He subsequently reported back to Orton that Bell's method was the only method for sending and reproducing speech. To Orton it seemed preposterous that a teacher of elocution could excel his own technical experts, so he decided to ignore the Bell patents. In December 1877 the American Speaking Telephone was formed with Western Union holding the bulk of the stock. Elisha Gray, an expert on telegraphy who had filed a caveat on the telephone shortly after Bell's first patent application, was retained, as was Professor A. E. Dolbear of Tufts University, who had frequented Bell's workshop and had actually carried out some electrical measurements for the latter. Orton's big ace was Thomas Edison, who, although having his own research organization at Menlo Park, New Jersey, was retained for part-time work on problems submitted to him by Western Union. Edison was now directed to devise some other means than that of Bell for talking over a wire.

Edison made several inventions relating to the telephone, the most important being his carbon transmitter. Bell's original telephone depended upon the vibrations of a diaphragm adjacent to the pole of a bar electromagnet. Edison employed two electrodes, one or both which were carbon. These were assembled together under mild pressure with one attached to a diaphragm. With Edison's transmitter the battery current did not flow through the main line but used an induction coil to generate much higher voltage than the current passing through the transmitter electrodes. With a higher voltage a greater resistance could be overcome and thus longer distances between stations were possible.

By early 1878 the Bell Associates had 3,000 telephones in use. By spring the American Speaking Telephone had incorporated Edison's transmitter with Bell's receiver and began to push its advantage supplying "superior telephones with all the latest improvements made by the original inventors, Dolbear, Gray, and Edison". Meanwhile the Bell Associates prepared to sue the American Speaking Telephone based on Bell's two patents (2, 3). Sanders was struggling to keep the Bell organization going. By early 1878 he had not only expended all of his own funds, but had borrowed heavily. Only by the help of Sanders' relatives did the Bell Telephone Company avoid bankruptcy. The Western Union subsidiary blocked the Bell group by Western Union's exclusive rights-of-way over housetops, along railroads and highways, and its monopolies in railroad offices and hotel lobbies.

Bell and his young wife spent 18 months in England, obviously leaving it to others to pioneer the telephone in America and fight their arch rival, Western Union. Bell was acclaimed by scientific and engineering societies. In October he was guest of honor at a special meeting of the Society of Telegraph Engineers. He attempted to raise capital for the development of the telephone in England. He lectured before learned societies on the education of deaf children. The Queen attended one of his exhibitions.

In the spring of 1878 the Bell interests formed the Electric Telephone Company in England with 39 subscribers. Bell's original patent was not filed in England due to the George Brown episode, but he filed improvement patents there including the metal diaphragm. Edison's London representative had set up the Edison Telephone Company using a so-called chalk receiver to replace Bell's diaphragm-electromagnet type. Edison's receiver was less satisfactory than that of Bell, but it did help the Edison interests to get a more satisfactory settlement with the Electric Telephone Company. The Bell and Edison interests combined in June 1880 to form the United Telephone Company with the Bell Company receiving 40% of the shares of the new company and the Edison Company 23%.

Meanwhile the American Bell group was assembling evidence for its forthcoming suit. Cable after cable came to Bell requesting written evidence of various dates, etc. Bell had loaned many of his written records, newspaper clippings, etc. to a newswoman who had written a brochure for the new British company and these records were lost.

Bell's Exeter shop was searched and valuable missing letters and records were found in dusty drawers and even the wastepaper basket. Bell became despondent over statements coming out of America that he was not the inventor of the telephone after all, and when he returned to Quebec on November 10, 1878 Mr. Hubbard had to send Watson to meet the boat to be sure that Bell came to Boston. Bell insisted on first going to his father's home but Watson stayed with him and only narrowly got him to Boston in time for necessary statements and signatures before the deadline of filing their deposition in the suit with Western Union.

Bell was retained by the Bell Company at $5,000/year as an "electrician", but his actual capacity was to assist counsel in its case against Western Union. After both sides had prepared their testimony, George Gifford, chief counsel for Western Union, advised his clients that Bell was unquestionably the first inventor. The suit never came to trial. Western Union settled for 20% of the net income from licenses and leases of speaking telephones used in the United States for the next 17 years. They agreed to go out of the telephone business and transfer all of their telephones, exchanges, etc. to the Bell Company at cost price. In December 1879 the stock of the Bell Company sold at $995 per share even though it had never paid a dividend. Growth then became phenomenal. In 1880 the number of telephones in use more than doubled over the total in use at the beginning of that year.

Never in the history of patents, before or since, has there been the array of litigations that poor Bell and his associates had to endure. The total number reached the unbelievable figure of 600. Most of them never reached the jurisdiction of the courts, but many did. In fact five suits were carried to the United States Supreme Court and all decisions were for Bell. Probably the reason for so many would-be inventors of the telephone was that it was the use of an undulatory electric current which was Bell's basic invention. The physical structure of the telephone had little to do with his patent coverage.

A decision relative to one of Bell's suits contained the following bit of wisdom:

It is an historical fact that the introduction of valuable and important inventions is productive of a host of rival claimants; and so the steady growth and assured success of the articulating telephone as a commercial venture had the usual effect of developing, reviving, and resurrecting all manner of inventions, and contrivances, both near and remote, upon which the mere shadow of a claim to priority could possibly be based, whereby the honors and profits justly due to its author could be secured.

Stimulated by visions of glory and profit, all manner of incomplete, dormant, unsuccessful, and abandoned inventions and devices have been brought to light, polished, and made to resemble as much as possible the real article, in order that their projectors might obtain, or at least participate in, the profits.

The development of the telephone in the United States led to one of the most successful businesses in our history. Although profitable to those who pioneered it, its success can best be measured by a job well done. In 1899 American Telephone and Telegraph Company became the central organization of the Bell system with numerous operating telephone subsidiaries. In 1882 Western Electric Company was acquired as the system's manufacturing and supply unit. In 1925 the Bell Telephone Laboratories was established. This research and development group invented the transistor, was a pioneer in radar, and continues to be the world's foremost research organization in the field of communications.

The litigation with Western Union was known as the Dowd case since the suit was brought against Dowd, an agent of the American Speaking Telephone Company in Massachusetts. In July 1879 Bell made a deposition in connection with this case. It constitutes about 100 pages of print. In 1908 the American Bell Telephone of Boston published this testimony plus additional testimony given in subsequent cases (4). This composite of material provides an excellent early history of the telephone. It shows also why Bell became exasperated because of the time and effort he had to give to this multitude of litigations.

Except for the time preparing depositions and appearing in court as expert witness in the many court cases dealing with his patents, after his return from England in late 1878, Bell had little to do with the telephone. He was interested neither in development studies which might lead to commercialization of an invention nor manufacturing operations. He did, however, maintain an interest in new things until the day of his death. Often this research dealt with subjects such as improved methods for teaching the deaf, where there was no opportunity to get patents or financial gain. Bell's researches after 1880 were supported by himself. In October 1917 at the unveiling ceremony of the Bell Memorial at Brantford, A. Graham Bell included the following in his remarks:

I cannot claim what you know as the modern telephone. It is the product of many, many minds. All I did was to initiate the movement of the transmission of speech by electricity.

While in England in 1877-78, Bell learned of some recent work there with selenium. A very unusual property of selenium is that it is a better electrical conductor when exposed to light than when in the dark. Bell visualized this phenomenon as another means of generating undulatory electric currents. In late 1878 the Bell family had moved to Washington, D. C. and he had a small shop and laboratory there. His assistant now was Sumner Tainter, who was an instrument maker and a former employee of the Williams shop, Boston. An apparatus was constructed using a crystalline selenium cell which was in circuit with a telephone receiver. A mirror so thin that it could be vibrated by the voice was used to reflect light rays to the selenium. Vibrations of the mirror resulted in light of different degrees of intensity to the cell which in turn varied its electrical resistance resulting in an undulatory current in the circuit which led to a telephone receiver.

Bell succeeded in transmitting sound a distance of 1¼ miles by what he termed a wireless telephone. He gave it the name photophone. In December 1880 four United States patents were granted to Bell on his new invention (5). He offered these to the telephone company, but they had already more problems than they could handle in getting the conventional telephone on a firm basis. The photophone never reached commercial success although the German government attempted to use it for sending messages from lighthouses to ships at sea.

In 1880 Bell was awarded the Volta Prize by the French Academy of Sciences for his invention of the electric-speaking telephone. This prize was established by the first Napoleon and named after Alessandro Volta, an Italian physicist. The prize was 50,000 francs, the equivalent of about 10,000 dollars at that time. With this very generous award, Bell set up the Volta Laboratory Association at 1221 Connecticut Ave., Washington. He was joined by his cousin, Chichester Bell, a chemist formerly on the faculty of the University of London.

One of the first research projects undertaken by the Volta Laboratory group was on the phonograph. Edison had invented the phonograph in December 1877 and then did little with it as he concentrated on electric lighting. The original machine consisted of a grooved brass cylinder wrapped with tin foil on which the recording was indented by a stylus. Apparently Bell felt that with his extensive knowledge of the mechanics of speech and technical knowledge of the science of the telephone, he and his associates should be able to greatly improve the phonograph. He was as usual thinking of the deaf; perhaps persons not wholly deaf might be able to hear a phonographic reproduction even if they could not hear the original sound. The associates spent several years on this project and developed a wax-coated cardboard cylinder for the recording surface. They got several patents dealing with the phonograph and organized the Volta Graphophone Company, later called the American Graphophone Company, to manufacture and market their machine. The Volta Associates sold their patents relating to the Graphophone, so Bell did not get involved in the business end of their development. Bell's share of this sale was $200,000. The Graphophone is covered in a thorough manner by Read and Welch (6).

This sale was a real windfall and that received probably greatly exceeded the true value of these patents. However, it did allow Bell to do something which was very near to his heart. He had already set up the Volta Bureau to collect and publish information relating to the deaf. He used the $200,000 which he received from the patent sale to set up this bureau on a permanent basis.

Bell remained a foremost authority on teaching the deaf until his death. The famous Helen Keller, who because of serious illness at the age of 19 months lost her sight and hearing and soon became mute, was one of the beneficiaries of Bell's teaching. Bell served as a consultant in her education which was by private instruction and at the Horace Mann School in Boston. Many years later in her autobiography, Miss Keller spoke of the first time she met Bell:

> Child as I was, I at once felt the tenderness and sympathy which endeared Doctor Bell to so many hearts . . . .But I did not dream that that interview would be the door through which I should pass from darkness into life, from isolation to friendship, companionship, knowledge, love.

Early in the 1880's Bell carried out an extensive study on the heredity of the deaf. He found to his dismay that the deaf-mute population was increasing more rapidly than the total population. This he attributed to intermarrying of the deaf. He used this information to urge teaching the deaf in their normal environment so that they would more likely marry hearing partners and thus reduce the likelihood of having deaf children.

The Bell family spent a vacation in Nova Scotia in the summer of 1885 and found the area near Baddeck so appealing that they decided to build a summer home there. A home, laboratory, and work shops were built on a headland across the bay. This became Bell's second home and as he became older the family lived and worked in these quarters the greater part of the year. It was here that he carried out aerial locomotion studies which led to the formation of the Aerial Experiment Association, a group that was second only to the Wright brothers in pioneering heavier-than-air flight in North America.

In the early 1890's Bell began studying aerial flight by means of giant kites. As they became larger they were pulled by manila ropes attached to the collar of a galloping farm horse. Bell risked his international reputation in proclaiming that man could conquer air as he had done land and sea. Samuel Langley aptly indicated the attitude of most scientists at that time:

> . . .a great many scientific men treated the whole subject with entire indifference, as unworthy of attention or outside of legitimate research, the proper field of the charlatan, and one on which it was scarcely prudent for a man with a reputation to lose to enter.

Lord Kelvin, Bell's famous friend who had given him great encouragement in the early days of the telephone, now warned the inventor not to waste his time on his aerial experiments. In a letter to Mrs. Bell, following a meeting with the Bells in the summer of 1897, Kelvin passed on some fatherly advice to Bell in this indirect manner:

> When I spoke to him on the subject at Halifax I wished to dissuade him from giving his valuable time and resources to attempts which I believed, and still believe, could only lead to disappointment, if carried on with any expectation of leading to a useful flying machine.

Simon Newcomb, the foremost American astronomer in the 19th century, echoed the dissent of the science fraternity when he said:

> . . .the construction of an aerial vehicle which could carry even a single man from place to place at pleasure requires the discovery of some new metal or some new force.

Since Bell was already using aluminum tubes in constructing his kites, Newcomb was wrong on both counts.

Bell's and Langley's common interest in heavier-than-air flight brought them together. Langley visited Beinn Bhreagh, which the Bells called their expanded home in Nova Scotia, and Bell had an opportunity to view Langley's experiments in May 1896 at Quantico, Virginia at which time an unmanned steam-driven plane model circled a distance of 3/4 mile. In 1901 Bell changed his kites from a box-type construction to multiple tetrahedral cells, which made possible equal strength in all directions and any possible shape. In 1899 Langley had received a $50,000 grant from the United States War Department for developing a flying machine for military purposes. In 1903 he attempted two manned flights from a houseboat on the Potomac, both of which were failures. Langley's design was basically sound and his failures were due to a series of unfortunate circumstances. It was left to the Wright brothers in December of that year to achieve the first powered, sustained, and controlled airplane flight in history.

The flights of the Wright brothers on the outer banks of North Carolina were carried out in great secrecy. After their initial success they spent about two years working at

Courtesy of American Telephone and Telegraph Company

Alexander Graham Bell, age 20 years

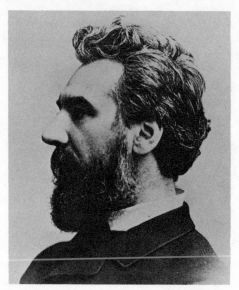

Courtesy of American Telephone and Telegraph Company

Alexander Graham Bell, age about 39 years

The Aerial Experiment Association; (left to right) Glenn Curtiss, John McCurdy, Bell, "Casey" Baldwin, and Thomas Selfridge

their Dayton, Ohio shop in perfecting an experimental plane and due to problems with business spies and inability to get capital to promote their invention, it was not until 1908 that their extensive flying experiments began.

By 1907 Bell's skilled workman, Hector MacNeil, had built a huge kite, 42½ feet from tip to tip, mounted on pontoons. In search of an engine to get it off the water, Bell approached Glenn Curtiss who was building motorcycles at Hammondsport, New York. Curtiss spent most of that summer working with Bell at Beinn Bhreagh. They were joined by J. A. McCurdy and F. W. Baldwin, graduates of Toronto University, and Lieutenant Thomas Selfridge of the United States Army.

On suggestion of Mabel Bell this group of five men in October 1907 formed the Aerial Experiment Association. She gave the organization $20,000 to get started and later added another $10,000. Curtiss was the senior member of the younger group and he became director of experiments at $5,000 per year. Baldwin was chief engineer and McCurdy his assistant, both with a salary of $1,000. Selfridge declined any pay since he was functioning as an observer on full pay from the army.

After getting scientific data by means of kites and other equipment at Beinn Bhreagh during the summer and fall of 1907, the group moved on to Curtiss' motorcycle factory at Hammondsport for the winter. Before leaving Canada Bell's huge kite, which he had christened Cygnet, was air-tested with Lieutenant Selfridge aboard. On being pulled by a steamer in Baddeck Bay, it rose 168 feet from the water and was aloft for seven minutes. Apparently due to a shift in the wind the kite came down gently on the water. Before it could be cut free it was wrecked as it was pulled through the water. Selfridge dove free of the kite and escaped with only a ducking. This mishap ended any prospect of putting an engine in the Cygnet, but it provided the first passenger carrying flight in Canada.

The Association built four useful flying machines. The first called Red Wing, because of the red silk fabric used on the wings, was a biplane equipped with a 40 horsepower V-8 cylinder, air-cooled engine designed and built by Curtiss. On March 12, 1908 Baldwin flew this plane a distance of 319 feet over the ice of Lake Keuka near Hammondsport. Baldwin was the first Britisher and the seventh person in the world to fly. It was also the first public flight in North America.

The three other machines were improved versions of the first. In July 1908 their third plane, the June Bug, piloted by Curtiss, won the Scientific American Trophy for flying the first measured kilometer (0.621 mile) under test conditions. Their fourth and heaviest machine, the Silver Dart, was the first plane with rubber-coated fabric on the wings. It was taken to Baddeck early in 1909 and there McCurdy piloted it eight miles in 11 minutes. A second Cygnet of tetrahedral construction was built and several engines were used in unsuccessful attempts to get it off the water.

The Association was dissolved after one and one-half years having achieved its objective of "getting into the air". The group then formed the Canadian Aerodome Company at Baddeck with financial backing by the Bells. Five aircraft were built by this company. One was tested by the Canadian military but they decided that airplanes held no promise for military purposes. No government support was given the Aerodome Company and in a short time it disbanded.

The activities of the Aerial Experiment Association forced the Wright brothers to publicize their accomplishments. Wilbur Wright flew in public for the first time in August 1908 near Le Mans, France. Orville remained in America and began making flights for the army near Washington, D. C. in September. On September 17 a fractured propeller caused his aircraft to crash, killing his passenger, Thomas Selfridge. Thus Bell's friend and associate became the first fatality in powered aviation.

McCurdy and Curtiss joined forces to "barnstorm" around North America. Aviation was still considered only suitable for daredevils with no practical civil or military use. By 1911 Curtiss had several firsts including the first practical float plane. This fulfilled one of Bell's basic objectives since he maintained that it was safer to operate aircraft off of water as compared to land. Curtiss and McCurdy both became famous in their own right in the aviation field.

Surprisingly accounts dealing with the history of aviation usually make no mention of Alexander Graham Bell. In the very extensive article on the history of aviation in *Encyclopedia Britannica*, there is nothing on Bell's work. *Encyclopedia Americana*, in an article on the history of aeronautics, states only of Bell that he financed the Aerial Experiment Association. The facts are, of course, that the Bells not only financed the Association but brought the men together who subsequently became members of it on Mrs. Bell's suggestion. Their early planes were built largely on data obtained at Beinn Bhreagh.

Admittedly Bell's tetrahedral structure found no place in aircraft manufacture, and he contributed little technically to the Aerial Experiment Association after it was formed. However, Bell was carrying out kite experiments directed towards heavier-than-air flight several years before those of the Wright brothers. He defied most of the scientific profession who maintained that a practical manned heavier-than-air craft was impossible. He supported Langley when the newspapers were branding his unsuccessful tests as a performance of Darius Green and his flying machine in person. When he was acclaimed at the annual banquet of the Aero Club of America for the epic flight of the "Red Wing", he gave sole credit to Curtiss, Baldwin, McCurdy, and Selfridge. He was instrumental in getting the Smithsonian Institution to establish the Langley Medal and to give the first award to the Wright brothers. Certainly in America, Graham and Mabel Bell were aviation's first patrons (7).

In July 1881 President James Garfield was wounded with two bullets from a would-be assassin's gun. One bullet was lodged in the lower abdomen near the spine. The attending physicians debated whether to operate to remove the bullet or to leave it with the hope it would become safely encysted. The exact location of the metal was necessary before an intelligent decision could be made. X-ray technology was unknown in 1881. Bell, believing that he could pinpoint the location of the bullet if not too deeply embedded by a combination of an induction coil and telephone receiver, offered his services. They were accepted and Bell, with his assistant Tainter, frantically began a series of tests on lead bullets of different shapes buried at various depths in meat obtained from the butcher. Tests followed on Civil War veterans who still carried rifle balls. Two tests followed on the President but they were inconclusive. The patient was moved to Elberon, New Jersey early in September to escape the heat of the city, and there he died on September 19. Postmortem examination showed the bullet too deeply embedded to have been detected by Bell's method.

Bell was ridiculed by the newspapers as a publicity seeker, but the physicians in attendance were appreciative of his efforts. Bell published later the details of the test and various laboratory data on bullets of different shapes (8). Subsequently he perfected his method for locating lodged bullets using a needle in combination with a telephone receiver and a metal plate placed on the patient's body; contact of the needle with a piece of metal, as a bullet, resulted in an audible click in the receiver. He made no attempt to gain financially from his many months of labor in developing this technique. For this contribution to surgery, the University of Heidelberg gave him one of its relatively rare honorary degrees of Doctor of Medicine.

Although Bell's most important contributions in the field of innovation were the telephone, methods for teaching the deaf, and pioneering in aviation, these were not all. After work on aircraft was dropped, Baldwin continued to work with Bell. During World War I they developed hydrofoil boats as possible submarine chasers. They built a 60-foot torpedo-like hull with fins on each side powered with air propellers. Weighing close to five and one-half tons, it reached a speed of 70.9 miles per hour, a world's speed record for boats (which held for about 10 years).

Bell was never happy unless he was working on something new. He had a flock of sheep at his Canadian estate and spent years trying to develop a breed which gave birth to twins rather than the usual single lamb. This he succeeded in doing but he overlooked the facts that his new breed were poor wool producers and the mutton of low quality! He spent days trying to determine why a cat can always land on its feet from a fall while most animals cannot. He sent letters to his medical friends suggesting techniques for treating cancer with radium, use of a vacuum jacket for applying artificial respiration, as well as many learned articles on the anatomy of the vocal organs.

Bell's early training was in public speaking and he

delighted in speaking before groups. He believed strongly in communication between workers in a given field both at meetings and by publication. He was founder of the American Association to Promote the Teaching of Speech to the Deaf. He not only initiated various publications for the deaf but sponsored and financed for 12 years the weekly publication of *Science*, at that time the foremost periodical dealing with original scientific articles. *Science* is now the official publication of the American Association for the Advancement of Science. Bell was one of the founders of the National Geographic Society in 1888 and became its president in 1898. He brought in young Gilbert Grosvenor as editor of the Society's magazine and the two of them modified drastically the format of the publication with more emphasis on meaningful pictures. The meteoric rise in Society membership began shortly thereafter. Bell was elected a regent of Smithsonian Institution in 1898. In 1918 he published his massive work on eugenics entitled "Duration of Life and Conditions Associated with Longevity".

Bell's inventive career brought him many awards including the John Fritz Gold Medal in 1907 and the Thomas Alva Edison Medal in 1914. He received 12 honorary degrees from American and foreign universities. Later in his life his formal title became Doctor Bell and, unlike Edison, he preferred the doctor prefix as compared to mister.

After inventing the telephone and marrying the daughter of a wealthy family, Bell had no need to seek further wealth. Mabel Bell's total deafness may very well have had a major effect on her husband's work and his scientific and social relationships. The marriage was a close one. Bell took part in few social functions unless his wife could also participate. At the dining table he would always try to sit across from her so she could read his lips and thus take part in the general conversation. Bell no doubt felt that his wife was at a disadvantage in a social-minded city as Washington, D. C. It is very likely that she was much happier in an isolated spot in Nova Scotia than the hubbub of the capital city. It has been suggested that the reason Bell gave up work on the telephone and photophone was that these were things in which his wife could play no part. She had to take it on faith that one could communicate by telephone; she was never able to use one. Kites and other aerial devices were different; she could see them. Thus it is safe to say that Bell gave up a part of his inventive and scientific career in order to be a good husband.

As an experimenter Bell was largely a dabbler rather than one carrying out a well-organized research program. While inventing the telephone, he taught by day and was an experimenter in somebody's attic or basement at night. He worked alone until success was eminent and then had only one assistant. His Volta Laboratory was the nearest of his workshops that one might call a well-equipped research laboratory, but he worked there only a few years and on a part-time basis. Although Bell spent the major part of his last 35 years in a vacation environment, he continued to experiment. He appeared to pick out important fields of research which needed major improvements before any degree of success was possible. He was ahead of his time in his aerial experiments, but instead of assembling a competent staff and moving ahead which he was financially capable of doing, he dabbled for about 15 years. It was not until he was joined by his young associates in 1907 that Bell's experiments converted to a quantitative basis and actual airplanes built, but by that time it was too late. Even so, the Aerial Experiment Association which based their know-how on Bell's early experiments and devices which he had constructed, was second only to the two Wright brothers in pioneering aviation in North America.

The many litigations in connection with Bell's telephone patents left their mark. The inventor saw how close he came to losing everything because of inadequate records kept of his early experiments. In later life the keeping of experimental records which would satisfy the most hostile court became a near mania with him. Every bit of experimental information, regardless how trivial, was written up in detail, signed, dated, and witnessed. All experimental devices were photographed. He spent a great deal of time dictating to his secretary various thoughts he had on research ideas to be filed away for record purposes.

Even at Beinn Bhreagh where Bell could set his own pace, he continued to work late. He would often not retire until three a.m. He would, however, sleep late and get seven to eight hours of sleep. Unlike Edison, he made no claim that he could get along with short periods, although while working on the telephone he slept much less than the conventional eight hours. He was a heavy eater and a poor patient when under a doctor's care. He usually decided what he should do as to medicine, diet, exercise, etc. rather than his doctor. Although he loved food he was not a gourmet. His favorites were lamb pie, ham-and-eggs, and porridge with plenty of heavy cream. He smoked a pipe and drank alcoholic beverages sparingly. He would not, however, allow liquor in his Washington home once the Prohibition Act had become law.

The Bells had two daughters, Elsie born in 1877 and Daisy in 1880. A son was born in August 1881 who, due to breathing difficulties, lived only a few hours. The mother was vacationing in Massachusetts at the time and the father was in Washington trying to save President Garfield's life. A second son was born prematurely in November 1883 and lived only a short time. This time Bell was in Hartford attending a convention of the National Academy of Sciences. The loss of their sons was a grievous blow to the Bells. Graham was proud of his ancestors and had hoped there would be a fourth Alexander Bell. Mable Bell was known to have said that God had taken her babies away because of some fault of hers.

Elsie Bell married Gilbert H. Grosvenor and they had seven children. Daisy married David Fairchild, a noted botanist, and they became parents of a son and two daughters. Thus the Bells had grandchildren galore to enliven their lives, particularly since Beinn Bhreagh was a favorite meeting place of the "clan" during the summer months.

Bell had ambitions to become a practicing scientist. In 1878 he sought without success to succeed Joseph Henry as physicist at the Smithsonian Institution. He published widely in both technical and nontechnical publications on many subjects and addressed many learned societies (9). Although he obtained only 30 U.S. patents (9), his invention of the telephone was such a grandiose achievement that it marks Bell as one of the greatest inventors of all time. Also the telephone overshadowed all else that Bell did, resulting in some lack of recognition for several other outstanding developments.

The reader seeking more details about the life of Alexander Graham Bell is fortunate in that the first biography in which Bell's personal papers were made available to the author has now been published (10). Following the invention of the telephone, Bell kept voluminous records of his personal, experimental, and business affairs. Because of extensive litigation proceedings relative to his telephone patents and his early correspondence to his parents and others, Bell's early life and activities are also well documented. Author Robert Bruce used this material well and his book should satisfy even the most diligent seeker of information on Alexander Graham Bell.

Alexander Graham Bell died at his Canadian home on August 2, 1922 at the age of 75. He suffered from diabetes and that was the day before insulin. He was buried on the hilltop at Beinn Bhreagh. Although born a Scotsman and living a large part of his life in Canada, Bell had become an American citizen in 1882. He was thankful for the opportunities his adopted country had given him. His grave is marked with a rock in which is set a tablet bearing only his name, dates, vocation of inventor, and the statement which he himself had specified: "Died a citizen of the U.S.A." His coffin of pine boards lined with airplane cloth, made in the laboratory workshop, was carried to his grave by his workmen. Few men so famous have gone to their final resting places with less fanfare.

Graham Bell was the crutch by means of which his deaf wife led a reasonably normal and happy life. Two months after his death she commented, "I thought I would always have him . . . " Although 10 years his junior, Mabel Bell survived her husband by only five months. She was buried beside him on the hill overlooking the bay.

Thomas Alva Edison

Thomas Edison, without the pretense of a public relations department, became the most popular scientist of all time. Whereas inventors of labor-saving devices, such as Elias Howe, inventor of the sewing machine, were originally denounced as enemies of the people, Edison's inventions brought only hurrahs. The difference was that the phonograph, the electric light, and the motion picture were entirely new things. The phonograph was so weird that many thought that the sound coming out of a box or from a cranked cylinder was a trick. Electricity was so new that few could understand how a light could be maintained connected only to a wire. Motion pictures brought the magic of active life to the remote village. These three Edison inventions took place and were introduced to the public within a period of less than 20 years. No wonder various polls taken during Edison's lifetime showed that he was considered the country's most valuable citizen or second only to the nation's President.

The appeal of Edison's inventions reached out worldwide. The following incidents illustrate that his name had become known outside the United States even to the common man.

In 1889 on a trip to France, Edison disembarked at Le Havre with a box of cigars under his arm. Since tobacco was a government monopoly in France, he was confronted by a French customs agent. The gesturing and flow of French language had no effect on Edison, who proceeded to move forward. Edison's secretary, Alfred Tate, rushed up, took the arm of the agent, and pointing to Edison said, "C'est Monsieur A-de-sohn! Comprennez? Monsieur A-de-sohn."

"Ah-a-a" breathed the French official gazing in obvious awe at Edison, "Ah-a-a M'sieu A-de-sohn." A handshake from Edison allowed the party, including the contraband cigars, to move on as the customs man kept murmuring, "Ah-a-a M'sieu A-de-sohn!"

A businessman from the United States, in Russia during the first part of World War I, described an incident which occurred in a barbershop there. Learning through an interpreter that his customer was an American and not an Englishman as he had assumed, the barber stood back and exclaimed, "Ee-di-son." This illiterate man apparently considered this name the most important thing he knew about America.

It is also amazing that during his long lifetime Edison did not descend from this apex of fame which he acquired at a relatively early age. His name continued to be kept before the public in a favorable light by such things as batteries for electric automobiles, his chairmanship of the Naval Consulting Board during World War I, Edison Cement, and his work on rubber from plants. At the time of his death in 1931, Edison's body lay in state at the West Orange laboratories, where thousands came to view him; many had stood in line for hours to pay their last respects.

Thomas Edison was born in Milan, Ohio on February 11, 1847. In 1854 the family moved to Port Huron, Michigan. Tom was the youngest of seven children. The three next to him died at early ages leaving the boy with two sisters and a brother much older than he, the next youngest being 18 years older than Tom. Tom had been a rather sickly child and shortly after the move to Port Huron became seriously ill with scarlet fever. This delayed his formal education, and it was not until the fall of 1855, at the age of eight and one-half, that he was enrolled in a one-room school. Tom proved to be completely incompatible with the teaching methods used and after three months his formal education came to an end. The schoolmaster felt the child was too stupid to learn and the father was reluctant to pay the small fee for a son who did not want to go to school. His mother, a schoolteacher before marriage, decided to teach her son. Realizing he had unusual reasoning powers, she ignored the ABC approach and began at once to read world history and the classics to him. The boy became fascinated by such books and was inspired to read them himself. Within a year he had become a rapid reader and had included science in his sphere of interest.

Since Tom did not attend school and had no playmates within the family, he tended to do things alone. By the age of 10, using some chemicals purchased at the local pharmacy, various scraps of metal which he had found, electrical batteries which he had made, and a science dictionary, he was conducting experiments. He and a neighbor boy set up a telegraph line between their homes, a distance of one-half mile. The need of money to buy supplies motivated the young scientist to undertake several ventures, all with an innovative approach. Tom constructed a crude steam engine to run a circular saw for preparing firewood to sell to the townspeople. A local physician had a theory that it was helpful to apply a mild electric current to certain of his suffering patients. Tom with battery was occasionally called on to perform this function at one dollar a visit. During the summer of 1858 Tom and another boy raised vegetables and sold them in Port Huron and surrounding area using a hired horse and cart.

Tom's big opportunity came at the age of 12 when he got the job as water boy on a passenger-freight train of the Grand Trunk Railroad running daily from Port Huron to Detroit. He soon graduated to newsboy and general vendor. He not only sold his merchandise on the train and at the various stops along the line but also established a news depot at Port Huron and, in season, a store selling fruits and vegetables not available in the Port Huron area. He bought a secondhand press, set it up in the baggage car, and published a weekly newspaper, selling it in addition to the newspapers and magazines he picked up in Detroit.

Tom's railroad job not only provided him with several dollars per day, but also gave him a much broader view of life. His train left Port Huron at 7:00 a.m. and returned at 9:30 p.m. with an approximate eight-hour layover in Detroit. Tom spent much time at the public library there reading literally hundreds of books. By frequent visits to the railroad shops, he learned about the various machines used in shaping metals into useful products. He had a chance to observe the operations of the telegraph, not only in sending messages and bringing the nation's news to the newspapers, but also being essential in the operation of a railroad. At that time the telegraph companies were foremost in the technology of electricity and primary electrical batteries. It was certainly the most sophisticated industry based on new technology with which Tom had come in contact. Thus it was not surprising that the science-minded boy resolved to become a telegraph operator.

Sam Edison, Tom's father, was sort of a jack-of-all-trades

with his most successful vocation being carpentry. He read poorly and could hardly write. Although the Edison family could not be classified as being poor, there was only money for the essentials of life. Sam was known to hike to Detroit, a distance of 60 miles, in order to save carfare. Certainly hiring a tutor or paying for a private school for Tom was out of the question regardless how brilliant the boy might appear to be. Furthermore, his father hardly knew what education was beyond the three R's, and by the time Tom was in his early teens, his mother's health was poor and her mind failing. Thus at the age of 15, Tom, entirely on his own, decided that the telegraph offered him the best opportunity to make his way in the world.

Beginning in the fall of 1862, Tom received several months of apprenticeship instruction from J. U. Mackenzie, the telegraph operator at the Mt. Clemens, Michigan station. By early 1863 he was qualified as a second-class or "plug" telegrapher. It took no school diploma to get such a job. One had only to demonstrate that he could send and take messages by the Morse code and keep the equipment in working order. The Civil War was on and telegraph operators were in short supply. Certainly Tom did not take up telegraphy with the idea of increasing his wage rate; his first job, which was at Port Huron, paid less than one dollar per day. One can imagine the chagrin of the hapless father when his son gave up a job paying several dollars a day for one paying only a small fraction of that.

From 1863-67 the youth held numerous telegrapher positions, usually of short duration, in cities from Canada to Memphis; Tom was an excellent example of the well known fact that one interested only in research and development makes a poor employee for routine work. He was fired from jobs for allowing messages to accumulate in order to tend to an experiment which he was running, or for changing the telegraphic equipment in attempts to improve it. However, because of the shortage of operators and his willingness to work the night shift, he never had trouble finding new employment. Despite his indifference to becoming a master operator, by late 1864 he had graduated from the plug class to a full operator, which meant he could take press as well as send and receive routine messages. By early 1865 he was making $105 per month at the Cincinnati office, an excellent salary in those days. Also, happily, his deafness did not interfere with his performance as a telegraph operator.*

As Tom went from job to job, his mind became filled with ideas and schemes for improving the telegraph. Most of the managers were not technically qualified to discuss intelligently his revolutionary ideas, and at more than one station he became known as the "loony one". In late 1867 Tom had a job at the Western Union office in Boston. At that time Boston was the educational center and the nation's Mecca for inventors and would-be inventors. His move there was an attempt to find support for his ideas on improving the telegraph, including the sending of two messages simultaneously over one wire. Young Edison soon had himself a corner in the shop of Charles Williams, the organization which later was so helpful to Alexander Bell. Tom worked at Western Union at nights and much of the daylight hours at the Williams shop. He began to receive some financial backing to develop his ideas, and by

---

*Apparently a combination of after effects from his early siege with scarlet fever and an injury to his ears when a train conductor grasped his head in helping to pull him aboard a moving train had made Tom partially deaf. Later in life he maintained that his deafness was an asset in receiving telegraphic messages since he did not hear extraneous noises which would be distracting to one of normal hearing.

mid-1868 he had given up his Western Union duties to devote full time to his own projects. Thus, at the age of 21, the self-made young scientist was on his own.

Although the one year Edison spent on his own in Boston left him penniless, he moved on to New York City and soon began his meteoric career to fame and fortune. Shortly after his arrival there he obtained a job with the Gold Indicator Company, which rendered ticker service on gold prices to about 300 brokers. Although his salary soon reached $300 per month there, he resigned within a few months to join Franklin L. Pope in the latter's consulting firm. He left Pope within a year and by early 1871 was carrying out research and manufacturing certain telegraphic equipment in Newark, New Jersey. In 1876 he gave up most of his manufacturing operations and moved to nearby rural Menlo Park where he built, equipped, and staffed the first truly industrial research laboratory in the United States, and probably the first in the world.

Although Edison directed all technical work and carried out a great deal of it himself, he had a staff up to about 30 people. Francis R. Upton, a mathematical physicist, was his most trusted professional scientist, who did most of the paper work relating to the research and development programs. Dr. A. Haid, chemist, was in charge of chemical analyses and preparing and purifying chemicals used in the research work. Dr. Otto Moses was in charge of the library and carried out literature searches in foreign publications. Edison also had an excellent machine shop staffed with the best craftsmen from his former manufacturing operations in Newark. He had numerous laboratory technicians with expertise in various fields, headed up by his trusted business and laboratory manager, Charles Batchelor. Last, but not least, Edison had his own patent department.

In a period of about six years, Edison's Menlo Park

group set an unbelievable record as an "invention factory". Not only were the phonograph and the first practical incandescent electric light born there but also various improvements in telegraphy, development and commercialization of the carbon telephone transmitter, a highly improved dynamo, and numerous developments relating to the setting up of the first central station for generating and marketing electricity. At Menlo Park Edison had his banner year as an inventor; in 1882 he filed 107 U. S. patent applications which were subsequently granted as patents. A replica of Edison's Menlo Park laboratory was enshrined as a part of Greenfield Village in Dearborn, Michigan by Henry Ford (1).

In February 1881 Edison transferred his headquarters to 65 Broadway, New York in order to be near the manufacturing operations and the installation of lines and equipment for the Pearl Street central station which began operations on September 4, 1882. A small laboratory had been set up in New York for testing the equipment going into the installation. By 1884 Edison had abandoned any idea of returning to Menlo Park as his headquarters. He was then concentrating on business matters relating to the organization of electric manufacturing and illuminating companies both here and abroad. Beginning in 1886 all of Edison's maufacturing operations, except that of electric light bulbs, were transferred to Schenectady, New York, the present site of huge facilities of the General Electric Company.

But the inventor disliked business and longed to get back to the laboratory. A new laboratory was completed in West Orange, New Jersey in late 1887. There were four one-story laboratories of the bench-scale type and a three-story building housing the library, offices, experimental rooms, a machine shop, and stockroom. Total floor space was about 10 times that at Menlo Park. Various Edison industries subsequently were built near the new laboratories beginning with those for manufacturing phonographs and phonographic records. These laboratories are now the Edision National Historic Site, National Park Service of the U. S. Department of Interior. The nearby former Edison home, Glenmont, is a part of the site.

Edison vacationed in Fort Myers, Florida in 1886 and 1887 and bought 14 acres bordering on the bank of the Caloosahatchee River in Fort Myers. Two houses were built and extensive botanical gardens developed. Beginning in 1901 the Edison family spent several months there each winter. Mr. Edison had a laboratory-office where he continued to work during his "vacations". When his interest turned to rubber from plants in the early twenties, a complete laboratory was built across McGregor Boulevard, which cuts through the former Edison property. Much of the work on rubber was done there, including botanical studies using the garden area. This 14-acre estate was subsequently given to the city of Fort Myers by Mrs. Edison and is now open to the public. A new museum dealing with Edison's inventions was dedicated in February 1966 and is now a part of Thomas A. Edison's Winter Home site.

On Christmas Day 1871, Thomas Edison married Mary Stilwell of Newark. They had three children, Marion, Thomas Alva, Jr., and William Leslie. Mary Edison died of typhoid fever in 1884. In 1886 Edison married Mina Miller, the daughter of Lewis Miller of Akron, Ohio, a manufacturer of farm tools. They also had three children, Madeline, Charles, and Theodore. The father's idea of proper education for his children was self education as he had done. This practice was largely followed with his first three children. The second Mrs. Edison had different ideas and her two sons attended Massachusetts Institute of Technology and Madeline, Bryn Mawr College. Charles, Theodore, and Madeline's husband, John Eyre Sloan, all chose not to follow careers in the family business. Thomas Edison's industrial operations have now been discontinued or sold to others.

Thomas Edison's accomplishments literally covered all fields of engineering and many of the sciences. Once asked what his primary interest was he replied, "Everything". In this single chapter it is impossible to do more than to describe his work in a very general way. The reader wishing a more complete story on any phase of Edison's inventions should consult reference material (2). However, it is hoped that the following summaries will give the reader an overall picture of the new things which Edison did and will be a guide for possible further reading. It should be appreciated that as an applied scientist and engineer, Edison was more than an inventor; in most cases he attempted to bring his invention to the marketplace. As research and development people well know, this often takes more ingenuity and skill than does the original invention.

Telegraph and Telephone

In the present age of telephone, radio, and television, it is easy to forget that the telegraph was the sole means of communication between distances in the early 1870's. Even urgent local calls, such as fire alarms, were by telegraph. Because of the chaotic financial conditions following the Civil War, trading in gold became an important feature of high finance. Indicators or tickers were developed by Callahan, Laws, and others for reporting gold prices from a central point to brokers within a city.

Edison's first job in New York was with a company using the Laws indicator. In his subsequent cooperation with F. L. Pope and shortly thereafter, Edison took out 46 patents on stock-printing instruments and devices, two of the patents being jointly with Pope. This work culminated into the ticker known as the Edison Universal Stock Printer. This device was controlled by Western Union and was used worldwide by stock exchanges. Thus Edison's inventive work on stock printers was a major factor in the development of the art whereby stock exchanges send prices in a continuous manner to stock brokers country-wide. Edison's development of the universal stock printer led to his manufacturing operations in Newark in 1871.

In the early 1870's, a group of private investors purchased the rights to a patent of George D. Little and founded the Automatic Telegraph Company. The Little process utilized a moving tape with perforations corresponding to the Morse dots and dashes used in sending. The dot and dash signals were recorded on another tape at the receiving end. Little attempted to develop not only an automatic system but one much faster than sending by hand. His equipment proved to be defective in a number of respects, and Edison was hired by the Automatic Telegraph group to see if the operation could be improved. He succeeded in developing equipment whereby over 200 words per minute could be sent as compared with 40-50 maximum by hand.

Early in 1873 Edison undertook further work on his duplex system of sending telegraph messages, a project which had interested him ever since his days as an operator. Western Union was interested and allowed him to use facilities at their New York station at night when the lines were free. Before long he had developed the quadruplex, a technique for sending four messages simultaneously over one wire, two in each direction. It operated successfully and was a major technical triumph for Edison. Its use greatly cut down on the need for new lines to handle the ever-increasing volume of telegraphic communication; after it was fully installed on Western Union lines in 1876, the company reported an annual saving of $500,000. The quadruplex was widely used for about 30 years. As pointed out in Chapter 2, it was Edison's quadruplex which caused Western Union to lose interest in Alexander Bell's harmonic telegraph. Edison received $30,000 for his patents covering the quadruplex.

Also as pointed out in Chapter 2, Edison was one of the inventors engaged by Western Union in their attempt to develop a speaking telegraph outside the Bell patents. Several years before Edison had constructed a rheostat — a current regulating device that works by varying electrical resistance — which consisted of an upright tube of insulating material filled with metallic discs separated by fine particles of graphite. There were metal plates at top and bottom. The upper plate was equipped with a screw for raising and lowering. As pressure on the graphite particles was increased, their conductivity increased. Edison now used this basic principle to develop a telephone transmitter and make possible the microphone.

Edison's carbon transmitter was a major improvement over Bell's method of generating an undulating current by varying a magnetic field around a coil of insulated wire. Edison used a pair of electrodes in contact, at least one of which was the carbon particle type. One was connected to a diaphragm on which sound waves impinged. Sound waves caused relatively large variations in the current passing through the electrodes. Buttons pressed from lampblack were first used as electrodes and these were found to vary from 300 to less than one ohm by pressure alone. Edison later found that fine particles of anthracite coal were superior to lampblack for this purpose and such transmitters are used in telephones today.

Edison made several other inventions dealing with the telephone, one of which was the so-called chalk receiver based on the motograph principle.* He also pioneered the use of an induction coil to amplify the varying current in the main line. Edison did, however, always give Bell full credit for inventing the telephone and he realized that in the United States, his telephone patents were dominated by those of Bell.

Phonograph

The American Association for the Advancement of Science held a memorial program honoring the memory of Thomas Alva Edison at their winter meeting of 1931. One of the speakers was Dr. F. B. Jewett, then vice-president of the American Telephone and Telegraph Company. The following is taken from his address (3):

. . .it is difficult to appreciate the degree of daring which Edison displayed in even imagining that he could imprison such a fleeting thing as the energy of the spoken word. Equally difficult is it for the average man of today to conceive of the daring involved in imagining that out of the prison thus created could come, at some remotely distant time, a reproduction of ancient words, possibly those of men long dead, with the full vigor and clarity of the original speech.

---

*The electromotograph was an early Edison invention relating to the telegraph. It was based on the principle that the friction between two surfaces can be varied by passage of an electric current at the point of contact.

Edison did not discover the principle of the phonograph by accident. Apparently he conceived that sound could possibly be recorded and later recovered because of the following observations:

(a) The basic principle of the telephone, which had just been invented, involved sound being recreated by a diaphragm vibrating in a manner similar to that of a diaphragm on which sound was impinged.

(b) Like Bell, Edison was impressed by the magnitude of the movement of a diaphragm on which sound waves impinged.

(c) Edison had worked on an automatic method for recording telegraph messages using a disc of paraffin-coated paper laid on a revolving table similar to that used in phonographs today. A pointed metal tool controlled by an electromagnet would emboss the dots and dashes on the paper. During the summer of 1877, while attempting to play back such a recording into an outgoing telegraph wire, he noted "a light musical, rhythmical sound, resembling indistinct human speech."

Thus Edison concluded that if he could indent a series of hills and valleys into a pliable solid by means of a sharp tool attached to a vibrating diaphragm, the vibrations from the diaphragm would be repeated when the indentations were retraced by a similar tool attached to a diaphragm. For his first experiment he chose tinfoil wrapped on a metal cylinder having a continuous helical groove. The playback of Edison's recitation of "Mary had a little lamb" was so clear and loud that even he was astounded.

It should be appreciated that until the early 1920's the techniques of recording and reproducing sound were purely mechanical. Surprisingly Edison, the inventor of the microphone and foremost in many electrical developments, played no part in the electronically controlled phonograph.

Edison carried out a more-or-less continuous research and development program on the phonograph extending over a period of about 40 years. Unfortunately there was a lapse of about eight years while he pursued the electric light and all its ramifications. This lapse allowed others to enter the field, since Edison's legal staff made no attempt to claim all methods for recording and reproducing sound. There was a paradox of the inventor of one of the most basic inventions of all time having little control over its use and manufacture.

The fabrication of record blanks* and records for the phonograph was the first large scale use of resins and plastics for making structural objects. Handling techniques were developed which became important later in other industries. Edison and his associates developed metallic soap-fatty acid mixtures for making record blanks. Unlike shellac, which was largely used by others until man-made vinyl plastics replaced all other materials for making records, the soap compositions allowed a wide range in compositions and thus ultimate properties. Edison records made with such materials are in playable condition after 80 years. For molding an innumerable number of records from a given master, techniques for depositing metals on plastics were developed. Molding techniques for precise reproduction of cylinders and discs having up to 200 grooves per inch with variations in depth of micro dimensions was no mean achievement. Prior to World War I Edison's phonograph business was the world's largest user of phenolic resins. Edison pioneered the use of diamond and sapphire styluses for the phonograph.

The phonograph was Edison's most original invention and one of the most unique of all time.

New Uses for Electricity

Electricity was known for centuries before Edison. Benjamin Franklin showed that lightning and that mysterious force were the same. Michael Faraday produced electricity from permanent magnets and in 1831 built the first electric generator. He also derived the basic laws of electrolysis. The first practical electric generator was constructed by Gramme, a Belgian, in 1870. It was Edison, however, who put electricity to work for mankind.

The commercial uses of electricity prior to 1870 were the telegraph and some small scale electroplating. The direct current was furnished by primary batteries. Following the work of Gramme, arc lighting began on a small scale using a generator for each or a small number of lights wired in series. All generators at that time converted less than 50% of the mechanical energy used in operating them to electrical energy. In fact it was accepted by the "experts" in the field that 50% efficiency was a theoretical maximum, a fallacy, apparently based on batteries, that the internal resistance of a dynamo must at least equal that of the external circuit.

Edison realized that in order to make electricity competitive with gas for lighting, a more efficient generator was essential. Batteries were never considered for a moment and he pooh-poohed the idea that a dynamo could not be more efficient than 50%. Efforts were directed to building a generator of minimum internal resistance. A laboratory program was carried out to determine the minimum wire winding required to saturate the magnets, the optimum thickness of wire and number of turns, and the best type of iron for the cores of the magnets. For the first time mica was used for insulating the armature bars from each other. All electrical connections within the generator were soldered to further cut down on internal resistance.

Edison's first dynamo was nicknamed "Long-Legged Mary Ann" because of the two field magnets which stood nearly five feet high. It was not only the largest dynamo built to date but was by far the most efficient, being the order of 90%. A test run at Menlo Park in 1880 used 10 such dynamos in series, with an additional one to supply current to the electromagnets.

Edison moved rapidly to manufacture dynamos of his improved design. In cooperation with Charles T. Porter, a noted steam engine manufacturer, an assembly using a common shaft for the engine and the armature was developed. It operated at 500 r.p.m. and the unit weighed 27 tons. It was labelled Jumbo, after P. T. Barnum's famous elephant. The first commercially manufactured Jumbo was shipped and exhibited at the Paris Electrical Exposition of 1881.

Many inventors had tried to develop electric lighting based on incandescence. Edison wrote to a friend in the spring of 1878 that he did not intend to take up electric lighting research because "so many others are working in that field." However, as early as 1876 Edison had already carried out some experiments on the amount of current required to bring various non-conductors to incandescence. In September 1878 he visited William Wallace, a manufacturer of dynamos, in Ansonia, Connecticut. Wallace, in cooperation with Moses Farmer, was also in the process of bringing out an arc light system. For the first time Edison became excited with the idea of working on electric lights. He gave Wallace an order for a generator to serve as a source of current for his experiments.

Edison dismissed arc lighting as being impractical and soon had a very definite plan for an incandescent light. He visualized an element of 100 ohms or more resistance which meant that it must be a poor conductor of threadlike thickness. It would have to be in a vacuum or inert gas to avoid oxidation. Edison was one of the first to appreciate that electric power was the product of voltage and current and planned to use a maximum safe voltage, thus holding current consumption at each light to a minimum. This would make possible parallel wiring with each light or group of lights being individually controlled.

Edison was the first to study filaments as the lighting element; others had used thick wire or rods. He first experimented with platinum since it could be drawn to fine wire and had a high melting point. Success came when he turned to carbon and employed a new type of pump to get an improved vacuum. Cellulose fibers from bamboo proved best for preparing carbon filaments. Degassing the carbon under vacuum while heating to incandescence was found to be crucial as was attaching the brittle filament to the lead-in wires.

Edison's original light had a screwcap type connection for holding it in place and connecting it to the circuit as is the practice today. The Edison light was not appreciably changed for 25 years, and the tungsten filament light bulb marketed today looks much like the original. In inventing the light Edison had other firsts including the development of carbon fibers which are now used in the fabrication of materials for use at very high temperatures. The Edison light was the first industrial product containing a permanent high vacuum.

The electric light was probably not as great an achievement as the multitude of innovations which were necessary in setting up the first central electric power station. The franchise for the historic Pearl Street Station in lower Manhattan covered one square mile. This station ultimately had 513 customers using 10,300 lights served by 18 miles of mains and feeders.

Practically none of the equipment going into the installation was available on the market when the franchise was granted in April 1881. In fact many of the devices had not yet been invented. Copper wire was available but its quality varied greatly so specifications had to be established. If Edison had used the "tree system" of distribution as used in arc lighting, the quantity of copper needed for conduits would have been prohibitive. Furthermore, a system had to be employed whereby each customer, whether near or far from the generating station, received current at the same pressure (voltage). Edison's feeder system solved the voltage problem and reduced the quantity of copper for conduits to one-eighth of that which would have been used by the tree system. His later three-wire distribution system reduced copper requirements another 62½%. A new insulation compound for underground wiring — another first — was developed.

One of the intricate accessories which had to be worked out was a meter to measure the amount of electricity which each customer used. Edison's chemical meter based on the deposition of zinc by electrolysis was the answer. Other accessories developed were safety fuses, switches, junction boxes, and light fixtures.

Six Jumbo dynamos were installed at the central station and assembled in such a manner that all or one could be used. This required large switches, resistance boxes, and test meters of various kinds.

The lights in lower Manhattan came on September 4, 1882 as scheduled. The new type of interior lighting won immediate acceptance. For example, within five months the *New York Times* increased its number of lights five-fold to a total of 288. All this was possible because Edison was able to subdivide electricity from a single source and market a uniform product, something his critics said was impossible when his plans for lighting by electricity were first announced.

In 1831 Joseph Henry, the American whose work paralleled much of that of Michael Faraday on electromagnetic induction, built a crude electric motor using short-coil magnets. He labeled it "a philosophical toy" and even as late as 1876 maintained that the electric motor was impractical as a source of power. On the other hand, Edison visualized from the start that an advantage of electric lighting over gas lighting was that once electricity was brought into home, office, or factory, it could also be used to operate devices and thus replace manual labor. At the open house held at the Menlo Park laboratories on December 31, 1879 to exhibit the new light, an electric sewing machine was operated from the same circuit used for lighting several bulbs.

Edison invented the first electrical appliance, the electric pen. A small impulse motor operated a needle up and down to puncture holes as a written message was traced, thus creating the first paper stencil. The pen was manufactured by Edison for a time and then by Western Electric.

Certain customers served by the Pearl Street Station began using electric motors in 1884. The first substantial use was for elevators in multiple story buildings. The motor soon became common place in factories. Isolated electric plants were installed in factories which did not have access to central stations. Henry Ford once stated that the modern factory would not have been possible without the electric motor.

One problem of the electric motor is the counter electromotive force which is generated. Edison reduced this to a minimum by using magnets of low resistance as he had done in case of dynamo design. In 1880 Edison constructed an experimental electric locomotive and tested it on a track built near the laboratory. However, commercialization was left to others.

Iron Ore and Cement

Edison had an early interest in metals and felt that methods for locating valuable deposits and mining methods could be improved. In the 1880's the blast furnaces of eastern United States, supplied from isolated sources of local high grade ores, were losing out to the midwest mills which received high grade ore from upper Michigan. Knowing that the Appalachian Range contained huge quantities of iron, but largely in concentrations below that considered feasible to mine, Edison decided that it should be practical to concentrate such ore. Based on laboratory experiments which he had carried out from time to time, magnetic separation was considered best.

Iron occurs in nature in primarily two forms, hematite, which is ferric oxide, Fe_2O_3; and magnetite, which is described as ferrosoferric oxide, Fe_3O_4. Only the latter is attracted by magnets. Others had attempted magnetic concentration of magnetite in certain beach sands and lean tailings from iron mines with indifferent results.

A geological survey of the Appalachian Range was made from the St. Lawrence to the Potomac using magnetic dip needles. Several large deposits of magnetite were found including one near Ogdensburg, New Jersey. This became the site of Edison's fabulous iron ore concentration plant. This project, which extended over a period of about nine years (1890-99), was the most stupendous research and development project ever undertaken by a private individual. Since it was a failure, it has been largely ignored by most Edison biographers.

Whereas a few years earlier the inventor of the electric light was working with such delicate things as carbon

111

filaments and evacuated glass bulbs, now the watchword was large scale. For this project Edison developed crushing mills weighing 130 tons each, capable of crushing a boulder weighing up to six tons; a tower dryer which could handle 300 tons of crushed ore per hour; rubber-fabric conveyor belting in cooperation with Thomas Robins; and briquetting machines, each capable of producing 60 cylindrical cakes a minute. At the high point of his operations at Ogdensburg, he employed about 400 men (4).

Edison brought in no mining experts but proceeded on his own to design and build his plant. Editors of *Iron Age* magazine visited his plant in 1897. The following quotation dealing with their visit is taken from the publication. (5):

> But to our mind originality of the highest type as a constructor and designer appears in the bold way in which he (Edison) sweeps aside accepted practice in this particular field and attains results not hitherto approached. He pursues methods in ore dressing at which those who are trained may well stand aghast.

Edison spent more time and more money on his ore concentration project than he did on his electric light-dynamo-central station development in 1878-83, excluding, of course, commercial installations. In the early 90's he was a multi-millionaire; at the end of that decade he was penniless and heavily in debt. If he had been forced into liquidation, it is doubtful if his physical assets would have covered his debts. Edison not only lost heavily but some of his friends also took losses. Welch points out that the abortive ore concentration project was a major factor in the faithful Charles Batchelor leaving Edison's employ (2c).

The ore project failed for economic reasons, not technical ones. The discovery of the fabulous Mesabi deposits in Minnesota reduced the price of high grade iron ore to a fraction of that when Edison began his project. Although one can excuse him to some degree that economics defeated him and not lack of innovation, the failure of this project points up his disregard of a good market survey before plunging into a major development project. The Merritt brothers had discovered several of the Mesabi deposits by 1890 and by 1892 shipments had begun. By 1898 the press was calling the ore concentration project "Edison's Folly" and mining engineers were describing it as "a monument of perseverance in original research which certainly deserves our admiration" (4).

However, the important thing was that this failure did not sour Edison on the value of research and development as such failures often do present-day companies. Rather, he turned to cement manufacture in order to utilize know-how and some of the equipment from the ore project. The laboratory began research on alkaline storage batteries, one of the most visionary projects he had yet undertaken. His phonograph business and the licensing of his patents on the motion picture provided financial recovery.

Cement rock had been discovered in 1898 in New Village, a small New Jersey hamlet located about 45 miles west of West Orange. After a survey by W. S. Mallory, former superintendent of the ore concentration works, Edison bought an 800-acre tract just south of New Village for his quarrying and plant operations. Since there was no limestone deposit at New Village, it was brought from Oxford, New Jersey, about five miles to the northeast. Building of the plant began in 1899 and manufacturing in 1902. By 1905 production reached 3,000 barrels per day, making the Edison Portland Cement Company the fifth largest manufacturer of portland cement in the United States.

Edison himself designed the plant which included several unique features. The large mills from the ore plant were used to crush the quarried rock. The cement rock and limestone were ground to fine powders — 97% through 100 mesh for feed to the kilns — by ball mills using both steel balls and rods. Whereas previously in cement mills the cement rock and limestone were proportioned with a wheelbarrow or other load units, Edison devised automatic scales with a hopper-closing device above each, electrically controlled by needles which dipped into mercury. Laboratory control chemists were responsible for adjusting the ratio of cement rock and limestone based on frequent analyses of the two feedstocks.

It was, however, the kiln itself where Edison made the most significant improvements. Kilns used in the industry at that time were about 60 feet long with a daily capacity of about 200 barrels of clinker. Edison's kiln was 150 feet long and had a capacity of 1,000 barrels per day. Most of the cement trade subsequently licensed under his so-called "long cement kiln patents", Edison receiving one cent per barrel royalty.

For several years Edison carried out a research program relative to new uses for concrete and new techniques for fabricating concrete structures. Molds for an entire house were built and a concrete mixture developed which could be poured to fill the molds in a matter of a few hours. Ten houses so constructed stand today in Union, New Jersey. Work was done on furniture using foam concrete. In cooperation with the state of New Jersey, several experimental sections of concrete highway were built, which led to the construction of several miles of concrete pavement of Route 24 near New Village in 1910 — probably the first successful concrete highway in the nation.

The Motion Picture

Photography is the art of producing visible images on sensitive surfaces by the action of light. Classical photography depends on the action of light in bringing about changes in silver compounds, usually silver chloride or bromide. The act of permitting the light to fall on the sensitive layer is known as exposure. The developer is a chemical reducing solution which converts the exposed silver halide to dark, metallic silver. The positive, the finished picture, is prepared from the negative by printing onto another sheet of sensitive material, the tones being reversed on the second sheet.

Visual persistence had been known since about 1824. Scientists had written learned papers on the fact that an object continues to be seen by the human eye for an instant after the object has been withdrawn. Utilizing this phenomenon, several gadgets were devised which gave the illusion of motion. One known as the zoetrope, or wheel of life, had figures on the inside of a revolving cylinder which appeared to be animated when viewed through slits. The figures in such optical toys were originally drawn by hand or still pictures taken in a series of intermediate positions.

It was not until about 1879 that relatively rapid photographic dry plates were on the market. There was then a desire to use photography to study the motion of animals. In this country Eadweard Muybridge took pictures of a running horse utilizing up to 24 cameras spaced one foot apart. The shutters of the cameras were released by thin strings stretched across the pathway of the horse. Exposures were as short as 0.0005 second. A series of such photographs placed in a zoetrope-type apparatus gave the illusion of the horse moving in a single spot while the scenery ran past. It was obvious that successive shots of a moving object should be done by a single camera.

Edison was familiar with the work of Muybridge and others but at first he considered it mere gadgetry. Upon moving into the new Orange laboratories in 1887, several new research programs were initiated. One of these was photography with which Edison now hoped to devise an instrument "which would do for the eye what the phonograph does for the ear". The early work which led to the first practical camera for taking motion pictures and their first projection by the peep-show Kinetoscope is described by a publication in 1894 by Edison's able assistant, William K. L. Dickson (6).

Transparent nitrocellulose film coated with photographic gelatin became available shortly after Edison began his work on the motion picture. He immediately gave up work with dry glass plates and coated paper and concentrated on the use of this celluloid plastic tape. The camera which was developed moved 1½ inch wide tape past the lens by means of rollers locked into perforations on the sides of the film. A locking mechanism held the film steady 90% of the time while taking 46 pictures a second. The Kinetoscope utilized a 50-foot length of endless film containing positive prints. The pictures passed under a magnifying glass at the rate of 46 per second with a revolving shutter making it possible to view each individual picture momentarily. The entire show lasted about 13 seconds. The speed of taking and reproducing individual pictures was later reduced to 16 frames per second and this remained standard throughout the era of silent films.

In the 1890's Edison was deeply involved in his iron ore concentration project and had little time for motion pictures. His first Kinetoscope machine stood idle in the laboratory for three years before more were built and the first motion pictures viewed by the public on April 14, 1894. When his agents handling his motion picture development called for a projector so that the pictures could be shown on a screen, he made no move to develop one, even though his camera design could have been easily used to make such a projector. The Edison shop eventually did make the first successful screen projector, based on a design by Thomas Armat of Washington, D. C. Such a projector was used in the first public showing of motion pictures on a screen in New York in 1896.

Other firsts for Edison in the motion picture world include standardization by the industry up to 1952 of his width of film (35mm.) and arrangement of sprocket holes for driving the film. Edison built the world's first movie studio, termed the "Black Maria", which could utilize either direct sunlight or artificial light of 50,000 candlepower by means of arc lights with reflectors. His film director, Edwin S. Porter, produced the first narrative film with his "The Great Train Robbery".

In 1924 the motion picture industry, then ranked in the top six of the nation, honored Edison at a dinner in New York at the time of his 77th birthday. Over 600 attended. Will H. Hays, director general of the industry, read many congratulatory telegrams including one from President Coolidge. In introducing Mr. Edison, after describing the wonders of the motion picture, Hays said, "Seated here is our friend and fellow American, who more than anyone else has made this instrument, which daily serves the leisure hours of nearly one-tenth of our population."

In Edison's reply, which was read by another, he included the following:

I believe as I have always believed that you control the most powerful instrument in the world for good and evil. Whatever part I may have played in its development was mainly along mechanical

117

lines. The far more important development of the motion picture as a medium for artistic effort and as an educational factor is in your hands.

In 1961 Gordon Hendricks authored a book entitled *The Edison Motion Picture Myth* (7). Hendricks' principal theme is that Dickson, Edison's employee who up to 1895 did much of the experimental work on the motion picture at West Orange, was the real inventor of Edison's camera and Kinetoscope. Also according to Hendricks, Edison was not beyond taking credit for things actually done first by others outside his organization. This unusual type of book is discussed in more detail in the appendix (7).

Hendricks does not seem to appreciate the accepted relationship between a technical employee and his supervisor. A laboratory technician may do all of the laboratory work on a given invention, but if he furnishes none of the new ideas which make a patent possible based on this experimental work, the technician, regardless of his skilled manipulations, does not share the inventorship. Since both the camera and the Kinetoscope were patentable because of their mechanical features, one would certainly surmise that Edison, the master designer of mechanical things, along with his machine shop and craftsmen who were second to none, would more likely invent such mechanical marvels rather than Dickson, the artist and musician. Although this author is not in a position to critically evaluate Hendricks' contentions, based on Edison's work which I have evaluated in detail (2b), it is clear that Edison was an ethical inventor. Regardless of inventorship, it should be obvious to all that it was Edison who provided the "hardware" to make motion pictures a commercial reality.

The Alkaline Storage Battery

Edison's major research project, following termination of the iron ore concentration work in early 1899, was the storage battery. The market which he foresaw was self-propelled electric vehicles. Initially the quiet electric cars were more popular than the noisy, hot, and troublesome gasoline driven vehicles. A survey made in New York in late 1899 showed that of 100 motorcabs in the downtown area, 90 were powered by storage batteries. Edison believed that the cost of such electrical energy would be low since the batteries could be charged at central electric stations when some of the dynamos would otherwise be idle during hours of minimum load.

Edison's two criteria for a new storage battery were both revolutionary: it would contain no lead and its electrolyte would be alkaline. He considered lead undesirably heavy to carry around in a vehicle and he wanted an alkaline battery so it could be housed in a metal container.

A battery is a device for converting chemical energy directly to electrical energy. One electrode acts as an oxidizing agent as the other is being reduced. The main difference between a storage battery and a primary battery is ·that in case of the former, it can be recharged by reversing the flow of current from an outside source.

Edison tested literally thousands of half-cells using test materials held in the pores of porous carbon strips. The best combination was found to be nickel oxide as the positive electrode and iron as the negative in a 25% potassium hydroxide solution. In the following equilibrium reaction, the reaction to the right represents discharge and that to the left, charge.

$$8 \text{ NiO (OH)} + 3 \text{ Fe} + 4 \text{ H}_2\text{O} \rightleftharpoons 8 \text{ Ni(OH)}_2 + \text{Fe}_3\text{O}_4$$

In order to achieve the desired purities, Edison found it necessary to manufacture his own chemicals. Nickel oxide was prepared from a nickel-bearing alloy. Iron of low manganese content, obtained from a Swedish source, was dissolved, precipitated and purified in the form of ferric oxide, and then reduced to metallic iron by means of molecular hydrogen. This was the first commercial direct hydrogenation process. The iron powder was so pure that some was sold to laboratory reagent suppliers to be marketed as pharmaceutical-grade iron.

The new Edison battery was placed on the market in 1904 with considerable fanfare. Within six months many of the batteries had lost power with use, some up to 30%. Edison decided to shut down manufacturing operations and purchasers were refunded in full for defective batteries returned. An intensive research and development program was resumed and an improved form of the battery was placed on the market in 1909. The nickel oxide electrode proved to be the principal source of trouble. In order to impart adequate electrical conductivity to it, the powder had been mixed with graphite before packed in porous steel pockets and 24 of these fitted into a grid. The expansion and contraction of the nickel oxide during charging and discharging tended to result in non-homogeneity of the mixture and also damage to the containers. In the improved battery, metallic nickel flake of 0.00004 inch thickness replaced the graphite. This tissue-thick nickel was prepared by a unique electroplating operation. Each four-inch container for the positive electrode now contained 300 layers of nickel oxide, interspaced with 0.001 inch layers of the flake nickel. The manufacture of this positive electrode was, and continues to be, probably the most intricate operation in the manufacture of any electrical battery.

ESB, Incorporated, in their modern plant at Sumter,

South Carolina, manufactures the Edison battery very much like it was in 1909. Due to the relatively high cost of nickel, the Edison battery is expensive. Its advantages over the lead-acid type include long life, no deterioration on storage, and its foolproofness when overcharged, over discharged, or reverse charged. The major uses for this battery are for industrial trucks and for standby power.

By 1909 the internal combustion automobile was well established and Edison did not find the major use in self-propelled vehicles which he had hoped. If the alkaline battery had been developed 10 years earlier, one might speculate that the electric automobile might have fared better in that early development period.

The nickel-iron alkaline storage battery was the first alkaline storage battery placed on the market. It was one of the most basic inventions made by Edison. During the nine-year period of its development, he encountered many discouraging situations which would have caused the average researcher to drop the whole thing. Certainly few research organizations today show the courage, faith, and tenacity that Edison did in the inventing and marketing of his storage battery.

Organic Chemicals, Naval Research, Rubber

At the start of World War I, Edison was the world's largest user of phenolic resins. A thin layer was used on the surface of phonograph records. In August 1914 the Allies imposed a naval blockade on Germany. They also placed embargoes on the export of most of their own chemicals. Phenol, the main ingredient used in the synthesis of phenolics, had been primarily imported. Synthetic phenol had not yet been manufactured in the United States. When no domestic chemical company would assure Edison of a supply of phenol in less than six to nine months, he proceeded to build his own plant. Within 60 days he moved from the drawing board to a plant operating at a design capacity of six tons a day. Demand from others resulted in his building a second plant of like capacity. Since the nation had practically no organic chemical industry at that time, most organic chemicals were in critical demand. Edison manufactured also six other benzene derivatives as well as setting up two plants for the recovery of benzene and other by-products from the manufacture of coke from coal.

All the organic chemical syntheses used by Edison were old but none had previously been carried out on a commercial basis in the States. Edison's ability to move rapidly into a new field of manufacturing was indeed impressive. His plants were of the improvised type and were shut down and dismantled as the American chemical industry met the demand, and in many cases, created surpluses resulting in distressed prices.

In the fall of 1915 the Secretary of the Navy, Josephus Daniels, set up the "Naval Consulting Board" with Edison as chairman. Each of the country's scientific and engineering societies selected two of its members to serve on the board. Edison soon gave up his position as chairman since he was now so deaf he could take little part in the board's deliberations. He was given the honorary title of president. Edison was instrumental in the board's recommendation that a $5,000,000 research facility be built and operated by civilians under the Navy Secretary. This recommendation was subsequently carried out but not until after the war.

Beginning late in 1916 Edison and about 40 members of his staff worked entirely on problems suggested by the Navy. Anti-submarine devices were emphasized. Other scientists were brought in from universities to assist in the effort. This group carried out a number of tests on sea-going vessels and some of their suggestions apparently were used by the Navy. In 1920 L. N. Scott published the official report on the work of the Naval Consulting Board (8).

In the 1920's Edison became concerned because of the fact that nearly the total source of supply of rubber came from the Far East. America's workers and its army travelled primarily on rubber-tired vehicles. Unlike others who attempted to produce alternate sources of rubber supply, Edison saw little chance of competing economically with the favorable growing conditions and, above all, the cheap labor of the Far East. Rather he visualized that the best solution was to develop a source of rubber from plants which, in an emergency, could be grown and harvested within a matter of months. Under such a situation, production cost would not be a significant factor. Edison was well on the way to attaining his objective when in 1931, in his 85th year, death came. Synthetic rubber ultimately provided the domestic source of supply which he sought and, in addition, proved to be competitive with natural in peacetime.

Edison built a chemical and botanical laboratory across the street from his winter home in Fort Myers. With financial help from Henry Ford and Harvey Firestone, the Edison Botanic Research Corporation came into being in 1927. Literally thousands of domestic plants were analyzed for their rubber contents. Leaves of the goldenrod were found to be the most promising source, certain species containing up to 12.5% rubber in the dried leaves if harvested at the optimum time. Although Edison's work on rubber from goldenrod did not progress far enough to be helpful during the critical rubber shortage during World War II, it was a milestone in the search for rubber from plants.

The U. S. Department of Agriculture subsequently published a comprehensive report on Edison's test results (9).

Miscellaneous

Edison's observation of what he called etheric force, which were scintillating sparks issuing from the core of a vibrating magnet, later became known as electromagnetic waves.

In 1883 while studying the cause of the darkening within electric light bulbs, Edison prepared an evacuated bulb containing two separate wire circuits. He found that when one was brought to incandescence, a current flowed through the other even though they were a half inch apart. Actually electrons were passing from the hot element to the cold one. This so-called Edison Effect constituted an important step towards the unveiling of the electron. Thus Edison was on the thresholds of two fundamental discoveries but did not pursue either.

After Roentgen showed that so-called x-rays pass through flesh and muscle tissue but not bones and inorganic material in general, Edison undertook a study of hundreds of chemical crystals to determine which was best to use on the screen of a fluoroscope. A fluoroscope is used to define the shadow in photographic x-ray studies. When he found calcium tungstate best, he manufactured and donated a number of such fluoroscopes along with x-ray tubes to hospitals where surgeons were taking up the new x-ray technique.

Edison, with his highly skilled shop, made substantial contributions to the development of a practical typewriter. Reproducing multiple written copies by his electric pen technique was followed by the development of a stencil sheet prepared by perforating wax paper. This became the grandfather of "office duplicating" and was commercialized by the A. B. Dick Company.

Edison founded the weekly magazine known as *Science*, the first issue being published July 3, 1880. Subscribers were few and it cost him about $135 per week to support the publication. At that time Edison did not have that kind of money; at the end of 1881 he paid the editor's salary in full and told him he could have the publication to do with it as he pleased. It ceased publication shortly thereafter. The new *Science*, sponsored by the Alexander Graham Bell family, began publication on February 9, 1883 as Volume 1, Number 1.

Edison took little part in the activities of scientific and engineering societies although he was a member of most and subscribed to their publications. His hearing problem no doubt caused him to shun such social contacts.

Personal traits, home life, work methods, etc. of the six highly successful inventors covered in these case histories will be discussed in Chapters 7 and 8. However, as an inventor Edison was in a class by himself compared with his contemporaries and it is appropriate to try to explain why this was true. Possible explanations might be that he was a miracle man, just plain lucky, or because of organization and work methods.

Edison was certainly a very intelligent person, learned rapidly, and had a phenomenal memory. However, he was the last to claim that he had supernatural abilities. His well known definition of genius was "99% perspiration and 1% inspiration".

One certainly cannot say that he stumbled on to any of his great inventions; in fact it is evident that bad luck often plagued him. As pointed out previously, Edison's iron ore project, which took the major part of his time for over nine years and resulted in the loss of $2,000,000 (9,000,000 based on 1970 dollars), was probably the greatest loss ever suffered by any individual in the field of research and development. Although his nickel-iron storage battery became a commercial reality, it did not capture a large market as he had anticipated. His all-concrete house was not a commercial success. Edison's work on rubber from goldenrod lasted for four years and was continued for several years after his death by the Edison family and Henry Ford. However by 1937, with several synthetic rubbers on the world market, the work on rubber from plants was dropped.

This brings us to a matter of methods. Even as a boy, Edison had the knack of bringing others into his operations. When a newsboy on the Grank Trunk Railway, he brought newspapers, magazines, fruit, and vegetables to Port Huron to be sold there by other boys. He "bribed" the telegraph operators along the rail line with magazines and produce at wholesale prices in the return for the latest news items to use in his weekly *Grand Trunk Herald*. When he undertook manufacturing operations, he assembled highly skilled craftsmen. When working on the electric light, he hired a highly skilled glassblower from Germany at twice the prevailing wage. Edison was operating well organized and functional research laboratories for 30 years before others did likewise. For a lone inventor competing with Edison, it was like present-day American Motors against General Motors.

Another factor was that early in his career Edison assembled enough private capital so that he had to spend little time looking for financial support. Also his research efforts were sufficiently diversified that if a major project failed, overall collapse did not result. He recovered quickly

126

Courtesy of Edison National Historic Site, West Orange, N.J.

Thomas Edison, age about 35 years

Courtesy of Edison National Historic Site, West Orange, N.J.

One of the last photographs of Thomas Edison

Edison took an active part in choosing artists for phonographic recordings.

from his catastrophic ore project and was able shortly thereafter to absorb high costs on the battery research because of income from his phonograph business and royalties from his motion picture patents. His profits went primarily into research and development. He had no stockholders to satisfy and had no inclination to accumulate a large fortune.

Although Edison had a fairly large staff at his laboratories both at Menlo Park and West Orange, it was not a matter of trained scientists or engineers carrying out independent research. His skilled people were primarily technicians and craftsmen. Edison felt that he had more ideas for research than time and personnel permitted and thus did not want his employees to get sidetracked on ideas of their own. By 1908 he did encourage certain of his employees to work on their own ideas and to patent. The New Jersey Patent Company was set up to handle such inventions. If Edison Industries used any invention, royalty was paid to the inventor. Charles Batchelor, Edison's key employee in the early days, always found time to invent on his own and got several patents.

Edison's career has been cited by certain psychologists as an example of the belief, held by some, that an inventor reaches his peak productivity in his 30's and then rapidly declines. It is true that Edison applied for more patents between the ages of 33-37 than in any other comparable period. Patents are only one of the yardsticks for measuring innovation. Some new things are patentable; others are not. Edison showed as much originality in his iron ore concentration work as he did with the electric light. However, during the period from 1893 through 1897, although developing many extraordinary operations in mining and ore concentration at Ogdensburg, Edison filed only six patent applications. Once his work again became more the bench-scale laboratory type, his fabulous patent record continued to grow. Twenty-five patents were granted based on applications filed in 1905. At the age of 80, he turned botanist. Actually the man who was granted 1,093 United States patents is an excellent example that age is not a significant factor in the ability of an individual to do new things.*

*Although Edison was 84 years, eight months of age when he died, he died considerably younger than did his immediate forefathers. His great grandfather lived to be 104; his grandfather, 102; and his father, 92. His grandfather on his mother's side also lived to be over 100.

Chapter 4

George Westinghouse

George Westinghouse was a man of quick decision and he usually got what he sought. This extended beyond his business affairs. One day returning by train to Schenectady, this lad of 20 years chanced to sit next to Marguerite Erskine Walker of Roxbury, New York; an animated conversation ensued. On returning home he announced to his parents that he had met the young lady whom he was going to marry. He hastened to get the minister of their church to write to Miss Walker and vouch for his good character. Within a few months the two were married even though George was forced to bring his bride to his parents' home in order to provide housing. Miss Walker was George's first and only love. Their marriage was a most happy one. Marguerite Westinghouse always appeared to understand the moods and actions of her sometimes difficult husband.

Although George Westinghouse became a famous man in industrial, engineering, and scientific circles and received many honorary degrees, awards, and titles, he preferred no fanfare. Before his death he chose his rather insignificant career in his country's service to mark his passing. The remains of him and his wife, who died three months later, were buried in Arlington National Cemetery where a simple marble monument bears the following inscription:

1846 — George Westinghouse — 1914
Acting Third Assistant Engineer, U. S. Navy, 1864-1865
His Wife
1842 — Marguerite Erskine Walker — 1914

George Westinghouse was born in the village of Central Bridge, New York, located about 36 miles west of Albany, on October 6, 1846. He was the seventh of 10 children of George Westinghouse, Senior and the former Emaline Vedder. The father was of German ancestors, noted for their large statures and mechanical traits. The mother was of Dutch-English background and was a person of great kindness and cheerful spirit. She became a semi-invalid at middle age and lived with her son George the last five years of her life. The older six children were three girls and three boys. Two boys, born after George, died in infancy while the tenth, Henry Herman, became famous in his own right as a builder of steam engines and as a business executive.

In Central Bridge the father was a combination farmer-mechanical shop operator. The latter activity soon expanded from repair work to fabrication of agricultural machinery. He made major improvements in a threshing machine as well as raking equipment, horse-power equipment, and a seed-separator for broom corn. He subsequently obtained a total of seven patents on mechanical devices made in his shop.

George Westinghouse, Jr.* never kept a diary, wrote practically no personal and few business letters, kept no notebook records of his experiments, and published little in scientific and engineering journals. We do, of course, have an excellent record of his inventions in his 361 United

*He dropped the title, Junior, after his father's death in 1890.

130

States patents. Very few pictures were taken of him and he refused to be interviewed by news reporters. No biography of George Westinghouse was written during his lifetime, probably because he wouldn't cooperate in furnishing information and forbade his employees or family to do so. Fortunately for posterity two good biographies were written following his death. That of Leupp (1) emphasizes the personal traits of his subject, while that of Prout (2) Westinghouse's scientific, engineering, and business careers. Each author carried out an extensive search and relied on memories of friends, corporate files, and public records wherever they might be.

In early childhood George, Junior showed no traits which would indicate that he would become a famous man. On the contrary he was noted for his continual revolt against the confinement of the schoolroom, his distaste for most of his studies, and his pugnacious disposition. If he had a strong desire and his demands were unavailing, he would fly into a rage, throwing himself on the ground or floor and banging his head. If an older member of the household would yield the point at issue, George's tears, cries, and self-torture would cease as suddenly as they had begun. Speaking of these outbursts in later life he said, "I have always known what I wanted, and how to get it. As a child, I got it by tantrums; in mature years, by hard work."

Westinghouse, Senior's interest in his machine shop increased and that in farming decreased. He had a bountiful supply of lumber in Central Bridge, but metal castings had to be purchased in Schenectady and moving them to his shop was tedious and expensive, especially under muddy road conditions. In 1856, with the help of two partners, Westinghouse purchased a building formerly used as a cement mill located on the south bank of the Erie Canal in Schenectady. A comfortable residence for the Westinghouse family was bought nearby.

The father's business prospered. The three older brothers subsequently, one by one, joined the family business. Jay, the eldest, first took a course at Rensselaer Polytechnic Institute in nearby Troy. George, then 10 years of age, was ordered by his father to come to the shop each day after school and learn how tools were used by skilled hands. Although the lad had already indicated a great interest in tinkering with various tools and machines on his own, he showed little interest in standing at the elbow of a skilled machinist and observing how surfaces were planed and holes bored. Soon he was doing some routine jobs, such as cutting pipe to proper lengths, earning 50 cents for a ten-hour day. He was expected to work full days on Saturdays and during school vacations. A kindly foreman fixed a small workroom in the loft where the lad could tinker during off-hours. In his workroom George could keep his trumpery, as the father called the toys and various gadgets which George often made instead of doing his assigned tasks, and not have them consigned to the scrap heap.

On insistence from his father, George was taking courses at school which would qualify him for college entrance. However, with the exception of mathematics and drawing, his marks continued to indicate that he was an inept pupil. He was particularly poor when called on for oral recitation, often to the amusement of his classmates.

George was less than 15 years of age when the Civil War began. The youth was smitten by the prevalent martial fever and attempted to run away and join the army. His father found him on the morning train, headed for New York City, in the nick of time. However, after his brothers Albert and John enlisted in 1862, George pestered his father to let him go also. George Westinghouse, Senior was a patriotic American and, now convinced that the rebellion was serious business, no longer stood in his son's way. In the summer of 1863, at the age of 16, George applied in person for an officer's commission at a recruiting station in New York City. His audacity amused the recruiting officer who suggested that instead the youth try a 30-day enlistment as a private in the army to see how he liked it. Since Lee was then moving into southern Pennsylvania, volunteers were in strong demand. Within two days George was off for the front.

His 30-day enlistment was uneventful, but he was more desirous than ever to see more of soldier life. He again inquired about a commission. It was suggested that he try to raise a company of his own and George set out for the Central Bridge area to gather 50 recruits. He found that most of the eligibles were already in the army. Although he did get 17 men, he had to go back to war as a private — this time in the cavalry. His assignment was in northern Virginia, primarily on scout duty. Although he became a corporal, he felt he was making little progress in the army so took an examination in marine engineering in an attempt to get a commission in the navy. On December 1, 1864 he was appointed Acting Third Assistant Engineer and subsequently served on several Union ships.

George was mustered out of the service in the summer of 1865. His father was pleased with his increased manliness. George, too, often expressed the opinion that his army and navy experience was highly valuable in teaching him lessons in discipline. Certainly his mercurial temper had changed to a sense of responsibility. However, the Westinghouse family had felt the bitter pangs of war. The elder brother Albert, a lieutenant in the cavalry, was killed in December 1864 while leading a charge. The mother was terribly broken by it and her health steadily decreased thereafter.

133

In the fall of 1865 George entered Union College, Schenectady. In three months he was back in his father's shop. It is not surprising that the college curriculum of 1865 had little to interest a lad who was primarily interested in practical things. His father was able and willing to send his son to college, but the ex-student was apparently welcomed back at the shop where he was allowed to work largely on what he chose.

Young Westinghouse had worked on a rotary steam engine before his sojourn in the armed forces and, while in the navy, saw the need for a source of power acting in a rotary manner for driving ship propellors. On his return to civilian life he filed a patent application on his rotary steam engine. At the age of 19, George Westinghouse, Jr. obtained his first patent (3). Although this engine was never a commercial success, it sparked his continuing interest in rotary engines, ultimately leading to his pioneering work with steam turbines.

At 20 years of age, an accident caused Westinghouse to become interested in railroads and their problems, starting him on his fabulous career. On returning home from Albany, where he had gone on an errand for his father's firm, his train was held up by a freight wreck. The two end cars of a train had leaped the track. George watched the repair crew working the cars back on the track by means of levers and then jacking them up to be lowered onto the rails. The young engineer wondered why the crew did not run a pair of rails at an angle to the wheels of the derailed cars and use the engine to pull the cars back on the track. This idea led to his second patent (4) and a partnership with two local men to manufacture the car replacer.

Westinghouse's contact with the railroads acquainted him with other problems which were crying for solutions. One of these was the "frog" used with railroad tracks; i.e., the device which permits car wheels on one track to cross a rail of an intersecting track. At that time these were made of cast iron as were track rails. Bessemer steel was just beginning to appear on the market. Westinghouse had read in a technical journal that the new material could be cast. He designed a cast steel frog which was reversible when one side became worn. This new patented product was marketed by the small firm making the car replacer, and his more durable product proved to have a useful life more than 20 times that of the cast iron frog. The car replacer and the steel frog were made on contract at Troy, New York and Pompton, New Jersey. The two partners were primarily the "silent" type, handling the necessary financing and business details. Young Westinghouse served as liaison with the manufacturers and handled marketing.

Another problem George had been thinking about was the problem of stopping trains. It was then the practice for brakemen, on a whistle signal from the locomotive, to apply brakes by hand at each car. Even under the best of conditions it required over a quarter mile to bring a train to a full stop and individual trains were restricted to four or five cars and speeds of a maximum of about 25 miles per hour. The crack New York Central pullman train operating between New York and Chicago required 36 hours for the one-way trip. The seriousness of the problem was brought to young Westinghouse's attention when a train on which he was riding was held up due to a collision of two freight trains. He learned that both engineers had seen the oncoming train but could not stop in time. The track was straight and the day was clear. It was obvious to Westinghouse that for effective braking the engineer must be able to apply the brakes of the various cars by some device from the locomotive.

George Westinghouse was not the first to tackle the

subject of braking trains. By 1867 there were already over 600 patents relating to the subject. That he was a latecomer did not deter the young man, his self confidence strengthened by the fact that he had already made two inventions relating to railroad operations. Young Westinghouse now concentrated on the brake problem using his father's shop for experimental work. The latter discouraged his son suggesting that he leave problems of the railroads to railway people. George's first approach was to consider a long chain running to the brakes of the cars and controlled by some device at the engine. In checking with railroad friends he learned that such a device was already in use on a four-car passenger train on the Chicago, Burlington, and Quincy Railroad. Westinghouse inspected this train and found that the chain was wound up by a windlass on the locomotive which could be revolved by pressing a grooved wheel against the flange of the drive wheel. The whole thing appeared so clumsy that Westinghouse dropped the approach of using a chain to actuate the car brakes.

He next considered steam, piped from the engine to the cars. Obviously this was impractical due to condensation and even freezing in the winter time. A hydraulic system not only acted too slowly but also suffered from low temperature problems. Antifreeze solutions were then not available and probably would not have been practical anyway due to losses when coupling cars.

One day at lunch in his father's shop, George was approached by a young woman selling the magazine, *Living Age*. He leafed through a sample copy and was just about to say no, when he noted an article dealing with the construction of the Mont Cenis Tunnel through the Alps in Italy. The girl sold a subscription and George was able to read an article which sparked an idea for a successful

136

railroad brake. In the tunnel construction air was being used to drive a drill like battering-ram against the face of rock in order to make holes for blasting. Previously steam had been used for driving the drill but since the ends of the tunnel were as much as 3,000 feet from the working area, compressed air had been successfully substituted. This apparently was the birth of not only the air-driven drill but also the present well-known air hammer.

At that time compressed air had not been used in this country for any commercial use. The inflated rubber tire was yet to be born. Gas pumps did exist but were used primarily for pumping illuminating gas into distribution systems. George Westinghouse was now convinced that air would allow him to do in a practical manner what he had considered doing with steam. He reduced his ideas to drawings and on July 10, 1868 filed a caveat in the Patent Office which marked the beginning of a series of patents relating to air brakes which totaled 103 in the United States and many abroad.

But Westinghouse was unable to create any interest in his potential air brake with the railway people, his two partners engaged in the car replacer and rail frog project, nor with his father. In 1867 George dissolved the partnership with his Schenectady associates. He then arranged with Anderson, Cook, and Company of Pittsburgh, a small steel manufacturer and fabricator, to manufacture the replacer and frog at their expense, and retain him as salesman. Late in 1867 George and Marguerite Westinghouse, married since August, moved to Pittsburgh and set up housekeeping in rented quarters. George became friends with Ralph Baggaley, a townsman of some wealth, who operated a small foundry. Baggaley was about Westinghouse's age, had received part of his education in Germany, and had a keen interest in technical matters. He became sold on his friend's idea of an air brake and was able to furnish a few thousand dollars from his own funds for development work. For one hundred dollars he hired a consultant, considered a foremost mechanical expert, to go over Westinghouse's drawings and laboratory data and give the two innovators an evaluation report. The subsequent report not only condemned Westinghouse's proposal as unsound but nonsensical as well!

Fortunately Westinghouse, backed by Baggaley, was not dismayed by the adverse report and proceeded to assemble the necessary apparatus for an actual road test. He continued to contact railway officials on his sales trips but with discouraging results. An interview was arranged with Commodore Vanderbilt, the leading railroader at the time, who dismissed Westinghouse after a brief interview with the satirical comment: "Do you pretend to tell me that you can stop our trains with wind?" Arrangements were finally made with the Panhandle Railroad to furnish a train for a test if the inventor would agree to equip it at his own expense and to reimburse the company for any damage done by the apparatus to the locomotive or the cars. Westinghouse and Baggaley agreed to these conditions although it meant going into debt for the necessary apparatus with no thought that any damage would occur to the train from the test.

The essential parts of Westinghouse's original air brake were as follows:

(a) An air pump driven by a steam engine which received steam from the boiler of the locomotive.

(b) A reservoir on the locomotive in which air was compressed to about 60 pounds per square inch.

(c) Brake cylinders for the tender and each car.

(d) A line of pipe run from the locomotive under the tender and cars with connections to each cylinder. Flexible rubber hose connections between cars provided couplings having valves which were automatically opened when the two parts of a coupling were joined, and automatically closed, when a coupling was separated. The engineer had a valve for letting air into the system from the high pressure reservoir. When air was admitted into the cylinders, pistons were thrust outward applying the brakes to the wheels. The brakes themselves were as used previously when operated manually.

Since Westinghouse had already built a specimen of his brake apparatus, it was a relatively simple matter to fabricate equipment for the four-car test which had been agreed upon. On the momentous day in September 1868, a locomotive with four cars equipped with Westinghouse's experimental air brake pulled out of the Union Station, Pittsburgh into a tunnel emerging on the Steubenville track of the Panhandle. In the rear car were several officers of the Panhandle Company and a few officials of other railroads. Westinghouse and Baggaley rode with them, leaving the engineer and fireman to carry out the scheduled program. The tests were not supposed to begin until the train reached open country beyond the Monongahela River. However, as the train pulled out of the tunnel a huckster's wagon and horses were standing on the tracks less than two blocks away. The driver applied his whip but in the confusion the horses reared upright and the conveyance was still on the tracks when the train came to a grinding halt. The alert engineer had sized up the situation and threw the brake valve wide open. The honored guests were thrown from their seats to the floor, but quickly emerged in none too jovial moods. Once the reason for the sudden stop was known, some felt no further testing was necessary; the brake had been proved. Lady Luck had smiled on George Westinghouse that September day as his brake was demonstrated in such a dramatic manner. However, the tests proceeded as planned with the engineer bringing the train to a series of quick, but not violent, stops.

With success now assured, Westinghouse resigned his position with Anderson and Clark. The firm with which Baggaley was connected was dissolved and its foundry converted to a plant for the manufacture of air brakes. In July 1869 the Westinghouse Air Brake Company was organized with a capitalization of $500,000. Two officials of the Panhandle Railroad and two of the Pennsylvania became members of the board of directors as did Baggaley and Westinghouse. Westinghouse, at age 23, became president of a company which subsequently became worldwide in its operations.

The Pennsylvania Railroad, now anxious to get on the bandwagon, made available a six-car train for testing the new air brake. In September 1869 this train was run from Pittsburgh to Altoona and air brakes alone were used to control the speed of the train on the eastern slope of the Alleghenies. In November a train of 10 cars demonstrated the brake at Philadelphia, Chicago, and Indianapolis. Orders poured in. By April 1, 1874, only five and one-half years after the first road test, a total of 2,281 locomotives and 7,254 passenger cars had been equipped with the Westinghouse brake.

However as most inventions, the air brake was not one hundred percent original. When Westinghouse filed his first air brake patent, he was only 22 years old. His knowledge of the previous art was only that which he had seen and heard in his dealings with railroad people. A search of railroad brake literature now revealed that a patent had been taken out in England about 30 years earlier in which air pressure had been used to apply brakes to rail cars. This development never got beyond the patent stage; it lacked

140

such pertinent features as a high pressure air reservoir, car couplings with automatic valves, and the three-way cock for controlling the air system. Competitive companies now entered the air brake business hoping to share in the profits. Westinghouse brought suit against the Gardner and Ransom Air Brake company for violation of his issued patents. The court's verdict, handed down on June 16, 1875, included the following:

> . . .Westinghouse was not the first to conceive the idea of operating railway brakes by air pressure. — A careful examination of these prior patents had led us — that there are substantial and essential differences between these prior patents and the Westinghouse apparatus, and that to these differences we may justly attribute the successful and extensive introduction of the Westinghouse air brake.

Although Westinghouse's basic patent was declared valid, it was soon obvious that his air brake had certain shortcomings. What if the air line broke or one or more cars broke away from the rest of the train? Other companies were promoting an electrically controlled brake or a combination electric-air brake. By 1871 Westinghouse was working on an automatic air brake in which his previous system was reversed, the air pressure held the brakes away from the wheels. If any part of the train broke away from that under the control of the engineer, the brakes of the loose cars would automatically set. His automatic air brake went through a series of developments and by 1875 it was replacing the initial straight-air brake.

Up to 1880 power brakes were confined wholly to passenger service. The railways wanted to employ such brakes for freights but it was obvious the brake must be standardized so that a car of any line could be inserted in the train of any other and be operated under the same brake control. The Master Car Builder's Association decided to invite all brake builders to demonstrate their brakes in a train of 50 freight cars. The contest was carried out at Burlington, Iowa in the spring of 1887. Six competitors took part, one using air alone, another electrical control only, and others using combinations of electricity with air or vacuum. The braking of freight cars was quite a different problem from that of passenger cars. Trains of the former were much longer and heavier and a major problem was to apply braking to the last car at substantially the same time as the first. For freights Westinghouse had reluctantly gone to a combination of compressed air and electricity with a tank of compressed air attached to each car. The verdict of the Car Builder's Committee was favorable to a brake operated by air, having valves actuated by electricity, although no brake tested was considered completely satisfactory.

Westinghouse's dominance of the power brake business now appeared to be at an end. His patent position on the electrically actuated air brake was marginal to say the least. Westinghouse set to work to perfect an all-air brake for freight cars which he felt would be more reliable than one actuated by electricity. Within three months he had developed what became known as the quick-acting brake. This was accomplished, in part, by an improved triple valve of larger openings. Each car had a triple valve with its own air reservoir. It was now possible to brake the last car of a 50-car train within two seconds of the first. Such a train speeding at 40 miles per hour could now be stopped in less than half its length with no appreciable shock from car to car.

Westinghouse proceeded to demonstrate his new air brake on a 50-car freight in various parts of the country at his own expense. Although these tests were unofficial, the Master Car Builders' Association recognized the superiority of Westinghouse's new brake and set up specifications which only it could meet. In 1893 Congress passed the "Federal Safety Appliance Act" which required power brakes on all railroad rolling stock used in interstate commerce. Westinghouse had won "the battle of the brakes".

In 1870 Westinghouse had gone to England with the objective of introducing his brake there. The British railway companies were not impressed by the fact that his new brake was finding use on American roads. They insisted on testing on a British railroad and this was successfully done in March 1882. The British were using wooden brake shoes, and it was necessary to use metal ones with the Westinghouse brake. A series of trips by Westinghouse to England and the continent over a period of 10 years led to wide acceptance of his brake abroad. Manufacturing facilities were set up in several foreign countries.

As Westinghouse became involved with railway safety in connection with braking, he realized that devices for railway signaling and switching were grossly inadequate. He gained control of two companies engaged in the manufacture of such equipment and used them as a nucleus to form the Union Switch and Signal Company. From 1881 to 1891 Westinghouse took out 15 patents dealing with electropneumatic devices for railway signals and switches. As one railway engineer expressed it, "Westinghouse used compressed air for the heavy work, and electricity to pull the trigger."

Another important Westinghouse invention for railroads was the friction draft gear. This was a coupling device between freight cars which absorbed the stresses and strains caused by "the play" between each car. Before its use it took a very skillful engineer to avoid breaking car couplings due to too rapid braking or too rapid acceleration of freight trains consisting of 30 or more cars. This problem was accentuated as steel cars began replacing wooden cars about 1890. Although purely mechanical in nature, the invention of the friction draft gear for the operation of large freight trains has been considered as important as that of the air brake.

After several locations in Pittsburgh, in 1890 the Air Brake Company was moved to a new plant in Wilmerding, just east of Pittsburgh. This plant is still in operation, being a part of WABCO, a manufacturer of control systems, air and hydraulic cylinders, air valves, and the like. The Union Switch and Signal Company was located at nearby Swissvale. For years it was operated as a subsidiary of the Westinghouse Air Brake Company.

It is doubtful if any single person has contributed more to railroad technology, and certainly not to safety, than did George Westinghouse. Railroads served to bring the two coasts of the United States together and make possible a coherent country, an essential for one with a representative form of government. Power brakes and an effective system of signals and controls made possible long, high speed trains which not only moved people and materials safely and rapidly, but also at relatively low costs.

The air brake is no doubt a very impersonal thing to most. However, to those of us old enough to have used the railroad as the chief means of long distance travelling on land, the sound of air swishing beneath one's coach or pullman as the engineer tested his brakes, after cars had been switched or added at a station stop, was a reminder that the air brake was on the job.

Westinghouse's second major field of research and development was electricity. Unlike railway power brakes, Westinghouse was not the pioneer. Before he had entered the field, Edison had developed the more efficient dynamo, the first practical incandescent lamp, the underground installation of electrical conduits, and the first central station for generating and marketing electrical power to numerous customers. Westinghouse's first use of electricity in his manufactured products was with his air brakes and signal equipment. At that time he considered electricity relatively unreliable and sought to use all-air systems. This may have been . a true evaluation at the time but subsequently electro-pneumatic brakes were developed into highly reliable systems as evidenced by their successful application on subway trains.

By late 1883 Westinghouse had become sufficiently interested in electricity to gather a small staff to work in this field at the Union Switch and Signal Company plant. His brother Herman had developed a high speed steam engine and the two brothers had founded the Westinghouse Machine Company to make it. One inherent feature of this engine was its self-regulating capabilities. George Westinghouse was no doubt aware that in Edison's central and isolated electric plants, manual control was necessary to maintain a uniform flow of electric power to all lights as the load varied. Westinghouse's first patent in the electrical field was an automatic electric current regulator (5).

Edison had successfully gone to a direct drive steam engine and had a working arrangement with Armington and Sims, a leading steam engine manufacturer of Providence, Rhode Island. The story goes that Edison was approached by a representative of George Westinghouse with a request that he test their high speed engine for direct driving a dynamo. Instead of telling him of his cooperative venture with Armington and Sims, Edison allegedly made the remark: "Tell Westinghouse to stick to air brakes. He doesn't know anything about engines." This episode apparently spurred Westinghouse to get into the electrical business. Certainly he foresaw that one of the big uses of steam engines would be for generating electricity.

Among the electrical experts Westinghouse employed in this early stage was William Stanley. Stanley had developed a self-regulating dynamo and in 1884 Westinghouse considered setting up a company to be known as the Stanley Electric Company to manufacture it and auxiliary equipment. He sought advice from Franklin L. Pope, a former partner of Edison and then a consultant, and was told that patents held by others might seriously hamper the operation of such a company, so the idea was dropped.

In 1885 Westinghouse learned of the work of Lucien Gaulard, a Frenchman, and his financial backer, John Gibbs, an Englishman, relative to their use of electrical induction for converting alternating current to lower and higher voltages, a process not possible with direct current. For readers not familiar with electrical technology, one can consider the analogy of water in a pipe in that direct current flows in one direction while alternating current flows first in one direction and then in the other. The common 60-cycle alternating current used in the United States is one which reverses its direction 120 times a second. The transformer is basically an electromagnetic induction coil. By varying the number of turns in the two parts of the coil, voltage can be lowered or raised with corresponding changes in amperage so that total power remains practically the same; i.e., volts times amperes to give what we today call watts. Present-day transformers are 96-99% efficient.

Electricity from batteries is the direct type and when

dynamos began replacing batteries, it is not surprising that direct current was considered the better, even though a special takeoff, called a commutator, was required on the dynamo to obtain direct current. Furthermore, direct current must be used for electroplating, the principal commercial use for electricity besides telegraphy, before the advent of electric lighting.

It had been known by the new electrical industry that an induction coil could be used to step down voltage and increase current, but it was considered too inefficient to be of possible commercial interest. The induction coil of Gaulard and Gibbs, developed in 1882, was of improved design with windings on iron wire in series. In 1884 a Hungarian group, headed by Otto Bláthy, invented a transformer with a closed iron core using primary windings in parallel. Bláthy is credited with having coined the term "transformer". In 1885 they used their new transformer in the lighting of over 1,000 lamps at the Hungarian National Exposition in Budapest.

Westinghouse was originally lukewarm about the future of electricity since it was uneconomical to transport it more than a few miles from the source of generation. In his work with natural gas*, he had found it practical to transport it long distances under high pressure and then reduce it to a low pressure at the customer site. When he heard of the transformer, he quickly grasped that here was a possibility of doing the same thing with electricity. He secured an option on the American rights of Gaulard and Gibbs and ordered several of their transformers shipped to Pittsburgh, as well as an alternating electric generator from Siemens of Germany. This equipment arrived in early December 1885 and within three weeks Westinghouse had

*Subsequently discussed in this chapter.

modified the transformer design to a practical and more efficient device. An H-shaped plate was used for the core and the primary and secondary coils were wound thereon using a lathe. The ends of the "H" were closed by I-shaped plates. A container for the transformer was designed which permitted cooling of the core by free circulation of air. Westinghouse patented the now well-known method of cooling and insulating transformers by immersion in oil.

The Westinghouse Electric Company was organized March 8, 1886. Among its assets were 27 patents and patent applications including those of Gaulard and Gibbs, Stanley, Westinghouse, and others. George Westinghouse became president and his brother Herman vice-president. Later in the year Henry M. Byllesby, a mechanical engineer who had been with Edison since the early days of Menlo Park, was hired as general manager. The first plant in the United States for distributing alternating electric current was built by Westinghouse in Buffalo, New York and was put into operation in November 1886. It supplied 1,000-volt power which was reduced to 110 volts for use by customers.

Westinghouse now moved rapidly to set up generating plants for lighting. Towns and even small villages could now be economically lighted from a power plant at a distance. Extensive tests showed that incandescent lights of the Edison type had as long a life with alternating current as with direct. A meter using a motor principle was developed to measure the amount of electricity used by a customer, the electroplating meter developed by Edison not being applicable with alternating current. However, the big hurdle was an electric motor which could operate on alternating current.

Nikola Tesla was born in Similjan, Crotia (Yugoslavia) and attended the polytechnic school at Graz and then the

University of Prague. He got a job in Edison's lamp factory at Ivry-Sur-Seine, France in 1882. Tesla was apparently used to his afternoon siestas and did not fit in well with the hard-driving American management at the factory and outside installation jobs. In 1884 he applied for transfer to an Edison company in the States and with the help of a family friend, Theodore Pukas, an agent of the Edison interests in Europe, Tesla was able to get a job at the Edison Machine Works located on Goerck Street, New York. Unfortunately for his future there, Charles Batchelor who had been his superior at the lamp factory in France returned to the United States in September 1884 and became manager of the Goerck Street factory. Tesla had a disagreement with Batchelor on salary matters and in 1885 Tesla left Edison's employ.

Tesla became associated with Westinghouse and later set up his own laboratory in New York City. He conceived the rotary magnetic field principle as an effective method of utilizing alternating current for power, making possible induction electric motors. Although Tesla was granted patents on an alternating-current motor in May 1888, it was not until 1895 that such a motor became practical. His motor was polyphase; *i.e.,* two or more alternating currents not in the same phase must make up the circuit. Furthermore the original frequency of 133 cycles per second was too high for any alternating current motor. Westinghouse was instrumental in setting up the 60-cycle standard which is still used today. Although Elihu Thomson invented an alternating current electric motor, the induction type as developed by the Westinghouse organization proved to be the best of all competitive devices, particularly as larger and larger motors came into use.

Westinghouse's alternating current got a big boost when

his company got the contract for lighting the Columbian Exposition which was held at Chicago in 1893*. Sealed bids were invited for lighting the fairgrounds. It was generally considered that the job would go to the General Electric Company which controlled the Edison light patents as a result of the merger of the Edison Electric Light Company and the Thomson-Houston Company in April 1892. When the bids were opened, it was found that the General Electric group had a minimum bid of $13.98 per light whereas Charles F. Locksteadt, president of the South Side Machine and Metal Works of Chicago, had submitted a bid of $5.49. Whether Locksteadt was an entrepreneur or a front man for Westinghouse is not clear, but in due course the Westinghouse Electric and Manufacturing Company advised the officials of the Exposition that it would honor the Locksteadt bid. After some negotiation new bids were called for. On this second round the Westinghouse group was low bidder at $5.25 and Westinghouse was awarded the contract on May 23, 1892.

Westinghouse Electric, as well as many other companies in the United States, including Thomson-Houston, had been manufacturing the Edison carbon-filament light with the supposition that Edison's basic light patent (6) was not valid. Following Edison's dramatic success, others came forward with claims that they, not Edison, were the true inventors. One of these was William E. Sawyer, who with his partner, Alban Man, had patented the use of carbon rods in a stoppered-type bottle which was either evacuated or filled with nitrogen. Certain speculators licensed the

*Although 1892 would have been the 400th anniversary of Columbus' successful voyage to the North American continent, it was considered inappropriate to hold an event of such magnitude during a presidential election year.

150

patents of Sawyer and Man, formed the Consolidated Electric Light Company in 1882, and attempted to copy the Edison light. As pointed out in Chapter 5, in 1884 this company hired Edward Acheson, a former employee of Edison who had specialized in the manufacture of the light while so employed, to head up their light manufacturing operations. Consolidated was in financial difficulties at the time, and in 1886 the Sawyer-Man Electric Company was formed and leased Consolidated's factory in Brooklyn. In 1887 Westinghouse acquired control of both the Consolidated and Sawyer-Man companies.

Now licensed under the Sawyer-Man patents Westinghouse proceeded to manufacture and set up electric plants using direct current. In his advertizing he boasted that his company would provide such plants at lower cost since they had not had the initial high development cost as had Edison. In 1885 the Edison Electric Light Company filed suit against several manufacturers of the Edison-type light, including Consolidated. Edison was enraged that others were brazenly ignoring his patents, and when Westinghouse began to push high voltage alternating current as well, the Edison interests decided to concentrate their attack on him. This constituted not only legal action for patent infringement but also a verbal attack that the high voltage alternating current was too dangerous to handle. Edison made some statements which he later regretted, but one can appreciate why he became bitter as he saw others moving into a field that he had pioneered nearly single-handedly.

In October 1889 a circuit court ruled in favor of Edison, but the Westinghouse interests appealed to a higher court. On July 4, 1891 Judge Wallace of New York ruled the priority of Edison's carbon filament patent over all others. However, the first and broader claim of Edison's basic patent (6), covering a carbon filament within an exhausted glass globe, was not sustained by the court. The second claim covering a globe "made entirely of glass", which the context of the specification showed to mean a one piece of glass with glass fused around the lead-in wires, was sustained. This was the Edison light, in universal use wherever incandescent lighting was employed.

The earlier adverse court decision in 1889 alerted Westinghouse to the possibility that the Edison light might soon be unavailable to him. Not one to admit defeat, he undertook to perfect a two-piece light bulb, the lower part holding the filament with fused in lead-in wires, and the upper part sealed on to the lower by means of cement on a ground glass joint. By 1892 Westinghouse had enough laboratory data to show that a useful two-piece light could be made which was outside the claim of the Edison patent sustained by the court. However, it would be more expensive and of shorter life than the Edison light. This lamp was never put on the commercial market. Making the number of light bulbs for the exposition plus those needed for other Westinghouse installations was a gigantic task. As pointed out in Chapter 5, grinding wheels for preparing the ground glass joints of Westinghouse's stopper lamps were the first sizable outlet for Acheson's new abrasive, Carborundum.

The bidding in of the Columbian Exposition lighting contract showed what a tough competitor George Westinghouse could be. He knew he would lose money on the project and his inferior light might cause serious problems. However, he rightfully saw the great advertizing value of his lighting the huge spectacle. When the World's Fair opened May 1, 1893, Westinghouse's lighting plant was one of the few large installations in place ready to go. It included 12 dynamos, each weighing about 75 tons, the largest of the alternating type constructed up to that time. They were constructed on Tesla's multiple phase principle with two armatures of each unit 90 degrees out of phase with one another. The voltage at the generators was 2,200 which was reduced to 110 for the 250,000 incandescent lamps operating in 40 separate circuits. The lights were so placed that only 180,000 were on at one time, the others being held in reserve. Never before had so much artificial light been produced in one place. A giant switchboard, controlling the entire system, was handled by only one man. Westinghouse's use of alternating current with voltage step-down on this large scale convinced such skeptics as Lord Kelvin — considered the leading authority in the electrical field — and the *Scientific American* that alternating current was the electricity of the future.

Although annual sales of Westinghouse Electric were up to $4,000,000 by 1890, their heavy expenses in connection with the litigation with Edison*, the high research costs in the development of alternating current, and the heavy capital expenditures and subsequent losses to be sustained in lighting the Columbian Exposition had forced the company into heavy borrowing. This resulted in a near collapse of this Westinghouse company during the economic depression of 1893. Westinghouse approached Pittsburgh bankers for a loan of $500,000. It was granted but with the reservation that they be allowed to name the general manager of the electric company. Westinghouse refused and went to New York banks for help. A reorganization of the electric company was carried out with banks and other creditors taking preferred stock for much of the loans.

---

*Litigation expenses from the various suits against those using the Edison light cost the Edison interests about two million dollars. It is safe to say that it cost the Westinghouse interests over one million.

Westinghouse's battles in the electrical industry had been costly, but his highly profitable air brake company and his outstanding record as an inventor and developer of new things helped him to weather this first storm.

In 1886 plans were initiated by certain residents of the Niagara Falls area to harness a part of the Falls for power. In 1890 the so-called International Niagara Commission was formed to implement some definite action. The chairman of this commission was William Thomson — later to be raised to the peerage as Lord Kelvin — the noted scientist of London. A decision had to be made whether the hydraulic power would be converted to direct current electricity, to alternating current, or to some other transportable form of energy such as compressed air. Following Westinghouse's impressive showing at the Columbian Exposition, the commission in October 1893 awarded the Westinghouse Electrical and Manufacturing Company a contract for three mammoth alternating current generators to be installed at Niagara Falls. In less than 18 months the first of the 5,000-horsepower dynamos was in place and the other two shortly thereafter. Originally it had been planned to supply electricity no further than Buffalo, a distance of about 20 miles. The project was so successful that within a few years a total of 11 generators had been installed, serving the entire western part of the state and as far east as Syracuse, a distance of about 195 miles. The generators were wound to deliver current at 2,200 volts, stepped up to 11,000 volts for delivery to points as distant as Buffalo. The Niagara Falls project pioneered the building of numerous large power plants designed to serve customers up to several hundred miles away.

In the late 1890's Westinghouse helped to pioneer the steam turbine, the workhorse of electrical power generation today. As larger and larger dynamos were developed, it was impractical to power these with reciprocating steam engines. The steam turbine had its origin, as did the steam engine, in England. By 1889 Sir Charles Parsons had not only made a 10-horsepower turbine but had some 300 in operation. His improved design used super-heated steam along with high vacuum. In 1895 Westinghouse took license under Parsons' patents and soon the Westinghouse Machine Company was manufacturing and marketing turbo-generator units. In 1899 a Westinghouse turbo-generator of 1,500-kilowatt (about 2,000 horsepower) capacity, running at 1,200 revolutions per minute, was installed at the Hartford Electric Light Company. The steam turbine helped to sound the death knell to direct-current generators, since commutators cannot be used on dynamos operating over a few hundred rpm, whereas steam turbines are most efficient at speeds of several thousand rpm. Multiple stages are used in steam turbine operation in order to use most efficiently the expansion of steam from 200 pounds pressure or more down to 29 inches of vacuum.

George Westinghouse had a great interest in turbines, dating back to his patent of October 31, 1865 dealing with a rotary steam engine. He made many contributions to turbine design following his licensing of Parsons' patents. He was also instrumental in the development of gears whereby a high-speed turbine could be used for driving a slow-rotating ship propellor.

The ever changing nature of the electrical and power business carried George Westinghouse into heavier and heavier expenditures. New plants had been and were being built. His electrical company issued no annual reports between 1897-1907. The reports from the news media continued good and the dividends were liberal. The stockholders appeared happy to leave it to "George". As expenditures skyrocketed, earnings per dollar invested declined. When the severe and widespread money crisis occurred in 1907, Westinghouse Electric had $43,000,000 in debts. The physical assets of this company were far beyond this amount but this was not a time for lenders to be optimistic. So many of the loans were called that both the Westinghouse Electric and Manufacturing Company and the Westinghouse Machine Company went into receivership in October 1907. The Air Brake Company and the Union Switch and Signal Company had no debts and rode out the storm.

Reorganized in December 1908, the new board of the electrical company consisted of 16 members, headed by Robert Mather, a lawyer of conservative bent. Although Westinghouse was left in the office of president, his authority was limited to the operating and sales departments, with all financial matters under Mather. The following year was poor in profits and in January 1910 the directors voted Westinghouse a six months' leave of absence. This proved to be a forced retirement. At the annual meeting in July, Westinghouse did not appear and his name was not on the slate of candidates for the board of directors. Edwin F. Atkins, a prominent manufacturer of Boston, replaced Westinghouse as president. At the annual meeting in 1911, Westinghouse attempted to regain control of his former company but failed. Like Edison, Westinghouse saw his electrical business, to which he had contributed so much, pass to the control of others. It was a blow from which he never recovered.

Although the air brake was Westinghouse's most original invention, and his developments in the electrical field his most outstanding in engineering, these were not all. The subjects of his 361 patents are ample evidence that he had much broader interests (7). Further evidence is that he organized 72 companies, the great majority of which were based on his own inventions or those which he had licensed and improved by further development.

Pittsburgh for all practical purposes is sitting on large deposits of coal. In addition, by 1880 petroleum had been discovered a short distance away, and natural gas even closer. Gas was beginning to find limited use as fuel in the area but due to poor distribution practices many accidents resulted from its use. Westinghouse, with his wife's consent, decided to drill for gas in the garden of their home in eastern Pittsburgh. At a little over 1,500 feet a high pressure area was struck which ripped out the casing head. The gas was set alight and the neighborhood was lit up by a roaring torch a hundred feet high. The well was finally brought under control and capped. With a gas well in his own backyard, in the spring of 1884 Westinghouse decided to go into the natural gas business.

Gas, obtained as a by-product in the early production of petroleum in Pennsylvania, was bled off and burned. If a driller struck gas instead of oil, he simply lit the well and allowed it to burn out. The commercial use of gas was hampered because of the inability to estimate reserves. A pipeline might be built to a well and then in a few years the gas supply become exhausted. Westinghouse was one of the leading pioneers in the production and distribution of natural gas in the United States. He took out 38 patents on the art, 28 of which were applied for during the two-year period of 1884-85.

In homes using natural gas for heating and cooking, it was common practice to let the gas burners run continuously, raising windows to cool the rooms if necessary. Gas pressure was unpredictable and if it fell too low and flames went out, resumption of pressure might

157

result in an explosion. Westinghouse invented and put into practice an automatic cut-off. It turned off the gas if the pressure fell below four ounces, and the supply remained off until restored by pressing a button at the regulator. How like our safety gas regulators today! He also devised a system of escape pipes to take care of any gas leakage underground. He developed devices for reducing the high pressures from the wells to low pressures for customers. He invented meters so that a customer could be charged according to amount of gas consumed.

In 1884 Westinghouse organized the so-called Philadelphia Company which marketed gas in Pittsburgh and other areas in Allegheny County. In 1898 eleven and three-quarters billion cubic feet of gas were sold. This company was operating 395 wells on land bought and leased and had 962 miles of pipelines. The availability of cheap natural gas drew many industries to Pittsburgh and thus helped to develop that city into a great industrial center. In 1889 Westinghouse resigned as president and as a director of the Philadelphia Company. He felt that he had gotten into an untenable position due to his major involvement in electricity which was becoming a competitor of gas.

For a time Westinghouse worked on gas engines, the forerunner of the present internal combustion engine. However when the steam turbine came in, it proved more practical for driving dynamos, primarily because of its increased efficiency at higher speeds, and his work on gas engines ceased.

In 1879 Westinghouse filed a patent application on the telephone followed by three others the next year. They dealt with setting up auxiliary telephone exchanges with the primary objective of saving wire. Although never exploited during the life of the patents, they did point in the direction of machine switching, a subsequent development of the Bell Company.

Once Westinghouse got into the electrical business, he saw the need for his own supply of copper. He bought several copper fields in southern Arizona and proceeded to do a limited amount of research on new methods of reducing copper ore. These experiments were not successful. However his choice of copper fields was a wise one. Southern Arizona leads the nation today in copper production.

After Westhinghouse lost control of his electric company, he not only remained active in his other companies but also continued to start new ones. His outstanding success with the air brake led him to thinking of new uses for compressed air. The result was the air spring. Its primary use was with automobiles in adjunct with steel springs. The air was held within a cylinder capped with another cylinder with a leather gasket enclosed in oil in the annular space. He was granted two patents dealing with the air spring for motor cars (8). Westinghouse died before the air spring was fully developed.

Although Westinghouse became a wealthy man at a relatively early age, in most ways he was a modest man. He had no yacht, he took no extensive vacations, and had no expensive hobbies such as fine horses, collecting art, or the like. However, he was extravagant when it came to homes. He had three permanent ones and two that were movable. Of the latter, one was his private railroad car, christened Glen Eyre, which was equipped with office, sleeping quarters, a kitchen, and dining room. The other temporary one was a suite in a New York hotel, the location of which changed from time to time.

In 1871 the Westinghouses bought a home in the Homewood section on the outskirts of eastern Pittsburgh.

George Westinghouse, age 18 years, a member of the Union Army

One of the few photographs available of Westinghouse as a young man

Mr. and Mrs. George Westinghouse in their Pittsburgh home

The elder George Westinghouse

The house was large and all of it was not furnished until several years later. It was only a few minutes' walk to the railroad station where on most days Westinghouse took the train to work. Mrs. Westinghouse named this home Solitude.

In the late '80's Mrs. Westinghouse's health was not the best, which caused her physician to recommend that she spend more time in mountain air in the country. The result was that a farm of about 100 acres, with a very substantial house, was bought in the Berkshire Hills near Lenox, Massachusetts. The home was named Erskine Park in honor of Mrs. Westinghouse's family. Adjacent land was bought from time to time and by 1911 the estate constituted nearly 600 acres. Marguerite Westinghouse spent a great deal of time there in the summers and took an active part in the gardening and other farm activities. The family displayed each year at the local florist show. A fine herd of milk cows was maintained and although George Westinghouse was not able to spend much time at Erskine Park, his wife did succeed in making a part-time gentleman farmer out of him.

The third permanent Westinghouse home was a fine brick mansion on the west side of Du Pont Circle, Washington, D. C. The family often occupied it for considerable periods of time during the winter months. In 1899 the American Society of Mechanical Engineers held their annual meeting in Washington. All members in attendance were entertained at the Westinghouse home, along with several members of the government and the diplomatic corps.

Westinghouse was a family man; he had no interests in clubs. He often chose to bring some business associates home with him for dinner, with technical or business discussions afterwards. Mrs. Westinghouse was a gracious hostess and always seemed to be able to provide a good dinner for many guests, even on a very short notice.

Westinghouse never smoked and took alcoholic beverages sparingly and then only at meal time. When a company associate was authorized to hire men for a new project, his only directive was that "they be gentlemen". He strongly disapproved of any off-color story at Company dinners or the like. During the verbal battle between the Edison interests and the Westinghouse group relative to direct current vs. alternating, George Westinghouse avoided bringing personalities into the argument.

Westinghouse was never a paid employee unless one chooses to call him such when as a youth in his father's shop. He had his own business at age 19 and at 23 was the president of a company which subsequently operated worldwide. He tended to be demanding of his technical and business associates but less so of the men in his shops than did most employers of that period. He inaugurated the Saturday half holiday at the Air Brake Company in 1871 — a first in any major industry. None of his companies ever had a strike while he was in charge, although the Pittsburgh area was the scene of much labor strife during the 1880-1900 period.

George Westinghouse never set up what one would call a research laboratory. A group might work for a time in a given location on a specific program and another group somewhere else, but there was no correlated research on a continuing basis. If he had an idea for a new or improved device, he would sketch it out and either build it himself in one of his shops or have one of his choice workmen do it. As most inventors of his time, George Westinghouse's knowledge and skills covered several technologies. For example, in his air brake there must have been some serious problems relating to rubber hoses for connecting the air pipes between cars. In 1870 the primary use for rubber was for water proofing coats and shoes. If one is to classify him by a single descriptive term, it would be mechanical engineer. It would seem that his great success as an organizer of new businesses has overshadowed in the minds of some that George Westinghouse was a great inventor (9). The invention of the air brake and his continuing improvements of it certainly rank high in the list of most original and important inventions. Although making no basic discoveries or inventions in the electrical field, he was one of the first to understand the technology of alternating current and to grasp its commercial possibilities. He had outstanding abilities on taking a crude invention and improving it to the degree that it became commercially feasible.

Westinghouse's difficulties in getting financial support for his early inventions appeared to have left him with a soft spot in his heart for young inventors trying to get started. As is pointed out in Chapter 5, he bought Acheson's first "successful" invention and thus helped him to get started on his inventive career. He helped Nikola Tesla with his early motor inventions even though many considered the fellow somewhat of a crackpot. He paid Gaulard and Gibbs $50,000 for American rights to their transformer patents, which were known at the time to be weak and later were declared invalid.

Westinghouse received many honors including the Franklin Medal, the John Fritz Medal, the Edison Medal, and the Grashoff Medal. He was the first American to receive the German Grashoff Medal. He received two honorary doctor degrees. The American Association for the Advancement of Science made him one of its two honorary members at the time. George Westinghouse never displayed his awards or used his titles. He preferred simply to be

George Westinghouse. His most illustrious award was posthumous; *i.e.*, his election to the Hall of Fame for Great Americans (10).

In 1905 the Equitable Life Assurance Society, then a stock company, was investigated for possible wrong doings by a commission appointed by the state governor. The investigation resulted in the recommendation that an illustrious committee be set up to reorganize this large insurance company. The committee consisted of Grover Cleveland, the only living ex-President of the United States; Morgan O'Brien, who had served as an esteemed justice of the state supreme court for 20 years; and George Westinghouse. Westinghouse was chosen to represent business and because he was accepted as a person of impeccable character.

George and Marguerite Westinghouse had one child, George III, born in 1884. The son took an interest in his father's business and headed up the Air Spring Company beginning in 1912. Today there is no Westinghouse descendant active in any of George Westinghouse's former companies. The headquarters of the Westinghouse Electric Corporation is still in Pittsburgh and their huge research facilities are nearby. Westinghouse Air Brake, now a division of WABCO, continues to be a leader in railroad braking. The original manufacturing facilities at Wilmerding are still in use. Air brakes for trucks are now manufactured by Bendix-Westinghouse, an independent company controlled by the Bendix Corporation.

Following his ouster from the electric company which continues to bear his name, George Westinghouse's health began to fail. While at Erskine Park in the summer of 1913, he had a severe coughing spell and his doctor was summoned from Pittsburgh. The latter insisted on a complete physical examination, the first that Westinghouse

163

had had since he joined the army. He was found to have an enlarged heart and other organic weaknesses. Shortly after Christmas he started for their Washington home but became so weak that his journey was interrupted at New York where he took residence in his hotel suite. He died there March 12, 1914. His wife, who had been a semi-invalid following a stroke in 1912, followed her husband to the grave the following June. The bust of George Westinghouse at the Hall of Fame for Great Americans bears the following inscription: "If some day they say of me that in my work I have contributed something to the welfare and happiness of my fellow men, I shall be satisfied."

Chapter 5

Edward Goodrich Acheson

Like Edison, Edward Goodrich Acheson made two outstanding inventions. The first, a synthetic abrasive approaching diamonds in hardness, is manufactured today in quantities exceeding 200,000 tons annually, by a process basically as that developed by Acheson. The second, his synthesis of artificial graphite, has made possible a multitude of processes and products ranging from the electric furnace process for manufacturing steel to lubricants. In spite of these two major developments, plus many minor ones, Acheson was little known by the public during his lifetime or later. The reason is that no Acheson product was marketed to the general public but rather to other industries where they were, and are being, used in their manufacturing operations.

Due to Acheson's lack of notoriety with the public, relatively little of a popular nature has been written about him. This is true in spite of the fact that he left a diary extending over most of his life as well as voluminous records of his research, his business, and numerous personal and business correspondence. In 1965 Acheson Industries, Inc. published a booklet of 63 pages entitled, *Edward Goodrich Acheson, A Pathfinder* (1). Much of this treatise is taken from *A Pathfinder* published in 1910, which was a short autobiography of Acheson, then 54 with 21 years of his life remaining. Recently a detailed biography of

Acheson has been published (2).

The Achesons had large families. William, the father of Edward, was one of 12 children of David and Mary Acheson of Washington, Pennsylvania. The William Achesons had two sons and six daughters, of which two daughters died in early childhood. William, Junior was the oldest and two of the surviving daughters were younger than Edward. The father was of Irish ancestry and the mother of English origin. The elder William had attended college briefly but was forced to withdraw for financial reasons. At the time of Edward's birth on March 9, 1856, the father, in partnership with his brother James, was operating a grocery store in Washington.

The Achesons had been natives of this small town for decades and apparently none had ventured far to seek his fortune. However in 1863 the father gave up the grocery business to accept a position as manager of an iron furnace at Monticello, Pennsylvania. The family moved from cramped quarters of a building, which housed the grocery store as well as two families in the downtown area of Washington, to a large house on an acre of ground. It was situated in a beautiful valley about 50 miles north of Pittsburgh near a creek which flowed into the Allegheny River.

In Washington Edward had attended a "private infants' school" which today, no doubt, would be classified as a kindergarten. He then attended public school which was continued after the move to Monticello. At that time Pennsylvania was one of the more progressive states in providing public education. At age 14 Edward was enrolled in a boarding school at North Sewickley, Pennsylvania. The following spring the school was closed because of an epidemic of smallpox. In the fall of 1871 Edward entered the Bellefonte Academy located in Bellefonte, Pennsylvania, a city of 3,500 inhabitants. Edward was a diligent student and greatly preferred mathematics and surveying over the languages. In a letter to the elder Acheson in 1872, the head of the academy, Reverend James Hughes, reported that, "Edward is doing well. If anything, he errs on the side of studying too hard. He is doing much more than the average of students. He seems determined to become an educated man."

The economic boom following the Civil War began to slack off by late 1871 and Edward's father came under great pressure from the mine owners to produce better iron at lower prices. The Monticello operation, as well as all iron blast furnace operations in the East, was beginning to meet stiff competition from midwest mills using the newly discovered high grade iron ore from upper Michigan. The father's health and the family's welfare deteriorated under the pressure and early in 1873 Edward was forced to end his formal education. On June 20, 1873 the elder Acheson was stricken with a fatal heart attack. Edward now shared responsibilities with his brother William for the welfare of their widowed mother and their sisters. William, Junior had taken over the operation of the blast furnace during his father's sickness but as the severe economic depression, known as the Panic of 1873, deepened, the operation functioned only periodically. In 1874 the company went into bankruptcy. The only source of income to the family then was from a half interest in a small coal mine which helped to provide the necessities of life.

As a child Edward showed an interest in mechanical and scientific subjects. He was a frequent visitor at the mine and blast furnace. His mother subscribed to *Scientific American* and she would read articles to Edward before he was able to read them himself. The boy came into possession of Orton's "Underground Treasures — How and Where to Find Them". With his know-how Edward searched the area for stones and Indian relics which might provide a boy's wealth. He built several small brick kilns to use in his fruitless attempts to obtain valuable metals from his findings.

Edward's father had encouraged his son's innovative traits. On his father's suggestion, during the summer vacation of 1872 the youth worked on an improved machine for drilling holes into rocks and slates in coal mines for placing explosive charges. Edward designed a "force auger" which was built in a machine shop in Pittsburgh at a cost of $154. The equipment proved to be too heavy and cumbersome for practical use. In 1873 Edward filed a caveat in the United States Patent Office on the auger, but since it proved impractical, the caveat was not followed by a patent application. It is significant that at the early age of 17 young Acheson was getting acquainted with Patent Office procedures and attempting to achieve the status of an inventor.

During the six years following his father's death, Edward held a total of 10 jobs, all in the local area. They varied from clerking in a dry goods and notions store in Reynoldsville to that of foreman in charge of about 60 men operating several small iron ore mines in the Allegheny valley. His varied experience included several jobs as a surveyor; a job as gauger of storage tanks in the budding petroleum industry provided opportunities for him to use his mathematics; and an unsuccessful private venture to market a device for sounding an alarm when the water in a steam boiler became dangerously low.

As Acheson moved from job to job he continued his scientific studies and experimented when facilities allowed.

168

He obtained a copy of Napier's "A Manual of Electro-Metallurgy" and from this learned the fundamentals of electroplating. This led to a profitable side job in that the young experimenter bought several watches with brass cases, silverplated them using some of his mother's silverware as anodes in his plating bath, and sold the silvered timepieces at a profit.

At an early age young Acheson showed the desire and ability to write on scientific subjects. In July 1875 he published an article entitled "Lightning Rods" in the Kittanning *Free Press*; in August of the same year, an article entitled "Silver Deposits of the Allegheny Valley" was published in the Pittsburgh *Commercial*. However, he did not fare so well with the more sophisticated publication, *Scientific American*. In a letter to the editor which was reproduced in the weekly issue of October 23, 1875, Acheson cited "a most wonderful explosive" which he had inadvertently prepared when shaking turpentine with nitric acid in a glass-stoppered flask. The flask had blown up in his hand but fortunately caused no physical harm except acid burns on his face. The editor commented that it was well known that nitric acid attacked turpentine vigorously and that he was publishing the letter ". . .in the hope that it may be of service in preventing accident, if not loss of life, to other amateur experimenters."

By 1879 Acheson had become greatly interested in electricity. He worked on a primary battery which contained no liquid and attempted to build a dynamo. Neither was successful and Acheson concluded that the best way to gain knowledge in this new field was to go to the New York area where "the action was". His mother had died in November 1878 and his two older sisters, as well as his brother, were now married. In the fall of 1880 the two younger sisters and Edward closed the house in Monticello;

169

the sisters left to attend a school of design in Philadelphia; and on the first day of September Edward, with a new suit of clothes on his back and one hundred dollars in his pocket, headed for New York City.

Edward Acheson was now 24 years of age. He had definitely reached manhood. Although he had been considered a good employee in his previous jobs, he had yet to demonstrate any degree of success when strictly on his own. However, it certainly could not be said that he lacked self confidence.

Acheson failed to find work with Edward Weston who was well established at Newark, New Jersey as a manufacturer of electrical instruments and dynamos. The applicant was equally unsuccessful with several electrical manufacturers in New York including Western Electric. Acheson then decided to try the seemingly impossible — get a job with Edison. Following are Acheson's own words on how he became a member of one of the most exclusive technical groups in America at that time (3):

> . . .I was getting desperate. Edison and his laboratory at Menlo Park were then much in the public eye. I had little hope of securing an opening there, but, as a desperate, final resort, took the train out to Menlo Park. I climbed the low hill from the station, entered a small brick building in the corner of a large fenced inclosure. The building contained the office downstairs and Edison's library upstairs. I handed my card to a boy in the office with the request to see Mr. Edison. He took the card and disappeared, presently returning, he opened a small wicket gate and inviting me to enter, conducted me out of a rear entrance of the office, across a vacant lot and into a long two-story frame

building. He took me upstairs and into a room covering the entire second floor containing a number of long pine tables, the walls being lined with shelves holding bottles. At one of the tables sat three men, the centre one in a colored calico shirt, without coat, was introduced as Mr. Edison. The one on his left I knew afterward to be Mr. William J. Hammer, and the one on the right as Mr. Francis R. Upton. Mr. Edison, placing one hand to his ear to indicate I should speak loudly, asked, "What do you wish?"; I replied "Work." He replied, with perhaps impatience, "Go out to the machine shop and see Kruesi," and returned to the work absorbing his attention. Mr. Hammer kindly told me to go downstairs, pass back through the laboratory, cross the yard to a one-story brick building and inquire for Mr. Kruesi, who was the Superintendent.

I followed Mr. Hammer's directions and entering the machine shop, found myself in a small office, almost completely filled with a large drafting table, over which a man was working. An attendant received my inquiry for Mr. Kruesi, and while he was gone I was very busy preparing myself, loading my gun, so to speak. The drafting table inspired me. I had had some experience using the tools of a draftsman in my civil engineering work. Presently a tall, foreign-looking gentleman entered and asked me what I wanted. This was Mr. Kruesi. On the spur of the moment, I am afraid I told a white lie. I replied, "Mr. Edison sent me to you for you to put me to work." "What kind of work?" he asked; "Drafting," I said. "All right," he replied. "Mr. Hornig needs an assistant. Can you report for duty Monday morning?" I assured him I could. So it happened that the 12th day of September, 1880, while still in my twenty-fifth year, saw me installed in Mr. Edison's employ at Menlo Park, N.J. Mr. Kruesi soon learned of the deception I had played upon him, and held me under suspicion for a long time.

Acheson was allowed to use the machine shop at night and soon he resumed work on the dynamo which he designed and built while living in Pennsylvania. One evening he showed Edison his dynamo design and asked him his opinion of its merits. Edison pointed out that it was similar to one developed by Siemens of Germany and told Acheson where he could find the pertinent reference in the library. This proved to be the case. Acheson was not to be outdone and in a few days asked similar comments on a meter which he had designed for measuring electrical power delivered to a customer. This brought the following reprimand from Edison, "I do not pay you to make suggestions to me; how do you know but I already had that idea, and now if I use it you will think I took it from you."

Although Edison expected his employees to work on assignments which he gave them and to follow the approaches he suggested, he did respect an employee who could think for himself. Although Acheson's idea for an electric meter proved to be a failure, Edison apparently felt that Acheson would be more valuable in the research laboratory than in the drafting room. This delighted Acheson (4):

. . .I was now in my glory. I had a large room under my supervison, equipped with all the conveniences required, balance room, muffle

172

furnaces, air pressure, gas, electricity, steam bath cabinet, etc. I was thrown into association with most agreeable companions. I, at this time, formed a close friendship with Dr. Edward L. Nichols, who had recently returned from Europe where he had followed an extensive course of study in the foremost universities of the continent. He was at this time doing special scientific work for Edison. The Doctor is now Professor of Physics at Cornell University. I made a number of special investigations for Edison – especially on the filament for the incandescent lamp. I had every opportunity to use my inventive faculties.

Acheson's joy was short-lived. The factory for making the carbon filament lights was just getting started under the supervision of Charles Batchelor, Edison's most trusted assistant. Batchelor was scheduled to go to Paris in the spring of 1881 to be in charge of the Edison exhibit at the Exposition to be held there that summer. Edison chose Acheson to replace Batchelor at the lamp factory. Acheson demurred saying he preferred research over production. However Edison gave him no choice by contending that lamp manufacture was so new that opportunities were as great there for "a thinker" as in the laboratory. Acheson was getting $7.50 per week at the laboratory (5). After a few days at the lamp factory he demanded $100 per month from Batchelor and on being refused, he quit his job.

This was one of the several episodes in Acheson's early life when his independent nature resulted in rash acts which might have ruined his career. Acheson had been with Edison for only three months when he was assigned to the lamp factory in one of the most important jobs in the organization. If manufacture of the new incandescent light had not been successful and at a reasonable price, Edison's entire electric light project would have failed. When Acheson quit, Edison replaced him at the light factory with his best professional man, Francis Upton, which showed the importance Edison attached to the job. If Acheson had not rebelled he would have received some increase in salary, but more important than salary, he turned down an opportunity to become top man in the manufacture of the important device which was spearheading the new electrical technology.

After sitting around his boarding house for several days, Acheson realized he had made a mistake. He returned to the laboratories and looked up Edison. The latter laughed and joked about Acheson not being able to take the hard work at the lamp factory and reassigned his former employee to the laboratories. Obviously Edison was convinced that Acheson was potentially a very valuable man for his organization.

Acheson did some good work on a technique for making filaments in quantity from a gunk containing finely divided natural graphite. Before these filaments found use in commercial light bulbs, a superior carbon filament was developed by carbonizing bamboo fibers. In the spring of 1881 Edison was making plans to move into Europe utilizing his exhibit at the Paris Exposition to attract customers and capital. Acheson was one of those chosen to go to Europe to help introduce the new lighting system. He learned all of the operations in making light bulbs and prepared a complete set of instruments for measuring the efficiency of electric lamps.

Acheson served as Batchelor's assistant at the Exposition and then joined the Edison group to set up a factory in France and to introduce the Edison light in Europe. In the interim, equipment was supplied from New York and soon

174

Acheson was travelling about Europe setting up independent light plants. One of his first assignments was at the La Scala Theater in Milan where 92 electric lights replaced a like number of gas burners. When an Edison company was subsequently formed in Milan, Acheson was offered the job as chief engineer at $300 per month, twice what he was getting from the French company. Acheson accepted in spite of the fact that he was advised by the manager of Edison's interests in Europe that the company disapproved of his independent action. Since the Italian affiliate got its supplies through the Paris company, Acheson's position became untenable. After seven months in Italy, he again severed relations with an Edison company.

With some accumulated savings, Acheson resolved to strike out on his own. He rented two rooms in a small Paris hotel, using one as a laboratory-workshop. He felt that since it was possible to convert electrical energy to heat energy, it should be possible to convert heat directly to electrical power. After five months of fruitless work, he was in debt and due to the strain and long working hours his health was impaired. Unable to raise any capital to support his experiments, he cabled his brother William for a loan of $1,000. Most of this was used to pay debts and patent attorney fees. He resolved to try his luck in London but shortly after his arrival there in June 1883, he was stricken by a severe case of jaundice.

Acheson moved into a cheap boarding house and although feeling extremely sick had no money for a doctor. One day while sitting in the sun in front of his lodging, he recognized a former Menlo Park colleague in the passing throng. It was James Holloway, who had been sent to London by Edison to assist in the installation of the electric light there. Holloway took Acheson into his home, procured a doctor, and the family helped nurse the patient back to good health. Acheson's failure to achieve worthwhile results in his energy conversion experiments during the five months in Paris, as well as considerable work he had done on his own time prior to coming to Europe, did not prevent him from selling his obsession to Holloway. The latter introduced Acheson to Frederick Gordon, owner of a hotel chain, who provided Acheson with capital to continue his experiments. In December, learning that Samuel Insull, Edison's private secretary, was in London, Acheson called on him and related his dire circumstances. Insull contacted Edison by cable and the latter directed that transportation be provided for Acheson to return to New York. Thus with promise of employment once again in an Edison organization, Acheson abandoned his experiments and returned to America.

Although Edison was in Florida on vacation, he had left word that Acheson was to work on an electroplating project using a corner of one floor of the Edison Machine Building in New York City as working space. This was followed by experiments with rayon which was then being developed as a substitute for bamboo fibers for making carbon filaments. Word also came from Edison that he wished Acheson to take the position of engineer at a new central electric station then being planned to supplement the original Pearl Street station in New York. Acheson refused this offer but continued to stay at the machine works where he was investigating several of his own ideas as well as his assigned tasks. In March 1884, about two and one-half months after resuming work with Edison, Acheson submitted his resignation. Not unexpectedly, Insull was chagrined by the turn of events. He refused to pay Acheson any salary for his last week, maintaining that he was working primarily on his own ideas, and demanded that Acheson pay for his transportation from Europe, which he did in part.

176

None of Acheson's pet ideas worked out and by July he was again broke and forced to seek employment. He obtained a job with the Consolidated Electric Light Company in Brooklyn. This company was attempting to manufacture the Edison-type light bulb and, because of their ownership of the patents of William Sawyer and Albon Man, hoped to escape infringement action by the Edison Electric Light Company. Acheson was a welcome addition to the staff because of his experience with Edison. Acheson improved their operations, which resulted in his salary being increased from 25 to 35 dollars per week. However, the company was in financial difficulties which resulted in Acheson severing his employment there after only a few months. While working at this company, he met Margaret Maher. Even though out of a job and practically penniless, he proposed and they were married December 15, 1884.

From two associates whom he had known while working for Consolidated, Acheson was now able to get some financial support for constructing a new type of dynamo. It proved to be a failure. Fortunately about the time the test data became available, Acheson happened to meet John Huyler on the streets of New York. Huyler had been a fellow passenger with Acheson on his boat trip to Europe in 1881, and the two had met again at the Paris Exposition. Huyler was in the confectionary business and apparently looking for investments in other fields. He informed Acheson that he was financing a project dealing with a new type of insulation for electrical conduits and he would like him to determine if the project had promise or whether it should be terminated. The upshot was that Huyler paid Acheson's supporters about $1,200 to release Acheson from the dynamo project, and Acheson began working at the small insulated wire plant. In a few weeks

177

Acheson convinced Huyler that the project was without merit and the plant was closed down.

Acheson now induced Huyler to support his effort on the development of an anti-induction telephone circuit. Telephone circuits, which are of low voltage, are subject to induction from neighboring electric lines. Acheson's approach was to take a rubber-coated copper wire, coat the rubber insulation with graphite powder thus making it conductive, and then to electroplate a tube of copper over the rubber. The assembly was then insulated in the usual manner by means of braided cotton subsequently impregnated with asphalt. The center wire and the copper tubing were the two conductors. Acheson's concept of a continuous process for depositing copper over the primary insulation to form the return conductor and an inductive protector for the primary wire was an ingenious one. Acheson's assignment with Edison of electroplating copper around the connections of the incandescent light filament and the lead-in wires likely led to Acheson's conception of his telephone circuit composite.

Although the development looked promising, Acheson was making only $15 a week and the family's rent for living quarters was $30 per month. In August 1885 their first child was born. Acheson's experimental working quarters left much to be desired and quoting from his autobiography (6):

. . .The sub-cellar was an abominable place in which to work, and I can now remember that I usually left there, after a day's work, cold and almost numb from my feet to the waist. Had I not had a remarkable constitution, I do not think I could have survived this period, and, indeed, it is possible that some of the loss of health I afterwards experienced

178

for some years, may be charged to my struggles at that time.

In the fall of 1885 William Acheson proposed that his younger brother return to Pennsylvania and conduct experiments on reducing iron ore with natural gas. William had continued to be active in the mining of iron ore and its reduction to pig iron in blast furnaces. His operations were in the area where there was extensive petroleum production and the by-product, natural gas, had little value at that time. The possibility of replacing the relatively expensive charcoal or coke used in blast furnace operations with the cheap gas was economically attractive. Since Huyler was not interested in putting up the necessary funds to pursue the telephone circuit development on a larger scale, he assented to Acheson leaving.

No doubt the return to rural Pennsylvania appealed to Acheson. One wonders if William did not originate the natural gas project largely as a pretense to rescue his brother and family from a pitiful situation in New York. One can hardly describe Edward's return as that of the prodigal son, but he was returning with less money than when he left five years earlier and he owed William $1,000 which he had borrowed while in Europe. Thus at the age of 29, Edward Acheson with family returned to the small town* where he had spent his boyhood, taking up living quarters in the household of William Acheson. It was no doubt difficult for the city-bred wife to become a subject of charity of the country cousins. It must have been apparent to all that, at least economically, Edward was the black sheep of the Acheson family.

Acheson's attempts to reduce iron ore with natural gas

*The name of the village had been changed from Monticello to Gosford.

179

were unsuccessful. He did, however, make an observation during one of his experiments which subsequently led to his first major success. Following the passage of natural gas over a clay crucible in a high temperature furnace, he observed that the crucible had not only become coated and impregnated with carbon but also appeared to have become harder.

With the iron ore project laid aside, Acheson again turned his attention to his telephone cable project. Two patent applications were filed on this technology resulting in the first patents granted to him (7). Acheson now felt he was in a position to approach a manufacturer of insulated wiring. Since Pittsburgh was the nearest industrial center, he contacted the Standard Underground Cable Company located there. His initial visit was encouraging but having no money to make the many trips he anticipated, Acheson pawned his watch chain and bought a monthly ticket on the Allegheny Railroad from Kittanning to Pittsburgh.

Following the rebuff by Edison to consider Westinghouse's steam engine for running dynamos, the latter resolved to contest Edison in the electrical field.* By 1886 this drive was in full swing with George Westinghouse acquiring electrical companies and hiring people who appeared to have special knowledge in this field. Due to the highly successful development of his air brake and other railway equipment, Westinghouse did not lack for money. About the time Acheson approached Standard Underground Cable, Westinghouse was negotiating for the purchase of a controlling interest in that company. Westinghouse made his purchase and on behalf of the Cable Company purchased Acheson's wire patents for $7,000 and $50,000 in stock of that company which was then capitalized at

*See Chapter 4.

180

$3,000,000. In addition Acheson was hired at an annual salary of $2,400 for three years.

Although the company was shortly reorganized with the capitalization being reduced from $3,000,000 to $1,000,000 with a proportional reduction in Acheson's stock equity, his economic status had suddenly changed from that of a pauper to one of substance with a guaranteed income. He at once paid Huyler $5,000 for the money he had advanced while Acheson was in New York and $2,000 to his brother William to cover the earlier loan, interest, and the expenses he had incurred when Edward's family was in Gosford. Acheson now moved his family to Pittsburgh, furnished a house, bought a cow, horse and carriage, and engaged a man to drive and to attend the barn. One can imagine the delight of Mrs. Edward Acheson on leaving the rural area where she had been discontented living with her in-laws.

In his new position, Acheson not only worked on problems in the local plant, but also supervised the installation of their underground cable in many cities. In his spare time he studied and planned for the future when he could return to his favorite subject — thermoelectricity. Acheson made several improvements in cable design and manufaeture during his three years at the Underground Cable Company, and likely there would have been a promising future for him there. However, once his three-year contract was up, Acheson resumed independent work on thermoelectric generators. He got financial support from several of Pittsburgh's leading citizens and beginning in May 1889, a laboratory was set up with one assistant. He remained as a consultant with the cable company until November 1889.

During the years Acheson had designed and constructed 33 forms of his thermal converter. Larger scale tests were now carried out which were not promising. After a year and spending $15,000, his supporters had had enough and abandoned the project. Acheson then conceived the idea of setting up an electric light plant in a small town with the hope that the income would pay expenses and he could use the plant facilities for experimentation when there was little demand for lighting. Monongahela City, 30 miles south of Pittsburgh, was chosen. A syndicate was formed, made up largely with Acheson's former supporters, including his brother William and his old associate from New York, John Huyler. A plant was installed and electricity ran to many of the homes. The stockholders were to share in the exploitation of Acheson's cal-electric patents, his thermal generators being given large scale testing in supplying current to the town. By 1892 Acheson finally concluded that conversion of thermal energy directly to electricity was a practical impossibility and he abandoned the field forever (8).

In 1890 the Acheson family had moved to Monongahela City where a house was purchased using the last of their Underground Cable stock and utilizing a sizable mortgage. Edward and his Catholic wife were upholding the Acheson tradition of large families; within six years after marriage they had four children. Although he had lost thousands of dollars in his private ventures, obtained several worthless patents both in the United States and abroad, and spent years of time unproductively, Acheson still had great faith in his own inventive ability. He now worked on what he considered "synthetic rubber" from turpentine and explored again the possibility of making diamond, *i.e.*, crystalline carbon, from a carbon compound or amorphous carbon.

Acheson's primary interest in synthetic diamonds was for abrasive purposes and his occasional contacts with

George Kunz of Tiffany's of New York served to remind him of the need for a new hard abrasive. Also Acheson recalled his observation five years earlier that clay appeared to get harder when impregnated with carbon in a gas furnace. He now had an abundance of electricity available. Why not try the action of carbon on clay at a higher temperature in an electric furnace? He was still thinking in terms of diamonds; he would dissolve carbon in molten clay and if successful, perhaps on cooling it would precipitate in the crystalline state.

In March 1891 Acheson prepared a mixture of clay and coke, put it within an iron bowl, and attached one lead from a dynamo to the bowl and the other to an arc-light carbon placed within the mixed powders. Enough carbon was present to permit a current to pass and Acheson was able to melt some of the clay near the carbon arc. On examination of the cooled molten mass, the material was found to be quite amorphous except for a few bright specks next to the carbon electrode. Acheson stuck one of these into the eraser end of a pencil and drew it across a pane of glass. It cut glass like a diamond!

Acheson next built a small furnace of refractory brick with two carbon electrodes which could be varied in distance from each other. After two months of experimentation using various mixtures of clay and coke, he had collected a small vial of the crystals. He took these to a diamond cutter in New York. They proved to be so effective that Acheson's sample was purchased on the spot for $60, which was at the rate of about $900 per pound. His wife was elated to learn of this unexpected income for the needy family, but her joy was shortlived on learning that her husband had spent most of the money for a microscope before leaving New York.

Acheson, with advice from a pharmacist friend who

knew some chemistry, named his new material Carborundum. Corundum is a natural aluminum oxide of extreme hardness. Knowing that clay is primarily an aluminum silicate and that aluminum oxide can be harder than silicon oxide, Acheson assumed his compound was a chemical combination of carbon and corundum. Subsequent analysis by an outside laboratory showed that the crystals to be silicon carbide (SiC), a new chemical compound. Acheson refused to believe the analysis until he demonstrated that Carborundum could be made from carbon and silica, no aluminum being present.

In September 1891 the Carborundum Company was incorporated with an authorized capital of $150,000. Acheson transferred $50,000 of the stock to the stockholders of the Monongahela Electric Light Company for their equity in his research carried out at the electric plant. Since it was not until the spring of 1892 that Acheson was sure of the chemical nature of his abrasive, a patent application was not filed until May 10, 1892. At the same time registration of "Carborundum" as a trademark name was also applied for.

Early production of silicon carbide amounted to only a few ounces per day. Acheson found that by putting a core of carbon embedded in the reaction mixture between the electrodes, they could be placed further apart and yield of product increased. Adding common salt which served as a flux also helped. In June Acheson hired a German chemist, Dr. Otto Mühlhaeuser, to work on means of increasing the yield. A furnace was designed using multiple electrodes and sawdust was included in the sand-coke-salt feed. Production was soon increased to 20 pounds per day. The sales price was reduced to $10 per pound.

At first sales were primarily for use as a dust in polishing precious stones. Later Acheson carried out an

Courtesy of Acheson Industries, Inc.

Edward Acheson, successful inventor-businessman

Courtesy of The Library of Congress, Washington, D.C.

Acheson remained an experimentalist until near the end of his life.

Mr. and Mrs. Edward Acheson

extensive program on making small Carborundum wheels to compete with emery wheels. Sales expanded and by April 1893, 500 pounds of Carborundum were being produced per day and income exceeded costs. Sales to the dental trade increased rapidly and Westinghouse ordered $7,000 worth of small grinding wheels to prepare the joints of the light bulbs to be used at the World's Columbian Exposition to be held at Chicago.* Acheson had a booth at this famous fair where he exhibited Carborundum and demonstrated its uses.

As the reputation of Carborundum grew, also did that of Acheson. He gave talks before technical societies on the synthesis and uses of his new product. In May 1894 he received the John Scott Medal, awarded by the Franklin Institute of Philadelphia for outstanding technical achievements. His foreign patents brought in substantial income. The early months of 1894 found the Carborundum Company 60 days behind in filling orders. In September the company decided to establish production operations at Niagara Falls, utilizing the cheap hydroelectric power made available there. The facilities at Monongahela City were retained for the fabrication of end products. Five electric furnaces utilizing 4,000 horsepower of electricity were built with a daily capacity of over six tons of Carborundum. Operations began October 1895, the Carborundum Company being the second manufacturer to contract for power from the Niagara Falls Power Company.

Because of the capital requirements in building a new plant during the financial depression of the 1893 period, new stock was issued highly favorable to certain investors. By 1898 the Mellon brothers** had gained control of the

*See Chapter 4.

**Andrew W. Mellon and Richard B. Mellon of the Union Trust Company of Pittsburgh. Andrew subsequently became Secretary of Treasury under President Coolidge.

Carborundum Company. Acheson's business associates were gradually replaced by others and on July 1, 1901 Acheson was removed as president. Although Acheson remained a susbstantial stockholder and at times a technical consultant to the company, he was not allowed to share in its management after it had reached ultimate success. By 1910, the company which Acheson had created from naught, was producing Carborundum at the rate of 10,000,000 pounds per year; by the early 1960's, over one quarter billion pounds.

The process of manufacturing Carborundum today is substantially as that developed by Acheson. An electric furnace of the resistance type is used. Anthracite coal has replaced coke as the source of carbon. The synthesis is one of the simplest chemical reactions employed by industry*:

$$SiO_2 + 3C \longrightarrow SiC + 2CO$$

The silicon carbide is formed as a mass of crystals of different shapes, sizes, and colors. The carbon monoxide burns at the surface to carbon dioxide.

Carborundum is next to diamond in hardness. The three hardest abrasives measure as follows on the Mohs' scale:

Diamond 10
Carborundum 9.5
Corundum 9

Carborundum is one of the most stable chemical compounds both thermally and chemically. It decomposes at a temperature of $2,830^{\circ}$C.

---

*The reaction is not as simple as indicated. Silicon likely forms as a gaseous intermediate which reacts with carbon monoxide to form the carbide.

Although originally developed as an abrasive, today silicon carbide has a multitude of additional uses including use in brake linings, in metallurgy to remove impurities, with graphite in rocket nose cones, and in the construction of nuclear reactors.

Following his invention and the commercialization of Carborundum, Acheson was subjected to the usual trials of a successful inventor. He was sued by Alfred Cowles because of alleged violation of certain electric furnace designs and operations. Others came forth as the true inventors of silicon carbide. Coslon, a Frenchman, claimed to have prepared the carbide as early as 1882 by the reduction of carbon silicates. Otto Mühlhaeuser, Acheson's former employee, had now returned to Germany where certain of his associates were claiming that he, not Acheson, had pioneered silicon carbide. A Frenchman, Henri Moissan, claimed that he had prepared the carbide when he had tried to crystallize carbon. Others claimed that silicon carbide was highly inferior to boron carbide as an abrasive. However, Acheson's early synthesis, his development of a practical process of manufacture, and his success in establishing industrial uses for the new material have indelibly correlated his name with silicon carbide, which is still manufactured under the misnomer, Carborundum.

Although the discovery and commercial development of silicon carbide was Edward Acheson's greatest scientific achievement, his commercial development of synthetic graphite was more important from an industrial standpoint. He was not the first to make graphite from carbon, but he was the first to produce synthetic graphite in quantity and to commercialize the operation. Acheson was able to establish his highly successful and profitable graphite business because of his know-how from Carborundum manufacture and his patents. Actually his graphite patents were based on a false premise, *i.e.*, that the mechanism of graphite formation from carbon is through the thermal decomposition of a carbide.

Carbon and graphite are identical chemically but differ structurally. Carbon is amorphous whereas graphite is crystalline. Graphite crystals may vary in shape resulting in different properties. Extensive deposits are found in Ceylon, Canada, and Mexico. Crude deposits run about 80% concentration, the mineral impurities being primarily clays. Natural graphite can be converted to 99% plus material by certain purification processes, but purified natural graphite is too expensive for run-of-mine uses.

It had long been known that carbon containing a minimum of volatile matter should be used in arc lights. Charles F. Brush, who pioneered arc lighting in 1878, prepared his arc rods from petroleum coke and pitch. In 1894 Acheson carried out work on making purified carbon by heating coke in an electric furnace. He also worked with Carborundum as an ingredient in arc-light carbons. This proved to be unpromising, but the work caused Acheson to become more interested in the so-called purified "carbon" which was a by-product in every Carborundum run. This material was gray, soft, and an improved conductor of electricity. Acheson realized that it was graphitic in nature.

It was generally considered that if any form of carbon was heated to a high enough temperature it was converted to graphite. The first evidence of this was the isolation of graphite from the tips of used arc lights. In 1882 Elihu Thomson had tried to improve without success the life of the incandescent electric light by submitting the carbon filament to graphitizing temperatures. We now know that

188

his failure was due to the fact that the carbon filament was charcoal, a type of carbon unsuitable for conversion to graphite (see below and Reference 9). In 1896 Hamilton Young Castner of the Mathieson Alkali Works discovered that if a carbon electrode was graphitized it had less tendency to disintegrate in electrochemical operations such as the anode in the manufacture of chlorine and caustic soda from aqueous sodium chloride. Castner approached the Carborundum Company to make the small anodes in their furnace operation. During 1897 more than 70 tons of such anodes were graphitized, an amazing amount considering that each anode weighed less than one pound.

The graphite formed in Carborundum manufacture was always found in the hottest part of the furnace. Thus, Acheson reasoned that it came from the thermal decomposition of silicon carbide, the silicon being volatilized (boiling point, 2,600°C). This was the primary basis of Acheson's theory that graphite could only be formed from carbon through intermediate carbides. His theory was further supported by the fact that neither lampblack nor charcoal, the purest forms of carbon available at that time, could not be converted to conventional graphite regardless of the temperature to which they were subjected. What Acheson and others did not appreciate was that lampblack is actually agglomerates of submicron spherical graphite particles and does not behave like graphite of large crystals. Lampblack was the first of the so-called carbon blacks. Charcoal comes from a strictly aliphatic compound, cellulose. As high boiling hydrocarbons are heated, they become polyaromatic in nature as they dehydrogenate to coke. Synthetic graphite crystals are primarily hexagonal in structure and thus polyaromatics, containing condensed six-membered carbon rings, are excellent precursors of graphite. Petroleum coke,

189

which is very high in polyaromatics, is the best raw coke for conversion to graphite; whereas charcoal, which is substantially free of polyaromatics, is entirely unsuited.

Over a period of about 10 years Acheson obtained a series of patents dealing with preparing graphite by heating various carbon-containing mixtures in an electric furnace. Although Acheson's theory that graphite can only be formed through the intermediate formation of carbides was incorrect, his patents served to give him adequate protection (9). However his most important patents dealing with synthetic graphite were those covering electric furnaces which made possible, for the first time, process temperatures of over 3,000°C (10). Firebrick constructed over concrete piers allowed air cooling of the bed. Graphite electrodes at either end extended outside the brick wall and were water cooled. Furnaces of this design are still in use today and are known as Acheson-type.

By 1899 graphitizing anodes* for the thriving electrochemical industry had taxed the capacity of the Carborundum Company. Also by this time Acheson felt that synthetic graphite could be manufactured and marketed in competition with the natural product. He decided to divorce graphite production from that of Carborundum and on January 25, 1899 the Acheson Graphite Company was incorporated under the laws of the State of New Jersey. In July 1896 Acheson had discussed with the Mellon brothers the possibility of setting up a separate operation for making purified carbon and graphite. The Mellons had agreed in writing to furnish the necessary capital in return for 40% of the stock. The interest in carbon and graphite waned and nothing was done. In 1899

---

*All graphitized carbon electrodes are called anodes although subsequently used either as anodes or cathodes.

190

Acheson had assumed that his agreement of July 1896 was dead. When he approached the Mellons to purchase some of the preferred stock of the Acheson Graphite Company, the latter stated that their 40% share of the common stock in accordance with their July 1896 agreement was adequate. Acheson scoffed at this but when the Mellons threatened to sue, a compromise was worked out with the Mellons receiving 25% of the common stock and Acheson 75%. Preferred stock was sold to finance the new company.

Acheson assigned his U. S. patents on purified carbon and graphite to the Acheson Graphite Company but retained his foreign rights. On March 14, 1900 Acheson organized the International Acheson Graphite Company to exploit his patents abroad. Subsequently the two companies were consolidated. This latter move was opposed by the Mellons but again the two parties compromised. This resulted in Acheson giving up part of his holdings in The Carborundum Company but gaining firm control of the graphite operations.

The Acheson Graphite Company was located near The Carborundum Company at Niagara Falls. The new company took over the graphitizing of anodes which was a rapidly growing business. Acheson began work on uses for the new synthetic graphite and readily found a market in paints, batteries, and brushes for dynamos and motors. Much work was done on the potential large volume use of graphite crucibles for the metal industries. When working on clay binders for his pure graphite, Acheson employed aqueous dispersions of clay using gallotannic acid as dispersant. He was impressed by the stability of the aqueous dispersion so obtained and studied also extracts from vegetation sources, including straw. Knowing the Egyptians had used straw in ancient times when making bricks, Acheson reasoned that they had made similar dispersions. He called his clay dispersions "Egyptianized Clay" and tried to exploit them commercially, but without success.

His work with clays led to similar dispersions of graphite. Acheson called this deflocculation of graphite and thought it was different from conventional colloidalization. He obtained the trademark name of Aquadag* for such dispersions of graphite in water and Oildag* for that in oil. The Acheson Oildag Company was formed to manufacture and market these dispersions. In 1910 this company was moved to Port Huron, Michigan to utilize the relatively pure water from the St. Clair River. Later a grease containing graphite, with the trademark name, Gredag, was added to this line of products.

Acheson had high hopes for his lubricant products and visualized graphite as the universal lubricant. He furnished samples of the concentrated dispersion to various oil companies for them to test in their own oils. None adopted a graphite-containing oil as a general lubricant, although some special high temperature lubricants containing graphite were put on the market. Actually the water dispersions proved to be more successful than those based on oil, finding diversified uses in industrial operations. For example, Colin Fink of the General Electric Company found that Aquadag solved the problem of rapid wear of diamond dies used in the drawing of ductile tungsten wire for use as filaments in electric lights.

Acheson took every advantage of the electric furnace operation to develop new businesses. He developed and patented a process for making elemental silicon by the reduction of silica with graphite in an electric furnace (11). He sold this patent to The Carborundum Company for $5,000. Frank Tone of that company further developed the

*The suffix "dag" stands for "deflocculated Acheson-Graphite".

process to a profitable operation. Silicon is now an important industrial product; its most important use is as a semiconductor in electronic applications.

Another by-product in the manufacture of Carborundum was a greenish-white amorphous powder. Chemical analysis showed it to be a silicon-carbon-oxygen compound of variable composition but predominantly Si_2C_2O. Acheson named it Siloxicon. Tests showed the material to be highly refractory and selfbonding at 2,500°C. Acheson visualized it could be marketed for high-temperature applications such as furnace linings and the construction of crucibles, muffles, and the like. He formed the Siloxicon Company in April 1903 and the Siloxicon Articles Company in September 1905. Again there was a squabble with the Mellon interests, but it was immaterial since the two companies never got "off the ground" and were dissolved in June 1908. Another company formed was the Acheson Ink Company, to exploit the use of synthetic graphite and lampblack in ink products.

The International Acheson Graphite Company, the name adopted following the merger of the two graphite companies*, was profitable from the start. Graphitization of carbon electrodes was a profitable business and was the mainstay of the company. Acheson not only brought his five sons into the family business but also his nephew, W. Acheson Smith, became a most valued executive. In 1903 Acheson set up a holding company, The Acheson Company, to centralize his business operations and interests. This company was superseded by the Acheson Corporation in 1915. The office of this holding corporation was located in New York and the family home was moved to that city shortly thereafter.

*Name was changed back to Acheson Graphite Company in 1916.

Although Acheson was a thoughtful man when providing living quarters for his family, several moves were necessary as his business underwent changes. After six years in Monongahela City the home was sold there and a house rented in Buffalo. In 1900 a large house on a 21-acre tract was purchased in Niagara Falls, Ontario. This was not only closer to his business operations but was an excellent private playground for his children, who at that time numbered nine. Probably because the word graphite predominated in the conversations there, this home later became known as "Graphilla".

In 1912 with his domestic operations doing well under the direction of W. Acheson Smith, Acheson decided to expand his European operations. Although retaining Graphilla, the family took residence in a 20-room mansion on Albert Road in London, overlooking a park area. Acheson set up a small laboratory at the rear of the house employing, among other things, a dynamo run by a steam engine. Not unexpectedly, this brought some severe protests from a nearby neighbor.

Factories were established in several European countries to make the Oildag line of products. Graphite was shipped from the United States for the preparation of these lubricants as well as graphitized anodes for marketing in Europe. There was some discussion of building a graphite plant in Sweden to utilize the cheap water power there, but this did not materialize. The Oildag business went poorly in Europe resulting in losses which severely taxed Acheson's financial resources in America. The sumptuous living standards of the Achesons in London plus high expenses on various business and lecture tours of the continent added to his financial woes. Early in 1914 all promotional efforts to market Oildag for automotive uses were abandoned and many members of the sales staff dismissed. Shortly after the war started, all of his factories on the continent were closed down.

E. G. Acheson Ltd., Acheson's British company and the headquarters for his European operations, was able to achieve profitable operations in 1915 filling orders from the Allies. Edmund Sprague, the works manager of the graphite operations at Niagara Falls, came to England in February 1915 to take charge. The Achesons returned to the States in April, supposedly for a visit but the trip proved to be a permanent return to their homeland.

Acheson found many things in America to demand his attention. The Acheson Graphite Company had electrode orders far exceeding their capacity but could not expand operations due to shortage of power. The power operations at Niagara Falls were limited by Government since only so much water could be diverted from the Falls for power generation. Acheson with other managers of industrial operations at Niagara Falls appeared before Congressional committees in an attempt to make more power available. Acheson subsequently turned to the Buffalo General Electric Company, which had excess capacity from a coal-burning generating plant. The Graphite Company built additonal capacity in Buffalo beginning in November 1916. The increased business due to the European war resulted in the overall Acheson interests making a net profit of $600,000 in 1916. For the first time, Acheson was out of debt.

On reaching age 60, Acheson no longer carried out bench scale laboratory experiments but was content to lay out experiments and outline test programs for his sons Edward and George. A small laboratory was set up in Newark, New Jersey with George in charge. Beginning in 1917 the senior Achesons spent a part of each winter in Florida. Although Acheson had led a strenuous life, he had suffered several breakdowns in his health. In the fall of 1898 during a period of stress due to his deteriorating position at The Carborundum Company, Acheson was confined to his bed for five weeks. His illness was diagnosed as nervous prostration and on recovery his doctors warned him to slow down in his business activities. Acheson had problems with his stomach since a young man and beginning in 1902 he would make periodic trips to Hot Springs, Arkansas for treatment. By 1904 his physical condition forced him to be absent from business for long periods. He spent three months under the care of the noted neurologist, Dr. S. Weir Mitchell, of Philadelphia. In May 1905 Acheson underwent exploratory surgery at the Buffalo General Hospital. It was found that the pylorus, the opening of his stomach, required enlargement. This operation brought excellent results and according to Acheson ". . .I was soon on the way to perfect recovery of my health."

In July 1922 Acheson suffered a mild stroke. Although his recovery was rapid, the use of his left arm and leg was impaired. Henceforth he always walked with a cane. Following this attack the Achesons spent increasing time in Florida during each winter. In 1925 they purchased a winter home in St. Petersburg. Thereafter Acheson's everyday activities in business ceased. They did spend about five months in New York each summer. His health continued to decline until his death, July 6, 1931.

In 1917 four independent companies banded together to form the Union Carbide and Carbon Company. One of these was the National Carbon Company of Cleveland. This company had utilized the services of the Acheson Graphite Company to graphitize electrodes and when Acheson started to graphitize anodes to market on his own, he was a good customer of National Carbon. In July 1928 Union

Carbide purchased the Acheson Graphite Company by an exchange of stock.

Why the Acheson family, the primary stockholder in this flourishing company, approved this sale is difficult to understand. One feels that the father would have wished to pass the business on to his many sons and sons-in-law who were active therein. Since Union Carbide would likely have done their own graphitization whether they bought the Acheson interest or not, this giant company may have appeared too great a potential competitor. Acheson's patents dealing with his furnace and other phases of graphite manufacture had long expired. Furthermore, Acheson himself still believed that the big volume use of graphite would be in lubricants, a field where he had spent much time and money, but which had yielded little profit (12).

Acheson was a slow starter. As a young man he was a good example of the old adage that "a bit of knowledge can be a dangerous thing", particularly if the host of that knowledge doesn't appreciate his limitations. Examples of Acheson's early ineptness include the following:

(1) At the age of 19 he thought he was "the discoverer of a most wonderful explosive" when he oxidized turpentine with concentrated nitric acid and created enough pressure to blow up a closed glass flask.

(2) At the age of 23 Acheson developed a dry pile (battery). He claimed in a letter to Edison that it had no internal resistance and had been giving off a constant current for months. Both statements were ridiculous and furthermore Acheson did not have the instruments to test for such properties. Edison agreed to test one of the piles but soon returned it with the message, "I will return it that

you may fix it or send another that will work."

(3) Acheson worked on a dynamo design before going to work for Edison and continued to work on it at nights at Menlo Park. He subsequently asked Edison what he thought of it and the latter pointed out that the design was old and had been the subject of a publication. At the age of 24 Acheson had not yet learned the basic principle of research — learn what has already been done on a given problem before undertaking experimentation.

(4) At the age of 30 Acheson wrote John Tyndall, the noted English physicist, about a theory which he (Acheson) had that radiant heat from a natural gas fireplace was "destructive to the water vapor" in the room; thus one should try "to reduce them to rays of low refrangibility before they are radiated into the room." Tyndall did not respond to the letter.

Acheson's principal problem in his younger days was that his reading, his interests, and experiments were too diversified. Before Edison went out on his own, he spent six years learning the fundamentals of telegraphy as a close observer, an experimenter, and a professional telegraph operator. Furthermore when he attempted to invent, he chose the field in which he was already an expert, *i.e.,* telegraphy. On the other hand, Acheson jumped from hither to yonder until, at the age of 24, he decided electricity was his field. His job with Edison could have started him on a successful career, but instead of staying there as an employee for five years or so until he became a true expert in the field, he was with Edison only a little over two years during three separate terms of employment. Then when Acheson did go out on his own, he concentrated on the conversion of heat to electricity, a problem of a highly theoretical nature which has not as yet been solved on a practical basis.

Early in his life Acheson tended to be reckless or thoughtless in his personal affairs as well. His attempts "to go out on his own" left him several times without food and shelter. He was rescued from a critical situation in London by his friend Holloway and later from a highly precarious one in New York by his brother William. He married when he was penniless and proceeded to raise a family with no prospect of an adequate income.

Although Acheson learned the hard way, he learned his lessons well. Once he synthesized silicon carbide by the electric furnace route, he exploited this technique to the utmost. He developed silicon carbide and synthetic graphite to the status of important industrial products, which are manufactured today essentially by processes which Acheson pioneered. Furthermore, he improved electric furnace technology to the degree whereby today it is widely used in many metallurgical operations including the manufacture of stainless steel and ordinary steel.

By 1905 Acheson had become the foremost world authority on electric furnace operations, as well as a noted authority on electrochemistry generally. When he was given the Perkin Medal by the Society of Chemical Industry in 1910, he was acclaimed by both academic and industrial scientists as a distinguished chemist and a great inventor. Early in 1913 Acheson was invited by the Russian Imperial Technical Society to visit that country where he was wined and dined, received by the Grand Duke Alexander, and lectured the military on his inventions. In the fall of the same year he made a similar visit to Sweden at which time there were rumors that he was being considered for the Nobel Prize in chemistry. He did not receive the Prize but the king conferred upon him the Cross of His Order of the Polar Star.

Acheson was an effective speaker and he readily took to

the platform. He not only lectured widely before scientific and engineering groups on his technical achievements, but also to college and government groups on more general subjects. Following World War I he spoke and wrote on hydroelectric power as a means of conserving natural resources. He was strongly motivated to gain recognition as a scientist and an inventor. After receiving an honorary Doctor of Science degree from the University of Pittsburgh in 1909, Acheson assumed and apparently preferred the title of Doctor Acheson. At one time he considered naming his art of "deflocculation of graphite" as "Achesonized graphite". However, he was talked out of this by some of his university friends. Acheson's drive to achieve recognition no doubt resulted, at least in part, from the fact that he was a slow starter and was in his thirties before achieving any degree of success as an inventor.

Many inventors are poor businessmen; not so Acheson. Even though he had to go to the bankers for financing, he retained control of the highly successful Acheson Graphite Company until it was sold to Union Carbide. He held important positions in industry but did it on the basis that he retained ownership of new inventions made while so employed. As such he is the envy of present-day industrial scientists.

Although appearing rather thoughtless in his demands on his early financial supporters, his wife, brother William, and others, once he was "in the money", he took care of his debts. Knowing the trials his wife had endured the first 15 or so years of their marriage, he not only bought the elaborate home at Niagara Falls, but also he equipped it with every known convenience. After there were no small children at home, Mrs. Acheson accompanied her husband on many of his business trips and speaking engagements. He returned manifold the kindness of Jim Holloway, when

Acheson was ill and in want in London in 1883.

Acheson's invention of Carborundum is considered one of the milestones of technology, being in the same league as the chief inventions of the other five inventors covered in this treatise. The invention of Carborundum was not only important in itself but also its synthesis opened up a new field of industrial technology utilizing the high temperatures obtained by means of electric furnaces. Acheson obtained a total of 70 United States patents.

Chapter 6

Alfred Bernhard Nobel

Alfred Nobel conceived the idea and provided the money for the international prizes which continue to bear his name. The establishment of these awards, which undoubtedly are the most coveted recognitions for workers in the fields of chemistry, physics, and medicine, has greatly enhanced achievements in these fields by providing incentives. Thus Nobel, although one of the greatest inventors of all time, no doubt made his greatest contribution to innovation when he set up the prizes, recognized as marks of excellence since the start of this century.

Nobel's objective in developing more effective explosives was for non-military uses, and that is where they have been primarily used. When Alfred's brother Ludwig died in 1888, several foreign newspapers mistakingly reported it as Alfred's death. The living Alfred had an opportunity to read his own obituary. In general he was pictured as the dynamite king who had made a vast fortune from weapons of destruction. This evaluation of his contribution to society — even by a few — shocked Nobel into doing something for peace. He was a friend of Bertha Von Suttner, the Austrian peace crusader. Although Nobel contended to her that "my factories will end war sooner than your congresses", her influence helped to germinate the idea for the Nobel Peace Prize.

Nobel had a keen interest in literature from the time of his childhood. He admired greatly the English poet Percy Shelley and wrote poetry himself patterned after Shelley's style. Just prior to his death, Nobel wrote a play of four acts called Nemesis*, which was a satire based on some unfortunate patent litigations which he had had in England. It is not surprising that Nobel included literature as another field for awarding prizes for excellence.

Alfred Nobel's ancestors were not only Swedes, but came from that Swedish group which had ousted the Danish conqueror in the 16th century and became the most feared people in northern Europe. Alfred, born October 21, 1833, was the third son of Immanuel and Andrietta Nobel. The original family name was Nobelius, which was subsequently changed to plain Nobell. Later the second L was dropped. Originally Immanuel was a self-made architect who later became involved in various inventive and manufacturing schemes, mostly of the "get rich quick" type.

Alfred was plagued with various illnesses all his life. As a child he had a spinal ailment, gastric problems, and a chronic susceptibility to colds. The doctor advised that he lie in bed not only at night but most of the day. He was ordered to have minimum exertion and was not allowed to play with other children. Nobel's childhood was not happy as evidenced by his following poems**:

*Subsequently his relatives suppressed its publication.

**Most of Alfred's poems were written at the age of 18-19 when he was traveling in Europe and America. They were composed in English. The author destroyed much of his literary writings and only a few poems – probably those meaning the most to him – were retained.

My cradle looked a death-bed, and for years
A mother watched with her ever-anxious care,
Though little chance, to save the flickering light,
I scarce could muster strength to drain the breast
And then convulsions followed, till I gasped
Upon the brink of nothingness − my frame
A school for agony with death for goal,
Thus passed some years, while life, with death contending,
Hung over chaos on a single thread;
But spun by destiny such threads will hold,
Till man is brought to tear them with a curse.
Not that to me life seems an idle burden:
I look upon it as a noble gift,
A gem from Nature's hand for man to polish
Till sparkling beams repay him for his toil.

. . . Now to my theme! We left the infant whining,
A paltry thing, conscious of nought but woe.
We find him now a boy. His weakness still
Makes him a stranger in the little world,
Wherein he moves. When fellow-boys are playing
He joins them not, a pensive looker-on;
And thus debarred the pleasures of his age
His mind keeps brooding over those to come.
When an imagination made to scale
The utmost heights to which the mind can soar
I had not judgment then to check its flights
Or trace the drawbacks to its golden dreams.
The past, the present with their conscious woe
Seemed but a stepping-stone to future bliss.

After one year of formal schooling in Stockholm, Alfred
moved with the family to St. Petersburg, Russia (now
Leningrad). His father had interested this foreign

government in military mines which he had developed. The family lived in high style in St. Petersburg in marked contrast to the near-poverty level in their former home. Now the boys had tutors. Alfred had a knack for languages and learned to speak and write Russian, English, and French. Later he added German and Italian. He also acquired the rudiments of history, philosophy, and science.

Soon it was apparent to the parents that Alfred was a superior student. Because of this and his frailty, at the age of 17 he was sent abroad to study and to purchase certain machinery for the family business. This was the time of the industrial revolution and Alfred visited the first International Exhibition held in 1851 in London. He visited also Germany, France, Italy, and the United States. In America he visited John Ericsson, a fellow Swede who had acquired a worldwide reputation in oceanic steamshipping. His trip abroad appeared to have rounded out his education and gave him confidence to move ahead on his own.

In the Crimean War (1854-56) the Nobels made mines and other military equipment for the Russian government. The factory at St. Petersburg was greatly expanded with much equipment bought on credit. At the end of the war the cancellation of orders and a fire in the plant led to bankruptcy. In 1859 the family returned to Sweden leaving the three older brothers, Ludwig, Robert, and Alfred, to salvage what they could from the business. Soon Alfred began his fantastic career in developing new explosives.

An explosive may be defined as a material which can undergo rapid decomposition or reaction of ingredients which liberates heat and expansion of gases. Explosives are used both as propellants and blasting agents. Black powder — also called gun powder — is a mixture of potassium nitrate, charcoal, and sulfur. This mixture of solids burns with great rapidity, the nitrate serving as an internal oxidant for the carbon and sulfur. The burning results in a great increase in volume because of the formation of such gaseous products as nitrogen and the oxides of carbon. The heat of combustion is high — 1,425 calories per gram. The proportions of ingredients in black powder vary depending on its end use; the following is a typical mixture used as gun powder:

Potassium nitrate	74.6%
Charcoal	13.5
Sulfur	11.9

Black powder was not only the first explosive but it was the sole one for centuries. The Chinese apparently used a mixture of the three ingredients for its pyrotechnic and incendiary effects a thousand or so years ago. The famous Greek Fire was some analogous composition. However, it was not until about 1250 when Roger Bacon studied compositions and properties of black powder that the material became an article of commerce. In 1313, with the invention of the cannon in Germany, it was first used as a propellant. In 1613 it was first used as a blasting agent in mines in Saxony.

Black powder, one of the most important inventions of all time, achieved its wide use because it was an explosive whose reaction could be controlled and handled with reasonable safety. Although nitroglycerin* was synthesized in 1846 by Ascanio Sobrero of Italy, it was used only as a

*Due to common usage the name nitroglycerin will be used for glyceryl trinitrate, the true chemical name of the ester derived from glycerol and nitric acid.

medicinal agent until the work of Alfred Nobel. Sobrero found that nitroglycerin could be exploded by shock or by rapid heating. Unlike black powder it could be burned without exploding if handled properly. Also unlike black powder, this single chemical substance provided both the fuel and the oxygen for combustion. The following equation illustrates the efficiency in which nitroglycerin forms gases:

$$\begin{array}{c} CH_2O\text{-}NO_2 \\ | \\ 2CHO\text{-}NO_2 \\ | \\ CH_2O\text{-}NO_2 \end{array} \longrightarrow 6CO_2 + 5H_2O + \tfrac{1}{2}O_2 + 3N_2$$

Professors Sinin and Trapp of St. Petersburg University called the attention of Immanuel Nobel to the explosive properties of nitroglycerin while the latter was manufacturing mines for the Russian military. After a few tests trying to set off the nitroglycerin in a controlled manner, work on it was abandoned.

After the collapse of the Nobel fortunes in Russia and Immanuel's return to Sweden, the elder Nobel began work on mixtures of black powder and nitroglycerin. Black powder was the major ingredient, the idea being that the sudden rise in temperature of the exploding powder would set off the adhered nitroglycerin. He studied also mixtures of black powder with "chloric acid" — very likely perchloric acid hydrate. The father reported these developments to his sons and urged that Alfred contact Russian army authorities about these "promising" new explosives. Alfred visited General Totleben, the hero of the defense of Sevastopol, and was assured that the new products would be tested if they looked at all practical.

207

Alfred visited the family at Stockholm to get samples to submit to the Russian military. He was highly upset to find that the "cloric acid" product was largely wishful thinking on Immanuel's part and the black powder-nitroglycerin proved to be effective only when freshly mixed. Brothers Ludwig and Alfred decided that neither should be submitted to the Russians, but that General Totleben should be assured that work on a new explosive was continuing. Alfred went to work on nitroglycerin on his own using work space in a small machine shop which Ludwig had rented.

Instead of investigating why a mixture of black powder and nitroglycerin became insensitive to a spark or fuse on standing, Alfred concluded that the practical way to set off nitroglycerin was by shock. He had already shown an interest and ability in inventing. In September 1857 he was granted a Russian patent on a "gasometer". Patents followed on a water meter and an improved barometer. In June 1862 Alfred succeeded in exploding under water a stoppered tube of nitroglycerin placed within a tube of black powder, and the latter ignited by means of a fuse. Surprisingly when a like experiment was carried out in air, the nitroglycerin failed to explode. Nobel concluded that a greater shock resulted in the overall system when immersed in water as compared to air. When the ends of the powder tube were strongly sealed, the system functioned as it did under water. He now reasoned that only a "powerful local detonation" was needed to explode any quantity of nitroglycerin. Subsequent studies led to mercury fulminate as the primary explosive or detonator. This invention, often called Nobel's greatest and certainly the first major advance in explosives since the invention of black powder, was covered by a Swedish patent in October 1863. This patent went beyond the mere technique of exploding nitroglycerin (1):

208

I therefore lay claim to the idea, so far as industrial use is concerned, of contriving by administering a mere initial impulse to develop an explosion in substances which, exposed, can be brought into contact with burning bodies without exploding . . .

By mid-1863 Alfred felt he was ready to demonstrate an improved explosive containing nitroglycerin and a meeting was scheduled with General Totleben. Then Alfred's father sent an urgent message for Alfred to come to Sweden at once to assist him in demonstrating his new explosive to the Swedish army. Immanuel and his youngest son, Emil, had improved the black powder-nitroglycerin mixture by using a coarser powder. The tests did not convince the army experts that such mixtures could be used in shells. However, while in Sweden Alfred demonstrated his nitroglycerin oil in a granite quarry at Huvudsta with results which amazed the quarry owner and workmen. Successful large scale blasting tests were carried out in December 1863. Alfred did not return to Russia but prepared to market nitroglycerin for blasting.

By early 1864 the Nobels were selling nitroglycerin. It found its first use in blasting granite, where black powder is largely ineffective. The manufacturing operations were moved from the home in Heleneborg, near Stockholm, to a small building on a rented lot. The main operation was to prepare the nitroglycerin which was done by adding glycerin to a mixture of nitric and sulfuric acids at a controlled temperature below 60°C. On September 3, 1864 disaster struck. The experimental factory-workshop was destroyed by explosion and fire, killing all five people present including Alfred's younger brother Emil, a student at Upsala University. Alfred was away on business at the time and the father was at home. In the course of the police investigation, Alfred admitted that Professor Sobrero had given up working with nitroglycerin because he considered it too dangerous. He also made the following statement which continued to be part of his personal philosophy, "One cannot expect an explosive substance to come into general use without waste of life."

The loss of his son Emil crushed the father, and he had a stroke one month later from which he never fully recovered. Although his two older brothers begged him to give up work on nitroglycerin, Alfred refused to be ruled by emotions. He was convinced that the explosion which took the life of his brother was caused by careless operations; nitroglycerin could be produced and handled safely. However, the authorities in Stockholm and the surrounding area thought otherwise. Further production of nitroglycerin was prohibited in the Stockholm district. Alfred proceeded to get a covered barge — literally an ark on pontoons — which became his new nitroglycerin laboratory and factory. He first anchored it just off the shore of Mälar Lake near Heleneborg, but a group of angry farmers armed with pitchforks forced him to carry out his operations in the middle of the lake.

The effectiveness of nitroglycerin over black powder as a blasting agent was so tremendous that the trial samples created a demand which could not be denied. Alfred received financial backing from two local merchants and a small factory was built at Vinterviken, a village outside the jurisdiction of the Stockholm district. Demand developed from neighboring countries. There was no shortage of venture capital now. In September 1865 Alfred Nobel & Co. was granted a license to build a plant at Krümmel, Germany, a few miles south of Hamburg on the Elbe. Nobel made his home here for the next eight years. This

210

factory shipped the explosive worldwide except to Sweden, Norway, and Finland where factories were already located.

With inexperienced people manufacturing, shipping, storing, and using nitroglycerin worldwide, the inevitable happened. In April 1866 a number of people were killed by nitroglycerin in Sydney, Australia; a shipment of the explosive blew up in a Wells-Fargo warehouse in San Francisco; and a few days later a ship carrying nitroglycerin and docked at a Panamanian pier exploded. The Krümmel factory had a severe explosion in May, as did the one at Lysaker, Norway shortly later.

High accident rates in industrial operations were then an accepted way of life. Also, the usual explosive, black powder, had a history of accidental death and destruction. In 1815 the Du Pont Company was just getting well underway in their pioneering manufacture of black powder when an explosion at their plant killed nine men and caused $20,000 property damage. Two years later a fire at the plant caused the death of the father of the du Pont immigrants, Pierre Samuel. On March 19, 1818 another series of explosions at the plant on the Brandywine left 36 dead and four mortally injured. Houses of workmen a half mile away were crushed. More than 85,000 pounds of powder had blown up within four minutes; however, the du Ponts rebuilt. By 1827 a total of 140 men were employed and 800,000 pounds of black powder were being produced annually.

However, the series of disastrous explosions with nitroglycerin coming within a few months was too much. The established manufacturers of black powder helped to pent up alarm over this competitive explosive. The then head of the Du Pont Company, General Henry du Pont, made the statement, "It is only a matter of time how soon a man will lose his life who uses nitroglycerin." In France and Belgium the possession of nitroglycerin was outlawed. Sweden banned its transport. Great Britain excluded the explosive oil from its realm. Senator Chandler of Michigan introduced a bill which would make death from the transportation of nitroglycerin, punishable by hanging.

Nobel still attributed the accidents to carelessness. However, he now realized that careless handling was impossible to avoid. Nobel was in New York when the storm broke. He filed without delay a patent dealing with an improved method for the transportation and storage of nitroglycerin as a solution in methyl (wood) alcohol. The customer would remove the water-soluble alcohol from the water-insoluble nitroglycerin by water washing and decantation just prior to use.

Nobel had already considered the liquid form of nitroglycerin as a basic disadvantage in its handling and use. It was shipped in metal cans or drums which were subject to attack by acids which might be present from its manufacture or nitric acid from the hydrolysis of the nitroglycerin ester by moisture. Leakage might go unnoticed, and even if detected, it was difficult to remove from the contaminated areas. As early as 1863 Nobel had attempted to convert the liquid explosive to a solid form by mixing with various powders. On his return from America in August 1866, he plunged into an intensive research program to that end. He decided to concentrate on inert powders which, although decreasing the overall power of the nitroglycerin, did result in mixtures that could be exploded by a detonator. He studied silicas, gypsum, clays, brick dust, cement, sawdust, charcoal, powdered coal, paper pulp, and the like. A particular type of natural silica mined at Hannover, Germany was found best.

Silica occurs primarily in its crystalline form called quartz, the major ingredient of sand. Diatomite, a sedimentary rock from marine deposition, is also primarily silica. Such deposits were formed from a prehistoric microscopic plant which had an encasing silica shell. These fossil remains resulted in silica particles of a few microns in diameter. Due to its low particle size and porosity, diatomite is a strong adsorbent for liquids. It has a low apparent density of about 10 lbs. per cubic ft., as compared to 62.4 for water and higher values for most minerals. The German diatomite is known as kieselguhr. In America the common name is celite.

Nobel found that kieselguhr could adsorb three times its weight of nitroglycerin*. The liquid was held tenaciously by the kieselguhr and the mixture could be pressed into hard non-tacky sticks. These were marketed enclosed in paper tubing ready for the user to place into boreholes. Nobel named his new product Dynamite after the Greek *dynamis*, meaning power. The trademark name came soon into common usage denoting nitroglycerin adsorbed on any solid. Although numerous other grades were marketed by competitors and later by Nobel, that with kieselguhr was the workhorse explosive for blasting for decades. It became known as guhr dynamite in some quarters to indicate that kieselguhr was used as adsorbent.

Nobel got wide patent coverage on his invention of dynamite (2) and then set about demonstrating to the world that it was not only safe, but highly effective. Although containing 25% less explosive than pure nitroglycerin, dynamite was at least five times as effective as an equal weight of black powder; when blasting certain

---

*The popular version is that Nobel discovered the nitroglycerin-kieselguhr composition when a can of the explosive packed in kieselguhr leaked, and he noted the strongly adsorbite powers of the mineral and the granular nature of the liquid-solid mixture. This story is apparently untrue.

types of hard rocks, it was said to be over 100 times as effective. Even so, as every manufacturer knows, if a new product fails for some reason and is taken off the market, the subsequent sale of an improved version of that product becomes doubly difficult.

The invention of dynamite was certainly one of Alfred Nobel's greatest achievements. One of equal magnitude was the salvage of his business after the accidental explosions with his liquid product which had resulted in embargoes placed on its transportation and use in most countries. Nobel & Co. notified the public, through the press, that liquid nitroglycerin would no longer be sold or shipped. Nobel gave scientific papers before learned societies in which the properties of black powder and the new dynamite were compared. He gave demonstrations which he himself directed and took an active part. As an example, at Surrey, England, Nobel demonstrated the safety of dynamite by burning containers of the explosive in a wood fire. He dropped 10 pounds of it from a cliff 60 feet high while he stood nearby. Then he exploded a like quantity in a 15-foot borehole which shook the earth beneath the group of illustrious onlookers standing several hundred feet away.

One country, which had not joined the others in 1867 in placing embargoes on the transportation and use of nitroglycerin, was Prussia. Its military, which had an installation near Nobel's factory on the Elbe, was impressed by this new explosive. However, they apparently were never able to adapt the liquid explosive to military use, but their experience with nitroglycerin helped them to move rapidly ahead when dynamite became available.

Prussia under Bismarck united with the other strong German state, Austria, to defeat Denmark in 1864. The so-called Seven Weeks' War in 1866 resulted in Prussia

214

dominating the area containing over two-thirds of the German people. The combined Germany was a surprisingly strong military power in the Franco-German War of 1870-71. This was the first war in which an explosive other than black powder was used.

France had refused permission to Nobel's interests to either import or manufacture dynamite in that country. Soon after July 1870 the French High Command was learning that the enemy was using dynamite to blow up bridges and roads with telling effects. Furthermore, before the conflict was over Krupp engineers had devised an improved high-explosive shell. A single hit would create a huge crater, demolishing any nearby buildings and causing panic among the populace. The shells were charged with dynamite. French chemists and physicists, as well as Nobel's French agent Paule Barbe, were mobilized by the nation to manufacture dynamite. Several tons were produced in the besieged city of Paris but it was too late. Subsequently dynamite achieved no appreciable success as the bursting charge of artillery shells and was never used as the propellant. The improved military explosives which came to the fore in the mid-1880's began to replace black powder, and the Spanish-American War of 1898 was the last major conflict in which it played an important part.

Although dynamite never became a truly military explosive, the Franco-German War showed the countries of the world they had better not ignore it. This, plus its demonstrated power in blasting, resulted in dynamite being accepted by all countries. Projects in mining, industry, and communications, which had previously been unthinkable, could now be initiated. Soon dynamite controlled the world market of industrial explosives. Its growth in sales was phenomenal; for example, the annual production grew from 424 tons in 1870 to 3,120 tons in 1874 — a 730% increase in four years.

Although the plant at Krümmel, Germany and later that at Ardeer, Scotland supplied export markets as well as domestic ones, Nobel built one or more plants in any country as soon as an appreciable market developed there. As shown below, the European area and the United States had a broad distribution of plants by 1873 (3).

Nobel Plants

	Erected
Vinterviken, near Stockholm, Sweden	1865
Krümmel, near Hamburg, Germany	1865
Lysaker, (later Engene), near Olso, Norway	1866
(Little Ferry, N.J., U.S.A. – U.S. Blasting Oil Co. – destroyed 1870)	1866
Zamky, near Prague, Austria (now Czechoslovakia)	1868
Rock House Canyon, near San Francisco, U.S.A.	1868
Hanko, near Helsinki, Finland	1870
Ardeer, Stevenston, near Glasgow, Scotland	1871
Paulilles, near Port-Vendres, France	1871
McCainsville (now Kenvil) near Dover, N.J., U.S.A. (Atlantic Giant Powder Co.)	1871
Schlebusch, near Cologne, Germany	1872
Galdacano, near Bilbao, Spain	1872
Giant Powder Works, near New York, U.S.A.	1873
Isleten, near Fluelen, Switzerland	1873
Avigliana, near Turin, Italy	1873
Trafaria, near Lisbon, Portugal	1873
Pressburg, Austria-Hungary (now Bratislava, Czechoslovakia)	1873

At the time of Alfred Nobel's death in 1896, there were Nobel companies in 20 countries, and explosives and accessories were manufactured according to his patents in hundreds of factories all over the world. For example, there were factories at 23 different locations in Germany. Many of the Nobel plants were nuclei for the later formation of large diversified industries. Dynamite A/G of Germany is an example. Nobel Industries of England was united with three chemical companies in 1926 to form Imperial Chemical Industries, Ltd., today the world's largest chemical company.

During the 1870-80 period Nobel took a very active part in the planning and operation of the new factories. Once each was in production with competent technical management, he left it on its own. He was a great believer in giving an employee authority to use his own judgment once he had demonstrated his ability. Nobel attempted to raise local capital for building new plants with his share of the stock in each usually obtained by his patent rights. Although he was a stockholder in each of the Nobel companies and an officer in most, he never attended a board meeting. He voted always by proxy. He hated strictly business matters and tried to spend the maximum time on technical matters – preferably laboratory research.

The guhr dynamite was only one of the several types of modified nitroglycerin explosives which Nobel developed. However, today, over a hundred years later, it is still extensively used in Europe. Nobel knew from the start that the kieselguhr used with the nitroglycerin acted as an inert diluent. Its role was to make possible a solid explosive of highly improved safety characteristics from a liquid explosive. The high porosity of the kieselguhr not only served to adsorb the nitroglycerin and prevent exudation on storage, but aided the explosion step as compared to the use of a more dense diluent. In 1869 Nobel invented straight or active-dope dynamite. It was found that if the kieselguhr was replaced by a mixture of sodium nitrate and an adsorbent, combustible material such as wood pulp, the resulting composition was stronger than the kieselguhr dynamite containing the same proportion of nitroglycerin. Such dynamites were variable in composition depending on the end uses.

However, in the mining of certain hard rock formations, liquid nitroglycerin was preferred in spite of its attendant hazards. Some mines rigged up crude stills to separate nitroglycerin from guhr dynamite. Nobel continued to seek a solid explosive which would have the power of nitroglycerin but the safety of dynamite. By 1875 he had the answer, blasting gelatin.

Cellulose is a carbohydrate polymer of empirical formula $(C_6H_{10}O_5)$. It has many free hydroxy groups and thus can be nitrated as can alcohols such as glycerin. Cellulose was nitrated as early as 1838, but it was not until 1845 that Christian F. Schönbein demonstrated that if cellulose is nitrated to a very high degree, the product is an explosive. However, it proved to be an unstable material with the acidic products of decomposition causing increased instability. Although there was some work on nitrocellulose as an explosive prior to 1875, no successful nitrocellulose explosive had been developed. Sir Frederick Abel of England did improve the purification process for nitrocellulose in 1868 and subsequently attempted to commercialize the product in England.

Nitrocellulose must have a nitrogen content of about 14% in order to have explosive properties. If the nitrogen content is 12% or less the nitrocellulose is completely non-explosive, although it does burn rapidly. Such non-explosive grades have found broad commercial uses. In 1868 the Hyatt brothers of New Jersey prepared celluloid, the first synthetic plastic, by mixing nitrocellulose with camphor. The first artificial silk was prepared by denitrating nitrocellulose fibers. This low nitrogen

218

nitrocellulose also found use as photographic film and in lacquers.

In an attempt to prepare high strength explosives of safe handling characteristics, Nobel had worked with mixtures of nitroglycerin with other compounds known to have explosive properties. Nitrocellulose (a solid) of explosive grade and nitroglycerin (a liquid) proved to be completely incompatible.

One day Nobel cut his finger while working in the laboratory. A solution of 12% nitrogen-content nitrocellulose in ether-ethyl alcohol was at that time a common laboratory reagent used for sealing cork stoppers and the like. Nobel applied some of this colloidion solution to his finger to stop the bleeding. His attention was called to the highly viscous nature of the colloidion, which contained only a few percent of nitrocellulose, and to the toughness of the film which formed on his finger. Nobel concluded by analogy that the lower nitrogen content nitrocellulose might be appreciably soluble in nitroglycerin even though the 14% grade was not.

An intensive study of about 250 blends of nitroglycerin with nitrocellulose of various nitrogen contents and molecular weights followed. Molecular weights of polymeric materials were unknown at that time although it was known that the conditions of synthesis could affect the solubility properties of a given nitrogen content nitrocellulose. Nobel and his assistant, Georg Fehrenbach, found that a seven to eight percent blend of 12% nitrogen content nitrocellulose in nitroglycerin was best. The product, a rigid gel, proved to be a more powerful explosive than nitroglycerin, one of the first examples of synergism in science. Nobel mixed an explosive with a non-explosive and the mixture was more forceful than 100% of the explosive. In addition it was substantially insensitive to shock and was strongly resistant to moisture. Production began in Nobel's four leading factories in 1875-76. It was marketed under such names as Nobel's Extra Dynamite, Express Dynamite, and Blasting Gelatin. Professor Abel, the advocate of nitrocellulose powder explosives, admitted that Nobel's blasting gelatin was "in every respect the most perfect explosive known".

Nobel introduced gelatin dynamites in which the nitroglycerin-nitrocellulose gel was used with the various solid adsorbents. Also, straight dynamites were developed in which part or all of the sodium nitrate was replaced by ammonium nitrate. This substitution resulted in an appreciable increase in the volume of gas as compared to those containing only sodium nitrate. The ammonium type was widely used in quarry mining. In addition ammonia-gelatin dynamites were developed by Nobel in 1879.

In 1887 Nobel invented his one and only military explosive, ballistite. Like celluloid, camphor was used as a plasticizer and, in this case, as a binding agent. Nobel used equal parts of nitroglycerin and a soluble grade of nitrocellulose plus 10% of camphor. This mixture can be made into a powder which has greater power and generates much less smoke and residue than does black powder. Like black powder it can be set off by means of fire. At this time there was much activity in Europe to make a more powerful and less smoky propellant. Shortly after Nobel developed ballistite, he licensed it to the Italian government. Since France was not on friendly terms with Italy, this caused friction between Nobel and French government authorities.

In England a government commission was considering all new explosives for possible use by its military. Two members of this commission got confidential information from Nobel and then used it to their advantage in getting a patent of their own. Their "invention", which was later sustained in the British courts, differed from ballistite only in that a less soluble grade of nitrocellulose was used. Their product was named cordite and this became one of the widely used smokeless powders. Thus Nobel's venture into military explosives proved to be a trying one and he was unable to dominate this field, even for a short time, as he had done for an extended period, with his industrial explosives.

Nobel always maintained an experimental laboratory where his home was at the time. This truly internationalist, who could speak and write five languages in grand style, continued to retain his Swedish citizenship. However, he lived where he thought best for his business and scientific activities. From 1865 to 1873 the inventor had a simple home and a small laboratory at Krümmel near Hamburg. Here, with no technical assistance in the laboratory, he invented guhr dynamite. Early in the business operations, Paule Barbe, a Frenchman, became an important partner. In 1873, with his factories and markets worldwide, Nobel chose Paris as his residence and center of business operations. At that time the French capital was the commercial and cultural center of continental Europe. The 40-year-old Nobel, now a rich man, bought an elegant mansion. The extensive garden included hothouses for growing orchids. He had stables for his fine carriage horses, one of his few hobbies.

Nobel had a small laboratory near his home at No. 59 Avenue Malakoff. In 1881 a larger and better equipped laboratory was constructed at Sevran-Livry near Paris. He engaged a young French chemist, Georg D. Fehrenbach, as his assistant. He was apparently the only technical help which Nobel had during the 18 years that he spent in

Paris. After Nobel sold the Italian government rights under his Italian patent to manufacture ballistite, he was accused by the French press of being a traitor since the invention was made in France. Nobel had rented a rifle range from the state for experimental testing of his new explosive powders. After the Italian affair, French police searched and closed his laboratory under the pretense that he had stolen secrets from the French military!

Nobel decided to leave Paris. He moved to Italy and settled in a newly furnished villa at San Remo on the Riviera di Ponente. By 1891 his health had taken a turn for the worse. His troubles in France and England over ballistite greatly depressed him. In addition, his trusted business associate Barbe had become involved in French politics and the unsavory $100,000,000 "lottery loan" by the Panama Canal Company. Nobel purged Barbe from his organization and reorganized the French companies under British management. Before his move to San Remo in 1891, Nobel resigned board membership in all the dynamite companies. He was obviously depressed as indicated by the following quotation from his correspondence at that time (5):

> I am sick of the explosives trade, wherein one continually stumbles over accidents, restrictive regulations, red tape, pedants, knavery, and other nuisances. I long for quiet and wish to devote my time to scientific research, which is impossible when every day brings a new worry . . . I wish absolutely to retire from business—and all kinds of business . . . To me it is a torture to act as a pacifier in a nest of vultures . . . There is not the slightest reason why I, who have not been trained in commerce, and cordially hate it, should be plagued with all these

commercial matters about which I know little more than the man in the moon. The American, Swedish, and Norwegian companies have been just as prosperous without ever troubling me with their business matters, and I don't see why the other companies should not do the same.

Nobel hoped that the mild Mediterranean climate would cure his chronic colds and "nitroglycerin headaches". A new laboratory was built on the grounds of the San Remo villa, and G. Hugh Beckett, an English chemist, was put in charge of a much larger staff than Nobel had at his laboratory in Paris. Fehrenbach did not want to leave France so Nobel allowed him to retire with a pension. At San Remo the laboratory was supplemented by a steel pier which was used when testing ammunition and firearms.

At San Remo Nobel's research became more general. He made an exhaustive study of solvents of nitrocellulose varnishes. Using nitrocellulose he attempted to make substitutes for leather and rubber. He developed a nozzle for extruding concentrated solutions of nitrocellulose to make fibers. The nozzle was made of glass and the multitude of fine holes were made by forcing platinum wires into molten glass, cooling, and then dissolving the platinum by aqua regia. He tried to make improvements in some of the newer inventions of others such as the telephone, the phonograph, electric batteries, and the incandescent lamp. It would appear that Nobel was at last enjoying himself in his scientific work.

Alfred's brothers Ludwig and Robert were pioneers in the refining of petroleum at Baku in Russian Caucasia. Alfred helped them with money and the setting up of their Nobel Brothers' Naphtha Company (called Branobel internally). He subsequently helped technically. The Nobels pioneered transportation of oil by pipeline on land and by tanker, instead of barrels, by sea. Also Alfred helped several young Swedish engineers in starting manufacturing operations. One was the initial financing of the Ljungström brothers' Svea bicycle, one of the first with a variable gear change. In 1896 he shared in the financing of S. A. Andrée's attempt to reach the North Pole by dirigible balloon.

Although Nobel found the new environment at San Remo beneficial to his health, for his work the resort location had many disadvantages. All laboratory equipment and chemicals were purchased from Germany, which meant a delay even for the smallest item. Skilled craftsmen were not available locally. Also his neighbors complained of his test firing on the jetty. Nobel was also getting homesick for his native land. He became 60 years of age on October 21, 1893 and with his frail health felt the need to be closer to relatives and friends. His brother Robert had already returned to Sweden from Russia because of ill health.

Nobel did return to Sweden in 1894, not to live in idle luxury, but to seek contentment in new fields of manufacturing and research. He bought two factories in Värmland, a province located northwest of Stockholm. Each had an extensive iron works. Sweden had, and continues to have, large, high quality iron ore deposits which Nobel no doubt saw as the logical raw material for his motherland to achieve industrial eminence. He set up private living quarters in an adjacent manorhouse at Björkborn and built a laboratory nearby. The latter was the type which today one would call a pilot plant laboratory; that is, one to carry promising laboratory developments to a semi-plant scale and to study current industrial operations on a reduced scale. He engaged a number of Swedish engineers under the leadership of Regnar Sohlman, who was

Courtesy of The Nobel Foundation, Stockholm

Alfred Nobel as a youth

Courtesy of The Nobel Foundation, Stockholm

The elder Alfred Nobel

Nobel's laboratory at San Remo. The mixing mill at lower right was used in connection with Nobel's broader research interests including plastics.

destined later to play a leading role in the Nobel Foundation.

The factory at Bofors in Värmland had an old munitions works. Nobel modernized this and broadened its scope of operations. He wrote at this time, "If there is one branch of industry which should be entirely independent of supplies from abroad, then it is manifestly the defense branch." Studies initiated in the laboratory included blast furnace operations, improved methods for utilizing water power, and electrolytic production of sodium and potassium. His factory at Bofors, now known as AB Bofors Company, is presently one of the large-scale industries of Sweden.

The harsh winter climate of Sweden restricted Nobel's stay there to the summer and autumn months. He continued to live at San Remo the rest of the year where he kept up lively correspondence with Sohlman and others. His last letter was to Sohlman on December 7, 1896, a fortnight after arriving at San Remo. It dealt with tests which he had carried out on an experimental sample of nitrocellulose powder which Sohlman had sent to him. Although written in a clear, firm hand, the letter ended with the following sentence: "Unfortunately my health is again so poor that it is with difficulty I write these lines, but as soon as I can I shall return to the subjects which interest us." A few hours later he collapsed at his desk from a stroke. Alfred Nobel died on December 10, 1896.

Alfred Nobel was an exceptionally versatile man. Even more so he was a man of contrasts. Although frail and in poor health most of his life, he led a strenuous life as exemplified by long working hours and quantity of work performed; by putting up with uncomfortable living

225

conditions in his extensive traveling; and because of the mental stress while developing new explosives. He was born in a family of very modest means but died as one of the richest men in Europe. In spite of little formal education, he not only became an outstanding scientist and business man, but also a versatile linguist, a poet, and a philosopher. Although an inventor and industrialist in the field of explosives, he loathed violence and sought peace for the world. Because of his business he spent most of his life in bustling cities, but he preferred seclusion. In spite of his outstanding successes and his great wealth, he never achieved happiness in his private life. He was kind and retiring in his contacts with most people, but when someone tried to take advantage of him, he could be ruthless.

The results of Nobel's research certainly indicate genius if one defines genius as does Webster: "A person endowed with mental superiority, inventiveness, and ability beyond ordinary limits." In competition with scientists, the staffs of manufacturers of explosives, and military establishments worldwide, again and again Nobel outsmarted them in solving problems and marketing new products. As few people have done in any field, he truly revolutionized the technology of explosives. His first development was of the very highest originality; use of a small detonation to set off the major explosive whereas a flame had always been employed before. His second was the taming of the previously uncontrollable nitroglycerin to make possible its use as an industrial explosive. His third was the use of a nonexplosive, but one having a chemical composition approaching that of an explosive, as a diluent for nitroglycerin to give a mixture more powerful than an equal weight of the explosive itself.

His greatest stroke of genius was conceiving and

226

providing the means of setting up the system which make possible the Nobel prizes. There was no precedent here; Nobel made possible this long-term program of international awards for excellence before the day when even awards of a limited national scope were commonplace.

Although a very rich man, Nobel did little to manifest that wealth. He did not have a yacht; he did not indulge in expensive vacations. During his 18 years in Paris he had a handsome town house; but he entertained little, shunned publicity, and detested social functions. His favorite relaxation was to visit the Scandinavian Club in Paris and converse with friends. He did not smoke and did not drink alcoholic beverages. He did not play cards and had no ear for music.

Unlike Edison, Nobel never had a well-organized research effort. Up until a few years before his death, his research was carried out with a maximum of one technically trained assistant plus a few helpers. As a technical man, Nobel would appear to have been primarily an idea man and a laboratory scale experimenter. However, he trusted only himself to demonstrate his new products to the first potential customers. He left the design of new plants, their start-up operations, and their production problems largely to others. Also unlike Edison, he preferred to bring in outside financing of his business operations and set up corporations with others in charge. Nobel did, however, keep enough control of each of the dynamite companies that if things did not proceed to his satisfaction, he could step in and, with the help of friendly stockholders, demand changes. The name "Nobel" became a magic word in the explosive field, and companies using his patents found it to their advantage to use it in their company names.

Nobel appeared to like desk work. He never had a fulltime secretary and took care of most of his voluminous correspondence himself in long hand. This not only included letters to his affiliated companies, but much of a personal nature. He mentioned at one time that he received, on an average, 25 requests daily for money. In general he was generous, giving away about $170,000 each year, particularly to young people who appeared to have worthwhile plans. He never retained a lawyer for any length of time and wrote most of his patents and contracts himself. In fact his final will was written without legal assistance or advice.

It is likely that Nobel would have preferred some field other than explosives for research and development. His first three patents indicated a broad range of interests but once he became involved with nitroglycerin when helping his father, the challenge was too strong for the resolute Nobel to put aside. Of the 120 patents and provisional patents* which he had in England, a considerable number do not concern explosives. If Alfred Nobel became a merchant of death, it was unwittingly rather than by inclination. Actually his explosives were primarily for industrial uses. Black powder was still the basic explosive for firearms at the time of his death. The invention of dynamite was a major factor in making possible the vast expansion in railroad building, harbor development, and the mining of minerals during the latter part of the 19th century.

Alfred Nobel never married. He had two love affairs in his late teens. In one his girl friend in Paris died suddenly (6); the other, the chosen one (a Russian), refused his abrupt proposal of marriage. After becoming rich he was highly suspicious of any female who showed an interest in

*A disclosure to the Patent Office similar to the caveat of the early United States Patent Office.

him. He considered himself unattractive and thus felt that only his money mattered with the fair sex. Once when asked by his brother Robert to prepare an autobiography for posterity, Alfred refused but added that, if such a sketch were ever written, it should begin as follows:

Alfred Nobel's miserable existence should have been terminated at birth by a humane doctor as he drew his first howling breath.

In 1876 Nobel met a 20-year-old beauty, Sofie Hess, in a flower shop at a health resort in Austria. A friendship developed and he attempted to educate her to the state of one who might be suitable as his wife — Pygmalion style. He installed her in a fine apartment in Paris with servants and tutors. However, Sofie was not interested in raising her intellectual standards and was critical of Nobel for spending so much time working. He broke off the affair in the early 90's but arranged that she receive an annuity. His agony over this relationship is illustrated by his following writing to her: "My whole life turns to bitter gall when I am forced to act the nanny to a grown-up child and be the butt of all my acquaintances." Following Nobel's death, Sofie threatened to publish the 216 letters from him which she had in her possession. In order to avoid this embarrassment and possible future blackmail, the executors of his will purchased them by agreeing to continue Nobel's annuity to her until her death.

One can speculate that Nobel might have had an even more productive life if he had been happily married. Although one wonders why one with such great wealth and outstanding intelligence was not happier, the fact remains that his greatest contribution to mankind — his will setting up the Nobel institutions and prizes — may never have materialized if he had had a family of his own.

Alfred Nobel's final will, a four-page document written in Swedish in his own hand, dated November 27, 1895, was prepared with no legal assistance. It read as follows (in translation):

I, the undersigned Alfred Bernhard Nobel, hereby do declare after mature consideration my final will regarding the property I may leave at the time of my death to be as follows: . . .(After listing the specific private bequests, the text continues:) The whole of my remaining realizable estate shall be dealt with in the following way: The capital shall be invested by my executors in safe securities and shall constitute a fund, the interest on which shall be annually distributed in the form of prizes to those who, during the preceding year, shall have conferred the greatest benefit on mankind. The said interest shall be divided into five equal parts, which shall be apportioned as follows: one part to the person who shall have made the most important discovery or invention within the field of physics; one part to the person who shall have made the most important chemical discovery or improvement; one part to the person who shall have made the most important discovery within the domain of physiology or medicine; one part to the person who shall have produced in the field of literature the most outstanding work of an idealistic tendency; and one part to the person who shall have done the most or the best work to promote fraternity between nations, for the abolition or reduction of standing armies and for the holding and promotion of peace congresses. The prizes for physics and chemistry shall be awarded by the Swedish Academy of Science, that for physiological or medical works by the Caroline Institute in Stockholm, that for literature by the Academy in Stockholm, and that for champions of peace by a committee of five persons to be elected by the Norwegian Storting. It is my express wish that in awarding the prizes no consideration whatever shall be given to the nationality of the candidates, but the most worthy shall receive the prize, whether he be a Scandinavian or not.

What a marvel of conciseness, simplicity, and brevity!

Nobel named two civil engineers, Ragnar Sohlman and Rudolf Lilljeqvist, as executors. Sohlman, only 26, had been in his employ for three years, They appointed Carl Lindhagen as legal counsel. These men did an excellent job, against great odds, in bringing Nobel's desires to reality.

Alfred's two brothers, Robert and Ludwig, were moderately wealthy when they died and their families had benefited therefrom. Furthermore, Alfred scorned inherited wealth as "a misfortune which merely serves to make men stupid." However, on publication of the will a storm of criticism broke out. The press led the way. It was contended that Nobel had been downright unpatriotic to overlook Swedish interests and to favor foreigners; it would put great burdens on the awarders and expose them to bribes; and giving the Norwegian government the task of awarding the peace prize would cause grave damage to Sweden's interest. The king originally opposed the will. There was the problem of establishing in what country was Nobel's official residence. The children of Alfred's brother

Robert threatened to sue. Since Nobel's interest in each company had to be liquidated in order to invest the money in "safe securities", dire predictions were made as to what would happen in some cases. One particularly sensitive situation was the Nobel Naptha Production Company in which Alfred had a large investment, and was now operated by Emanuel Nobel, son of brother Ludwig. However, Emanuel along with other members of the Ludwig family refused to contest the will and were highly instrumental in bringing the Nobel Foundation into being.

In the liquidation of Nobel's holdings, lawyers had to be hired in each country. Expenses and taxes took their toll. The net yield to the Nobel Trust was about $8,000,000. All obstacles were overcome and on June 29, 1900 the constitution and bylaws of the Nobel Foundation were set up by government resolution (7). The first prizes were distributed in 1901, about $30,000 each. The choices for Nobel prizes over the years have received wide acclaim and instead of causing problems for Sweden, Alfred Nobel's legacy has been highly instrumental in creating for that nation, as well as for Norway, a reputation of high integrity and fair play.

Nobel prize winners have varied from heads of state to plodding laboratory workers. In the scientific fields, academic people have been favored (8). None of the previous inventors discussed in this treatise won a Nobel prize although all but Goodyear were still active after the Nobel prize program was initiated. All possible candidates fervently hope to win a Nobel prize. Through his legacy, Alfred Nobel has probably contributed collectively to science, the arts, and hopefully to peace, more than any other person.

Chapter 7

Backgrounds, Personal Characteristics, and
Research Methods

We shall now proceed to examine the backgrounds, personal characteristics, and inventive careers of our subject inventors. The primary objective of this book is to determine why Goodyear, Bell, Edison, Westinghouse, Acheson, and Nobel were so outstanding as inventors. Any common trends should be helpful to educators who hope to impart true creativity to their students, for those hoping to identify potentially creative people, and to individuals who wish to enhance their abilities in the fields of research and development.

Some may contend that any conclusions drawn from a study of only six people would have little or no value since the number of references under scrutiny is small. This author believes that a comprehensive evaluation of the inventors considered here can reveal more about successful inventing than can statistics from data dealing with hundreds of inventors whose products, backgrounds, and methods are only qualitatively defined. Each of the six considered here was himself an institution. Such case histories are quite meaningful.

Ancestral Background and Family Relationship: The ancestral backgrounds of parents and their religions, or lack of it, do not appear to be significant factors. The financial status of the parents was middle class in all cases. None was a professional person based on mid-19th century standards;

i.e., none was a physician, lawyer, or minister. Based on today's standards, Bell's father would have been considered a professional and possibly Edison's mother, a teacher before marriage. Except Melville Bell, the fathers' occupations were craftsman, small manufacturer, or shopkeeper. At that time in America most people lived on the land; it is surprising that none of the parents were farmers. Also none of the fathers worked for others for wages.

It is believed quite significant that all the fathers of the six subject inventors had above average innovative traits. Goodyear's father was a small manufacturer utilizing water power. He introduced the spring steel hay fork, a closed lamp for burning oil, and was the first to manufacture pearl buttons in America. Westinghouse, Senior had seven patents on machinery which he manufactured. Edison's father engaged in a number of private ventures and was a skilled carpenter. Shortly after the family's move to Port Huron, Sam Edison built a 100-foot observation tower on the corner of his property for which he charged 25 cents for one to mount the winding stairs. At middle age Acheson's father left the grocery business to become manager of an iron ore operation. He worked with his sons to improve the mining and blast furnace operations. The elder Nobel was sort of a mad genius trying many ventures. One was to train seals to deliver mines to enemy ships. Bell's father had grandiose ideas as to the future of his system of "visible speech", but it made little headway until his son promoted it as a method for teaching the deaf.

As a whole the fathers did little to encourage the innovative traits of their sons and actually opposed them in some cases. George Westinghouse, Jr. got no assistance from his father for the development of the air brake even though the latter was in a position to manufacture parts and help finance development costs. Melville Bell was highly critical of his son for his early work on the telephone and strongly suggested that Alexander Graham tend to his teaching duties and the promotion of "visible speech". The antagonism between the Nobel father and son began early. The father, a robust individual, resented Alfred's "softness" and his interest in poetry and appeared to feel that the boy was putting on an act to avoid helping in the family business. While a young man Alfred was embarrassed several times by commitments which the elder Nobel made to certain Swedish and Russian military authorities that he could not subsequently live up to. Alfred was called in on at least two such occasions in attempts to rectify the situations. The father ridiculed Alfred's early attempts to explode nitroglycerin by detonation rather than by fire. Both blamed the other for the tragic explosion which killed five people including the youngest brother.

These differences between fathers and sons tended to bring the latter closer to their mothers. After Edison's father had agreed with the teacher to remove his son from school, it was the mother who stepped in and saw that Thomas got a rudimentary education and then encouraged him to continue it on his own. Bell's mother was a gifted musician and inspired her son to excel at the piano. Bell's knowledge of music led him, at least indirectly, to the harmonic telegraph and telephone. His mother's deafness, which became quite severe about middle age, gave added impetus to Graham to improve communications with the deaf. Nobel and his mother were always very close and later in life he always managed to return home on her birthdays. He lavished her with gifts and provided for her to the degree that she died a wealthy person.

All of our six inventors were from families of several children. Westinghouse was the seventh of 10, Edison the fourth of six, and Nobel the third of four sons and two later children died at birth. Only Goodyear was the eldest child of the family. It would appear favorable, at least in the 19th century, for the potential inventor to be one of the younger brothers. The older sons were expected to help in, and ultimately to take over, the father's business. All three of Westinghouse's older brothers entered into the family business and there was little pressure for George to do likewise. Nobel's two older brothers largely ran their father's business in Russia. Alfred was allowed a corner in his brother Ludwig's factory for his early experiments. Acheson's older brother ran the family iron business following their father's death. Later he helped Edward financially several times and provided support for the experimental work which sparked the idea for the subsequent synthesis of silicon carbide. It is also worthy to note that of all the brothers of the six inventors, none showed inventive traits except Herman Westinghouse. Of the five brothers, only he was younger than George.

Charles Goodyear, the eldest child, entered his father's business and the concern became Amasa Goodyear and Son. Charles served an apprenticeship in the hardware business and then became largely responsible for marketing the products from the family business. If this enterprise had not failed, Goodyear would very likely have carried on as a dutiful son in that business. Thus because of unusual circumstances, Goodyear became a famous inventor even though the first born.

Childhood and Education: All of our six inventors showed innovative traits as children, with Edison being most pronounced in this respect. None was particularly interested in competitive sports with the possible exception of Westinghouse. Those who attended school excelled in such subjects as mathematics and drawing, but did poorly in Latin and Greek. None was the child prodigy type unless it was Edison, and there we can only surmise since he did not attend school. Bell received the best education, but he did not attend college except for a few courses which he took at irregular times. We can conclude that a high degree of formal education is not essential to becoming an inventor.

At age seven Edison became seriously ill with scarlet fever. This was followed by periodic infections of the middle ear which were unattended. Also as a child he suffered greatly from respiratory diseases. His poor health was one reason why he was not enrolled in the one-room school until over eight years of age. Bell also had scarlet fever as a child but was reasonably healthy in his youth. In his late teens he was plagued with headaches and his symptoms of tuberculosis led to the family's migration to Canada in 1870. At age six Acheson was stricken with typhoid fever. He was ill for many weeks and for a while his recovery seemed doubtful.

Of the six, Nobel suffered most from childhood illnesses. Before age 15 he had a weakness of the spine which forced him to lie in bed for days on end. Goodyear at age 10 was said to be much smaller and more delicate than other children of his age. At age 21 he had his first physical breakdown which was to occur periodically the rest of his life. We know little of George Westinghouse's childhood but he was apparently a robust individual.

In the past century children had many duties in the house, barn, and garden. Also there was usually wide open spaces for playing. It is reasonable that children confined to periods in the sickroom, and within the house following an illness, would have more time for reading than their more healthy playmates. For example, this would appear to have been a major factor in Nobel's education. Even when not bedfast, he was so frail that he was not allowed to play in vigorous games. In his confinement he learned several languages, did very extensive reading of the classics and science, and even wrote poetry. Westinghouse, the healthy member of our six, never did as much reading as a child or adult as did the other five. Although childhood illnesses can have negative effects, they may actually be beneficial in creating an interest in reading, certainly a primary requisite of an educated person.

None of our inventors was a "man-about-town" as a young man, nor was he a favorite with the ladies. Westinghouse was the youngest to wed at age 20. It was his only courtship and a short one. Nobel never married. The other four were 24 years of age or older when married.

Personal Traits As An Adult: Our six inventors show no definite trends in size or stature and in personal appearance. All could be charming and persuasive people when they wanted to be. They had few friends other than their business associates. None sought wealth for the sake of wealth. However, each liked comfortable and even luxurious living quarters once he could afford them. None was active in politics or community affairs.

Of the six, only Goodyear was a highly religious man. He did no work on Sundays regardless how dire his circumstances. He never spoke harshly of Hancock who obtained a sample of vulcanized rubber from him and then proceeded to file on sulfur vulcanization in England. On his deathbed he asked his wife to forgive "that certain person", meaning Day, who had caused him so much misery.

Edison often remarked, "There is a great engineer up there." Near the end he said, "If there is a hereafter, it's all right; if there isn't, it's all right. I've lived my life and done my best." Edison's wife was, however, a very religious person.

238

Nobel included the following in a letter to a pastor who had requested money of him:

> Our religious views differ, perhaps, more in form than in substance, since we agree that we should treat others as we want to be treated by them. As regards my theoretical religious views, I admit that they depart considerably from the beaten path. Precisely because these problems are so far beyond us, I refuse to accept solutions made by the human intellect. Any thinking person must, of course, realize that we are surrounded by an eternal mystery, and on that is based all true religion.

Nobel was a Lutheran by baptism.

All six were plagued with solicitations for charity. Nobel averaged about 25 requests per day. He was considered a fairly easy mark and after he became wealthy, he gave away about $170,000 annually. A considerable proportion of this went to young inventors and those engaged in unusual projects. For example, he provided half of the estimated cost of Andrée's expedition to the North Pole.

Bell was approached for contributions to numerous projects for the deaf as well as to deaf individuals. In general Bell favored contributions to general projects. During his lifetime he and his wife gave about $450,000 to the deaf. Bell supported *Science* magazine to the extent of $60,000 until it had other continuing support.

As did his friend Henry Ford, Edison felt that charity to individuals did the recipients more harm than good. However, he helped his relatives liberally. His father lived with him beginning in Menlo Park days. In 1889 the elder Edison toured Europe at his son's expense. Goodyear supported his parents even when his own family was in need. Westinghouse's mother lived with him for the last several years of her life. Certainly each of our famous inventors never thought it beneath his dignity to associate with, and to help, his less affluent relatives.

Not one of the six was a heavy drinker. Goodyear, Edison, and Nobel were total abstainers of alcohol.

Although a heavy smoker of cigars, Edison prohibited the smoking of cigarettes in his laboratories. At that time the softener-flame retarder used in cigarette papers was glycerin. The thermal decomposition of glycerin was known to produce acrolein, a severe poison. Edison reasoned that cigarette smoke led to acrolein poisoning and inferior employee performance. Edison's ban on cigarette smoking did not appear to affect his son Charles, who in early manhood was a cigarette smoker. Bell was a heavy pipe smoker and occasionally would smoke a cigar. Goodyear, Westinghouse, and Nobel did not use tobacco in any form; Acheson only sparingly. Thus, there was no common trait of the six inventors in the use of tobacco.

All six were fairly healthy adults although Goodyear and Nobel were sickly the last few years of their lives. Goodyear spent his last seven years on crutches. After middle age Nobel and Acheson took occasional treatments at health spas, although both continued business correspondence while there. All lived to a reasonably old age so each had time for a productive life. Goodyear died the youngest, age 59; Edison the oldest, nearly 85.

All were good sleepers. Nobel fell to sleep easily and slept well. Even as a youth, Bell preferred to retire late and get up late. After he became financially independent, he worked or read up to about 3:00 a.m. and slept until late morning. Getting Bell up before his usual waking time was a major task; Bell's valet usually had to call on Mrs. Bell to complete the operation. Although sleeping during an unusual time of day, Bell usually got the conventional eight hours.

Edison had the most unusual sleeping habits. As a telegrapher and while at Newark and Menlo Park, Edison slept only four to five hours a day in a conventional manner. However, he might take one or more brief naps each day. On lying down he could fall asleep immediately even in a noisy room. On getting up he was quickly alert. He was known to go as long as 60 hours without sleep. However, after such an episode he might sleep for 24 hours. Alfred Tate, his former secretary, described a visit to Long Beach, New Jersey where Edison slept the entire 36 hours they were there except for one hour off for eating a dinner of steak, fried potatoes, apple pie, and coffee (1)!

Edison said he never dreamed. In fact none of our six inventors complained of loss of rest due to dreaming or insomnia.

Nobel considered stupidity World Enemy No. 1. However he questioned the methods of teaching then used in schools. When solicited for money to support Stockholm College, he wrote: "I have not made up my mind whether it is better for young people to graze like Nebuchadrezzar or to pore over books." Edison favored self education beyond the elementary level, but when Mina Edison insisted on sending their children to college, he saw that the two boys went to an applied science-engineering school — Massachusetts Institute of Technology. Although Acheson's and Bell's children went to college, their parents did not press them to go for advanced degrees. Bell lamented that neither of his daughters appeared interested in his experimental work. We can conclude that our six inventors did not consider book learning beyond a reasonable education necessary to attain success.

None of our six inventors considered art of great

importance. After his trip to Europe in 1889, Edison contended that the famous paintings of the old masters were not valuable because of their inherent beauty, but rather because there were so few of them. Westinghouse and Nobel had few expensive works of art in their homes. Acheson showed no interest in art even though he travelled extensively in Europe. Even if he could have afforded it, Goodyear would have considered it sinful to spend money on expensive art.

In 1904 Charles Freer of Detroit offered his large collection of oriental art, plus one-half million dollars to maintain it, to the Smithsonian Institution. Bell, as a regent of Smithsonian, was one of the committee authorized to inspect the collection and to decide if the offer should be accepted. Bell was for rejection of the offer on the spot. His daughter Daisy, who had accompanied him to Detroit to view the collection, got her father to withold judgment until their return to Washington. After due deliberation the committee voted to accept Freer's offer. In 1965 this collection was evaluated at 17 million dollars.

Classical music had no great appeal to any of our six. Bell enjoyed playing the piano and leading a family group in singing. Edison could play the organ and piano but had had no formal training in either. In connection with his phonograph recording, Edison went into the mechanisms by means of which the various instruments produce music. Although he recorded from a number of opera stars, and used them in his famous tone tests where the artist's voice was compared with his recordings before audiences, for his own entertainment Edison preferred marches and heart songs. Edison wanted a minimum of tremolo in his recordings. Of the great composers, he preferred Beethoven. He contended jazz was for "the nuts".

Other than Bell and Edison, our other inventors appeared

242

to have no interest in music. Except for Bell as a young man, none cared for dancing.

Sports played little or no part in the lives of our chosen six, either as participant or spectator. Edison did a little fishing while on vacation in Fort Myers, and late in life Westinghouse played some golf. All six were sufficiently active in their laboratories and plants that adequate exercise was probably so obtained in most cases.

Of the five who were married, all had devoted wives. In case of Mrs. Westinghouse and both of Edison's wives, their husband's work came first with few questions asked. The first Mrs. Goodyear suffered great deprivation but she stood by her husband. Mrs. Acheson had a heavy burden raising nine children with her husband gone so much on business trips. Also she was forced to move her home several times as the location of Acheson's business interests changed. They were, however, a devoted couple and later in their lives she accompanied her husband on many of his trips.

Mrs. Bell loved to travel and due to her deafness her husband felt he should accompany her although he came to detest it. The family made nine trips to Europe, besides the 16-month stay in England following their honeymoon, as well as a trip to Mexico and two to the Orient. In 1879 Bell hired Charles Tainter from Charles Williams' shop in Boston, brought over his chemist cousin, Chichester Bell, from England the following year, and set up his Volta Laboratory. He expected this research laboratory to be self-supporting and a continuing effort. However, work was just getting well underway when Bell left with his family for Europe and was gone from September 1881 to May 1882. He was back in Washington for only a month when the family left for Newport, Rhode Island to spend the summer. By 1885 Chichester decided he had had enough and returned to England. The Volta Associates were dissolved in January 1886. If Bell had had a wife more like Mina Edison, it is possible that he would have continued a permanent laboratory and his inventive career following the telephone would have been more impressive. Instead he began to spend the major part of his time in an isolated area in Nova Scotia where lack of laboratory supplies and skilled labor made effective research and development substantially impossible.

The number of children in an inventor's family does not appear to be an appreciable factor in his success. None of the five married ones was too good a father, leaving the rearing of the children largely to their wives. The bachelor, Nobel, turned out an amazing amount of work as he nearly singlehandedly developed his own fabulous inventions, did his early manufacturing, established numerous factories in many countries, did most of his own correspondence, wrote his patents, and ran one or more households. He is certainly an example that marriage is unnecessary for a successful inventive career.

Inventive and Business Career: It goes without saying that all of the six subject inventors were hard workers. In 1901 Edison stated that his daily work schedule was eight hours of manual work and eight hours of mental work. After dinner each evening he planned the work for the following day. During most of the 1870's, Bell taught during the day and experimented about six hours each evening. When Acheson was employed, he would spend his evenings working on his own projects. Westinghouse had a terrific work load with his many businesses as well as his experimental work. Since Nobel wrote to each of his affiliates in the language of the subject country, he could find no qualified secretary. He did most of his business correspondence himself during evenings at home.

None of the six practiced a hobby; in other words, their

work was their hobby. Each can be described by the adage, "Happy is the man whose work is his hobby." Asked why he worked so hard, Edison replied, "I like it. I don't know any other reason. Anything I have begun is always on my mind, and I am not easy until it is finished."

Self motivation is no doubt the most important factor in the success of an individual. It is well known that need motivates; the lean dog is the better hunter. Our six inventors were originally in the "lean dog" class but each had a higher motivation than immediate financial return. Acheson left a $90/month job in the oil fields to seek his fortune in the New York area. Nobel left the employ of his brother in a promising established business to undertake the precarious future of manufacturing nitroglycerin. Westinghouse left the security of his father's factory to strike out on his own. Goodyear resolved to solve the problem of hot tackiness and cold brittleness of rubber come what may. Edison left a $250/month job with the Gold Indicator Company to become an independent inventor and businessman.

All were egotistical men and all sought fame; man does not live by bread alone. Each was the type of person who got great satisfaction in excelling. In their early careers, each was a target of criticism and ridicule that "it wouldn't work". Each accepted the challenge and proved that he was right.

Each participated in experimental work even after one or more successes. None preferred to desert the laboratory and concentrate wholly on a business career. Nobel's idea of retiring was to be able to spend fulltime on experimental work. The 80-year-old Edison, a multimillionaire, did extensive menial laboratory work on his project of rubber from plants. After middle age, experimentation of a broad nature was Bell's "hobby". Goodyear licensed his patents in order to concentrate on developing new uses for his vulcanization process, even though he could have set up one of the most exclusive business monopolies in history if he had chosen to be a manufacturer.

None of the six dropped a project at the laboratory stage and turned it over to others for development, manufacturing, and marketing. Edison got down in the trenches and made many of the connections at the junctions of the 20-foot underground conduits of his first electric central station. He spent several days each week at Ogdensburg, New Jersey when his iron ore concentration pilot plant was in operation there. He designed his cement plant. Acheson not only carried his Carborundum process to commercial production but went into the manufacture of grinding tools containing Carborundum. Westinghouse spent much time at the drafting board.

All took an active part in the initial marketing of products from their inventions. Westinghouse put air brakes on the first test train with little help from workmen, and no financial help from the railroads. He carried out testing at his own expense until his brakes were accepted worldwide for both passenger and freight trains. When emery wheel manufacturers alleged that they were unable to make grinding wheels using Carborundum, Acheson went into an extensive wheel-making program of his own. He and his wife fabricated 12,000 dental wheels and discs and mailed them out to dentists all over the country. This brought an onrush of orders and established Carborundum as a commercial abrasive. Bell created interest in the telephone by holding public lectures in which he and various members of the audience talked with someone at a distance. Bell was largely responsible for convincing his backers and the public that the telephone was a means of two-way conversation and should not be promoted as a

Bell, extreme right, views one of his tetrahedral constructed kites raised by a 10-mile-per-hour wind.

The good friends, Henry Ford and Thomas Edison, exchange greetings with mock formality.

substitute for the telegraph to send one-way messages.

Edison was a great believer in demonstrations for introducing and promoting new products. At New Year's Eve following the successful testing of a carbon filament electric light on October 19-21, an open house was held at the Menlo Park Laboratories. There were 53 lamps and one electric motor in use. A serious obstacle in the introduction of the new light was that insurance companies rated buildings having such lights as "extra hazardous". To combat this adverse propaganda, Edison draped strings of lights around the shoulders of several employees and, led by himself, they paraded the streets of New York at night, current for the lighting being supplied from a dynamo mounted on a wagon. Edison promoted his phonograph by staging tone tests in which an operatic artist sang from a stage from which his recordings from a phonograph were also produced. It was demonstrated that the audience could not distinguish between live and recorded renditions.

After the series of lethal explosions from liquid nitroglycerin, which resulted in the material being prohibited in most countries, Nobel faced a major problem in getting his safe-handling dynamite accepted. By means of a series of demonstrations carried out by himself he was able to get these embargoes removed. His ability to turn this defeat into a stunning success has been called one of Nobel's greatest accomplishments.

Most of our six inventors used exhibits at fairs and expositions to promote their new products. Acheson staffed his own exhibit of Carborundum at the Columbian Exposition in 1893. Bell's exhibit and demonstration of the telephone at the Philadelphia Centennial was a major factor in its successful introduction. Edison's exhibits at the Paris Expositions of 1881 and 1889 were highly instrumental in his success in Europe. In the latter exhibit, Edison occupied about one-third of the space allotted to all United States industry. Goodyear exhibited very effectively in the London and Paris Fairs of 1851 and 1855 respectively, but they failed to help him because he was unable to get patent protection in these countries.

Our six inventors believed in spending the money necessary to get proper materials and equipment for carrying out their experiments. None farmed out experimental work except on a temporary basis. Edison used some equipment at nearby Princeton University (then College of New Jersey) during the early days at Menlo Park. However, when he established his West Orange laboratories, he made provisions for carrying out all operations on the premises. He even had a music room and later a movie studio. His stockroom was a marvel, containing over 8,000 items. He kept a standing order with Eimer and Amend, chemical reagent supplier, to ship a sample of every new chemical which became available.

Next to Edison, Nobel had the best research facilities. He always had a laboratory near his home. He was fortunate in working in Germany or a nearby country since the Germans had the most extensive supply of reagent chemicals and laboratory equipment of any country. Bell had extensive shops at Beinn Bhreagh for building his huge kites. Goodyear used his brother's rubber factory at Naugatuck, Connecticut to carry out experimental coating, mixing, and molding operations.

Our subject inventors not only had experimental facilities available but they used them. All were sold on the experimental method. Edison was once asked if he read much literature dealing with theories. He replied, "No, I prefer facts. I don't know the why of many things I do."

Bell was probably the nearest to a theoretical scientist of the six inventors. His first patent on the telephone was based on the theory that the undulatory electric current was the only way to transmit speech, not the make-and-break technique used by others. However, Bell did not figure this out sitting at his desk. It was a stuck reed in the apparatus he was using in his harmonic telegraph experiments which gave him the clue.

Acheson had a theory that heat could be converted directly into electricity. This proved to be a costly mistake. It was not until he based his experiments on keen observations that he became an outstanding inventor. Another erroneous theory which Acheson had was that graphite was formed from amorphous carbon via intermediate carbide formation. If one of his competitors had shown that this was not the usual mechanism, Acheson's patent position on synthetic graphite manufacture would have been largely annulled.

Nobel determined some very fundamental information relative to mild detonation for setting off certain explosives and synergistic mixtures as exemplified by that of nitroglycerin and low-nitrogen nitrocellulose. However, this information came wholly from experimentation.

Warren has described an interview which he had with Edison relative to the latter's methods of inventing (2). Asked the question "Is it true that an inventor has to be more or less abnormal," Edison replied, "Abnormal persons are never commercial inventors." Pressed further by a comment from Warren that he understood that inventors worked in sort of a frenzy of illumination, Edison continued,

Nothing to it. Those long-haired fellows that act queer and figure out queer things, I don't call them real inventors. Once in a while they may hit something, but not often. There are perhaps five hundred real inventors in the world — men with scientific training, and imagination. They have made about ninety-five per cent of all the good things in the way of inventions and improvements. They are usually connected with some big plant; you may not hear of them, but they are there, working out all kinds of machines and processes. They are the real inventors, not the long-haired kind.

Certainly a characteristic our inventors had in their research work was tenacity. The remarkable comeback which Nobel made with nitroglycerin in the form of dynamite has already been cited. Edison's initial marketing failure with his alkaline storage battery took him back to the "drawing board", and it was not until a total of about nine years of research and development that a successful battery was marketed. Westinghouse spent over 15 years getting an air brake perfected for freight trains. Goodyear's struggle to solve the curing of rubber is tenacity at its extreme.

A remarkable characteristic of the six was that of withstanding failures and not becoming discouraged or bitter. Edison once said, "Spilt milk doesn't interest me. I have spilt lots of it, and while I have always felt it for a few days, it is quickly forgotten and I turn again to the future." Edison's loss of his electric business in the General Electric merger and his huge monetary loss and eight years of time in his iron ore project appeared to have left no "scars on his soul". Acheson's many failures during his early career did not cause him to lose faith in himself. Westinghouse's ouster from the Westinghouse Electric Corporation was a severe blow to him, but he was back pioneering a new field, individual springs for wheels of motor vehicles, when death ended his remarkable career.

Goodyear consoled himself over the loss of his French patents in that it was likely a good thing, otherwise he might have settled in Paris permanently and thus expose his children to the worldly environment of the French capital!

Optimism was a common trait which went with their abilities to withstand failures. Bell was predicting that one would ultimately be able to talk by telephone to Europe, even though there were then difficulties when he and Watson conversed from Boston to Salem. Westinghouse foresaw the transformer as a means of making feasible the transportation of electricity over long distances even though the transformer at the time was highly inefficient. Nobel vouched that his explosives, which made possible roads, tunnels, and bridges which could not be built using black powder explosives, would improve communication between countries and thus a more peaceful world. Goodyear saw rubberized, waterproof clothing as protecting mankind from diseases brought on by inclement weather. Edison sought a domestic source of natural rubber, should supplies from the Far East be shut off, even though he knew little about botany and there was no indication that such a source could be found or developed.

In his experimental approach Edison stated that he first found out everything that others knew about the problem and then began where they left off. He appeared to have the ability to shut off from his mind everything except his specific problem. However, if he got to a point where he had no more ideas on a problem, he would set it aside. Asked if he might force himself to think hard along a given line he replied (2):

> Oh, no. I never think about a thing any longer than I want to. If I lose my interest in it, I turn to something else. I always keep six or eight things

going at once, and turn from one to the other as I feel like it.

However, in development-type research he did not hesitate to try long-shot approaches. In searching for the best organic material to pyrolyze to carbon filaments for electric lighting, he tested the hair from the beards of some of his employees. M. A. Rosanoff, a chemist employee closely associated with Edison for over a year, has described that the Old Man, as he was called around the laboratories, did not give up easily (3).

Late one night, having spent the evening editing some troublesome encyclopaedia articles, I was weary and yearning for bed, when my telephone rang. It was 'Santcho Pantcho'.* 'Say, we are working all night to-night. The Old Man says to ask you if you want to come up?' I groaned under my breath and said, 'All right, tell him I'll be right up.' The laboratory was brightly lighted up, Edison and Santcho Pantcho and a group of Muckers were there. Edison's son Charlie was there, pottering with something at one of the desks. The Old Man hailed me with exaggerated cordiality. 'Say,' he called, 'let's you and I go to work on your damned problem to-night and make a resolution not to go to sleep until we have solved it!' This sounded to me like an invitation to join a suicide club. I pleaded, 'Mr. Edison, you know I have been at my problem for months; I have tried every reasonable thing I could think of, and no result, not even a lead!' — 'That's just where your trouble has been,

*The nickname for Fred Ott, Edison's assistant.

you have tried only reasonable things. Reasonable things never work. Thank God you can't think up any more reasonable things, so you'll have to begin thinking up unreasonable things to try, and now you'll hit the solution in no time. After that you can take a nap,' he added reassuringly.

Bell also did not use obvious research methods. Some of his best leads to the telephone were when experimenting with a human ear. He continued with his air flight experiments even after most of his friends, including Lord Kelvin, had warned him that he was wasting his time and likely would become an object of ridicule.

Observation of unexpected results served to lead our subject six to several inventions. This was Goodyear's primary source of success. He noted the curing effect of nitric acid on rubber following its use to remove metal deposition from the surface of rubber. His keen observation of the thin layer of cured rubber, sandwiched between the layers of burnt rubber and uncured material of the sample placed on the stove, led to his ultimate success. Others present could not detect the phenomenon even when pointed out by Goodyear.

Acheson observed that when attempting to reduce iron ore with natural gas at high temperatures, the clay impurities became harder. Subsequent experiments with clay, carbon mixtures heated in an electric furnace led to the synthesis of Carborundum. Acheson's observation that some of the unreacted carbon in his Carborundum process became gray in color and soft in texture, led to his process for making synthetic graphite. Observation of the behavior of a toy, which Edison had made for his children, led him to believe that it might be possible to record and reproduce sound. Nobel's observation of the behavior of colloidion when treating a finger injured in the laboratory, led to experiments from which came blasting gelatin, one of his most important inventions.

Edison did not consider that he had any special powers of invention. He detested the term "wizard" which some of the newspapers used in describing him. He claimed that if he had any special traits as an inventor it was due to 99% perspiration and 1% inspiration. As Edison, our other inventors claimed only imagination, ambition, and hard work to be the sources of their successes.

Warren wrote as follows of Edison (2):

> Edison regards the art of inventing very much in the light of a profession which may be 'learned' almost as successfully as soldiering or acting or even 'doctoring'. Thousands of men, he thinks, might have become inventors had they but cultivated their ideas, for the creative germ lies hidden in most minds.

None of the six was a specialist by training or practice. Bell's early training and practice was in speech, but the telephone got him into electricity. His subsequent research concerned the phonograph, hereditary of the deaf, sheep breeding, aeronautics, and other fields. Although Acheson's first successes dealt with use of the electric furnace, subsequently he became an authority on electrochemistry and colloidal dispersions of solids. Although Nobel's great successes were in the explosive field, at the time of his death he had broadened his research activities to cover steel, electrochemistry, and the generation and use of electricity generally.

Although all of our subject inventors delegated authority on a rather broad basis in their business operations, each ran the show in their research laboratories. Acheson always laid out the research program in detail, even after two of his sons were active in research. Although Nobel had at least one professional in his laboratories in France, Italy, and Sweden, they worked as assistants to him. Only Edison had a large enough staff to justify organization. Although several of the laboratory people had specific responsibilities, all those doing technical work reported directly to him. Although the practice varied with time, in 1903 as reported by Rosanoff (3) there were no reports to write, no staff meetings, no clicking of typewriters – just experimental work. No one was expected to report to the boss until he had some positive results. However, Edison valued negative results; he felt that since they showed what didn't work, they were a guide to further experiments.

Edison had a large group, of what we would today call laboratory technicians, working directly with him. Each evening at home he wrote out in detail the experiments to be done by this group the following day and expected them to record their results in notebooks. Edison would not only read these results but usually visited their laboratories each day to observe samples, procedures, etc., and perhaps work with one or more of them for a time.

Edison's great success as an inventor is even more remarkable when one considers his deafness. He was partially deaf even as a youth and following a mastoidectomy in 1905, his hearing loss became progressively worse. At times he suffered from severe ear aches. During the last 10 years or so of his life, people communicated with him by writing or tapping the Morse Code on the back of his hand. Although Edison realized that his defective hearing was a liability in many ways, he refused to let it interfere with his career. He often joked about it, saying it was a blessing since he didn't have to listen to his wife and her lady friends so much. He worked out techniques to hear phonograph recordings by holding a pencil between his teeth and pressing it against the phonograph cabinet or its horn. Although Edison had a negative attitude towards hearing aids, two were found in his safe following his death. Apparently they had been too ineffective or clumsy to handle to interest him.

It is possible that Edison's loss of hearing enhanced his productivity as an inventor. His ability to sleep soundly and get adequate rest with relatively short periods of sleep may have been due, at least in part, to his deafness. His hearing problem prevented him from attending social events, or at least gave him an excuse for not doing so. Thus he had more time for research and development. Since his employees could talk back to him only with difficulty, it made it easier for him to dominate literally all situations. Because of Edison's great abilities, this may have resulted in more effective research than if others had had a greater part in running the programs.

As an example of how hearing loss can affect a person, Mrs. Alexander Bell once said that she would rather be blind than afflicted with her total deafness. Edison's pretention that his deafness was an asset rather than a liability is an excellent example of his approach to life and his work.

Although Nobel's "nitroglycerin headaches" and Goodyear's gout — or lead poisoning — caused them great discomfort in their later years, neither allowed his affliction to prevent him from working. In the cases of all of our subject inventors, problems of health were something to be tolerated and not used as excuses for living a life of leisure in retirement, something each was financially able to do many years before death.

Once a subject inventor began to get patents, he

continued to invent his entire life. Westinghouse got started at the early age of 19, whereas Acheson was 30 before he made an invention of value. This would appear to have been primarily a choice of problems rather than relative inventive skills. Westinghouse began working on steam engines and problems relating to railroading, both fertile fields for invention at that time. On the other hand, Acheson concentrated on the direct conversion of heat to electricity, an objective unattained today. As pointed out in Chapter 3, Edison's rate of getting patents was more affected by the nature of his fields of research rather than by age. In fact the careers of the six inventors emphasize that the "fertility" of the field of research under investigation is a major factor in the apparent creativity of the investigator.

Edison commented as follows on the effect of age in general:

The man who has reached the age of 36 has just about achieved readiness to discard the illusions built upon the false theories for which instructions and youthful ignorance previously made him an easy mark. He is just beginning to get down to business. The useful man never leads an easy, sheltered, knockless, unshocked life. At 36, he ought to be prepared to deal with realities; and after about that period in his life until he is 60, he should be able to handle realities with a steadily increasing efficiency. Subsequently, if he has not injured his body by excess indulgences and if he has not eaten to excess, he very likely may continue to be achievingly efficient up to his 80th birthday and, in exceptional cases, until 90.

Bell and Acheson were very active in technical societies. They were effective speakers and enjoyed addressing meetings. Westinghouse and Nobel were less active in the societies of their choice. Nobel enjoyed most the meetings of the Royal Swedish Academy of Sciences. Although Edison was a member of numerous scientific and engineering societies and institutes and received their technical publications, he took no active part in them. Based on our six case histories, attendance and participation in meetings of technical organizations are not significant factors in an inventive career.

With the possible exception of Westinghouse, all of our subject inventors preferred research and development to manufacturing. Goodyear licensed his patents and did no manufacturing. Nobel manufactured nitroglycerin and dynamite in their introductory stages but as a business spread to various countries, each factory had local management. Nobel would bring in one of his experienced managers temporarily to direct start-up operations. Nobel retained only technical liaison with his affiliated companies; he never attended a board meeting. Bell took no part in the business end of the telephone company. Fortunately his father-in-law was a shrewd businessman and took over this responsibility for the Bell-Hubbard interests. Both Acheson and Westinghouse were very active when new operations were set up, but each left routine operations to others. Westinghouse at one time was president of 29 companies. In spite of his apparent interest in being a businessman, he found time to get 361 United States patents!

As a youth Edison showed much skill in business; e.g., he made $45/month from his weekly *Grand Trunk Herald* which he printed in the baggage car. He "bribed" the trainmen with produce at wholesale prices and was allowed to haul, without charge, magazines, newspapers, and produce to sell at the station stops. He likely could have been a successful businessman. He certainly had an opportunity to become one of the giants of industry following his founding of the electrical industry. Instead he turned these operations over to others and concentrated on his new laboratories at West Orange. Soon he found himself frozen out from his former companies. He neglected his phonograph and allowed others to come into this profitable field, but he came back and established a very successful, but highly competitive, business. Although Edison delegated most of his business operations to others, he couldn't resist the temptation to step in and make changes when he saw fit.

Although all of Edison's laboratory people addressed him as Mr. Edison, he had a very informal relationship with them. In Menlo Park days he was usually dressed no better than the janitor. Francis Jehl, his youngest assistant, has described trips to New York the two occasionally made on Saturday nights to see a show, have a lunch afterwards, and possibly get Bergmann, a former Edison employee and now a manufacturer on his own, out of bed to join them at their midnight lunch. In the late 1920's Edison had about 15 "old timers" around the laboratory who were largely useless but he refused to dismiss them. One was Meadowcroft, Edison's secretary, who was nearly blind.

When first coming with Edison at Menlo Park, Upton felt superior to his new employer. After all, he not only had a college degree from what is now Princeton University but he had studied abroad under the famed Helmholtz as well. However, he soon learned to respect Edison and as an old man he once remarked, "The pride of my life is that for several years I was able to be near such a leader as Mr. Edison."

Edison set up the first industrial training school in New

York in 1881 to train men for the electrical industry. They met in Edison's office on Fifth Avenue at nights. Laboratory personnel from Menlo Park were instructors.

There was no unionization of any Edison plant during the founder's lifetime. It is of interest that William Green, president of the American Federation of Labor, was one of the guests of honor at the 50th anniversary of the electric light, held in Dearborn, Michigan, in October 1929.

Nobel never had a strike in any of his factories. His explosive factories in England had a better safety record than the coal mines there. Westinghouse's air brake company was a model in employee relations. We can conclude that our six inventors respected the man who worked with his hands and as employers maintained an above average relationship with their labor forces.

One is inclined to overlook the part that venture capital played in the days of the lone inventor. None of our six was able to finance his early inventions. If the Rider brothers had not financed Goodyear, his secret might have died with him. He did not apply for his vulcanization patent until 1843. Westinghouse's first railroad test of his air brake was financed by a chance friend in Pittsburgh. Acheson received early financial support from Huyler, whom he had met on the ship during his first trip to Europe. Sanders, in his early support of Bell and commercialization of the telephone, became so deeply in debt that he nearly lost his prosperous leather business. Edison was advanced $50,000 by those who formed the Edison Electric Light Company and later another $50,000, although at the time he had nothing but failures from his work on incandescent lighting. Our inventors must have inspired confidence in their potential backers in order to get such financial support.

In summary, based on the six biographies covered in Chapters 1 - 6, the potential inventor has a greater likelihood of success if he comes from a middle class family, if his father is a craftsman who has shown innovative traits, and if he is one of the younger children. As a child our successful inventor may have been relatively weak and sickly, he did not excel at sports, and although not necessarily an outstanding student, he did well in science, mathematics, and the mechanical arts. He persisted in innovative activities even though discouraged by his father. His education was general and had no high degree of specialization. He was little interested in social affairs and married later than the average.

As an adult our inventor is not active in politics or community affairs and has little interest in the arts. He indulges in alcoholic beverages sparingly or not at all. He likely has unusual sleeping habits and at times sacrifices sleep in order to work longer hours. He has a devoted wife whose primary interest is the welfare and success of her husband. Their friends are largely her husband's business associates.

In his vocation our successful inventor prefers research and development over business, but he takes an active part in the early manufacture and marketing of products from his inventions. He is highly motivated, extremely self-confident, tenacious, optimistic, and not discouraged by failures. He has the keen foresight of choosing a field, yet unplowed or unsuccessfully plowed by others, and proceeds to invent by extensive imagination, keen observation, and hard work. Once he feels the "cream has been skimmed" from a given field, he moves on to another. He maintains close contact with his research assistants and directs their work in detail. He is a member of several technical societies but he takes a minor role in their activities. He is basically

261

an experimentalist who follows through on an invention until it is a commercial success or has been abandoned. He does not allow any physical disability to impede his desire to excel and he has no plans for retirement from his research and development activities due to age.

—

Chapter 8

Inventors and the Patent Office

Products and processes covered by patents constitute the only legal monopolies in the United States except, of course, the utilities which are government regulated. Such monopolies are the rewards to inventors for disclosing their inventions to the public. A patent monopoly is not a monopoly in the usual sense; it covers only something which did not exist before the subject patent was issued. All are free to use the old process or product. Furthermore, the monopoly ends 17 years after the date of issuance of the patent.

Another unique feature of patents is that they are one of the few types of property which are not taxed. However, the income from patents is taxed.

The United States patent system has always been one of the best in the world and has been credited with encouraging Americans to be the most inventive of any nation, particularly during the period when our subject six inventors were active. As discussed in Chapter 9, the situation is less favorable today.

Thomas Jefferson, himself an inventor, had this to say of our patent system while he was President: "The issue of patents for new discoveries has given a spring to invention beyond my conception." Abraham Lincoln, the only holder of a United States patent to become President,* said, "The

---

*Jefferson took out no patents on his inventions.

patent system added the fuel of interest to the fire of genius." Dwight Eisenhower, who saw at first hand the part that technology played in winning the world's greatest conflict, is quoted as follows: "The U. S. Patent System is soundly based on the principle of protecting and rewarding inventors, this system has for years encouraged the imaginative to dream and to experiment − in garages and sheds, in great universities and corporate laboratories."

Although the inventor has a theoretical monopoly for a limited time, in most cases his invention is not accepted rapidly enough to make his reward a generous one. Even in high places, men may fail to recognize what inventions are truly the important ones. In the "Annual Report of the Commissioner of Patents" to Congress for 1891, Commissioner William Simonds attempted to point out how important the Patent Office was to the welfare of the nation: "The following are a few and only a few of the American inventors whose reputation has become national and whose improvements have formed the foundation of manufacturing industries of great magnitude." There were subsequently listed 44 such industries and 81 American inventors. However, there was no mention of Westinghouse and his air brake, Bell and his telephone, nor of Edison and his electric light or phonograph, all of which had been invented over 12 years before. In contrast, there were listed those for making inventions relating to horse cars, wood screws, hat making, hand shovels, and pin making. Of our subject inventors, only Goodyear's name appeared among the 81 and it was grouped with those of Nathaniel Hayward and Horace Day "as to India-rubber".

The Constitution of the United States gives Congress the power to enact laws relating to patents. The first patent bill was signed into law by President Washington in 1790. A board consisting of the Secretaries of State and War and the Attorney General had the responsibility for granting patents. In 1802 the Patent Office was created and placed within the State Department. An act of 1836 set up the American system of granting patents largely as it is today. It had four primary features:

(a) The Patent Office was set up as a special unit.

(b) The Commissioner of Patents is to be appointed by the President.

(c) A corps of experts was established to examine incoming patent applications and establish their novelty.

(d) The inventor was required to take an oath that he believed he was the first to invent that claimed in his patent application.

Thus America led in setting up a liberal patent system. The most humble inventor has the services of experts in determining the novelty of his invention. After visiting the Centennial Exposition in Philadelphia in 1876, Sir William Thomson (later Lord Kelvin) reported, "If England does not amend its patent laws, America will speedily become the nursery of useful inventions of the world." England did so in 1887 as well as Germany in 1877 and Switzerland in 1887. All were patterned after that of the United States. Werner Von Siemens, the famous inventor and manufacturer, spearheaded the drive in Germany to establish an adequate patent system in that new empire.

The life of a patent in 1836 was 14 years after date of issue, subject to an extension of seven years. In 1861 the term of a patent was increased to 17 years and the power of the Patent Commissioner to extend the term was withdrawn. The Act of 1836 provided for the filing of caveats. A caveat was a written notice to the Patent Office from an inventor who was not yet prepared to file his application. It gave him the right for the period of one year to be notified if someone else applied for a patent on the same invention. Caveats were abolished in 1910.

In 1849 the Patent Office was transferred to the newly formed Department of Interior and in 1925 to the Department of Commerce, where it remains today. In 1932 the Patent Office was moved to the Department of Commerce Building, occupying over eight acres of office space. During World War II most of its activities and personnel were moved to Richmond, Virginia on a temporary basis. The Patent Office is now located in spacious quarters in Crystal Plaza on the Jefferson Davis Highway, Arlington, Virginia. Today about 2,600 people work there, of which nearly half are Examiners. Its annual budget is over 50 million dollars, of which over half is collected as patent fees. Over 100,000 patent applications are received annually.

The ten-year period beginning in 1880, during which all of our subject inventors were active except Goodyear, was one of the greatest decades of invention of all time. The following were invented or introduced during this period:

Incandescent light	Automobile
Improved dynamos	Pneumatic tire
Electric welding	Cash register
Electric furnace	Smokeless powder
Trolley car	Transparent film
Induction electric motor	Cyanide process
Steam turbine	Manufacture of aluminum

Thomas Edison filed 481 applications which were subsequently granted as United States patents during this ten-year period.

All inventions are not patentable and all patents are not

inventions. The statute provides that any person who "invents or discovers any new or useful process, machine, manufacture, or composition of matter, or any useful improvements thereof, may obtain a patent." In order to be new the invention must be made before it is used or described in a printed publication in this or any foreign country. Furthermore if an inventor or anyone else describes an invention in a printed publication, uses the invention publicly, or places it on sale, the inventor must apply for a patent within one year, otherwise the invention is not patentable. Thus, an invention is not patentable if one does not act within the specified time limits, and prior disclosure by another in a printed publication of a mere idea may make an invention reduced to practice nonpatentable. On the other hand, many patents are on subjects which do not prove to be truly "useful", and thus do not constitute inventions. A patent may be technically sound, but uneconomical to use.

Obtaining a patent in the United States carries no obligation to practice it or to license it to others. If desired, it may simply be filed in a drawer. Although some patents may be worth millions, unfortunately most are worth little or nothing. Whether in use or inactive, a patent excludes others from using commercially the invention so covered. However, a patent does not exclude anyone from using the information disclosed therein in research and development work.

If a patent application is to be filed in a foreign country, in order to be valid it must be filed within one year after like filing in the United States. Even so a foreign patent may be issued before that filed in the United States, since many countries do not examine an application for priority before publishing it as a provisional or final patent.

All new things are not patentable. Business methods, new

plays on the football field, or even computer programming are not. New devices or machines which are considered mere gadgetry, *i.e.*, something that anyone skilled in the art could contrive if he so desired, are not patentable. Also the term, "any useful improvements thereof" is hard to define. Thus it is impossible to define patentability on an absolute basis which results in differences between the potential patentee and the Patent Office, between rival inventors, and the patentee and the courts.

Besides patent applications covering the subjects quoted above, the Office processes applications dealing with trademarks, design patents, and patents on plants. A fourth category, copyrights, is now handled by the Library of Congress. Patent applications dealing with atomic weaponry are not accepted by the Patent Office.

An inventor need not patent his invention in order to practice it; he may choose to keep it secret. This is a fairly common practice when it is a process invention which can be confined within one's laboratory or factory. Furthermore, often a new process is a difficult one on which to get patent coverage, and may be even more difficult to enforce − if it is one that competitors could use behind their factory walls. Secrecy may be preferred over patenting in case of compositions of mixtures which undergo chemical change during manufacture, or are too complex to chemically analyze. Examples are rubber compounds in which the secret ingredients undergo change during vulcanization, as well as some compounded beverages and medicines. A famous example of the drink category is Coca Cola.

Unfortunately many people who are unfamiliar with patenting procedures consider it is too difficult and expensive to attempt patenting their inventions. Actually one may prepare his own application, file it in the Patent

Office, and conduct the proceedings himself. In 1974 the filing fee is $65, and if a patent results, an additional $100 fee for issuance is required. However, most inventors employ the services of persons known as patent attorneys or patent agents. Lists of such personnel are available as well as other information helpful to the potential inventor (1). If an application is deemed unpatentable by the Examiner, the "invention" will remain secret within the Patent Office.

Patents of every industrial nation constitute a vast storehouse of information. For example, on August 7, 1973 the U.S. Patent Office issued Patent No. 3,751,726. This total number does not include the 10,032 granted prior to July 4, 1936 and the thousands of plant patents and hundreds of thousands of registered trademarks. However, most writers of scientific and engineering articles and books ignore the patent literature. A good example of this was the failure to recognize until recently that Thomas Edison was likely the foremost American applied chemist of his time (2). Edison's chemical achievements are recorded primarily in his patents, not in chemical periodicals and books.

Getting patent protection is only one of several steps in developing an embryonic invention. A practical method of preparation must be worked out, capital must be obtained for constructing manufacturing facilities, and the product must be marketed. Also unfortunately, and particularly if the invention is of major importance, competitors may ignore one's patent or attempt to declare it invalid. Here the Patent Office offers no help to the inventor. There is also the problem of foreign patent coverage which is complex since patent laws vary from country to country. How our subject inventors fared in the patent offices of the world, in the courts, and in the exploitation of their inventions is a story which further exemplifies the know-how of inventing.

Charles Goodyear

Goodyear's struggle to get and maintain patent protection is described in some detail in Chapter 1. He did make several mistakes relative to patents, some of which can be attributed to his lack of funds. He should have filed a patent immediately after his epic observation in January 1839. Instead he felt the need for more experimental data although his invention was so unique that he did not need to define optimum temperatures and the like as he did in his U.S. Patent 3,633. He should not have submitted samples of his vulcanizate to anyone prior to the filing of his patent. Failure to observe this fundamental rule of inventing lost him all rubber business in England, the most industrialized nation at that time. As soon as he had adequate income, he should have hired legal counsel and surrounded himself with technically trained personnel. Instead he largely maintained a go-it-alone policy. However, since there was no alternative method to sulfur vulcanization, Goodyear enjoyed a good royalty income in this country following the successful defense of his patent in 1852. His failure to get patent coverage in any foreign country, on one of the most basic patents of all time, is certainly no credit to the patent laws and policies in vogue at that time.

Goodyear knew a surprising amount about patents as indicated by the chapters entitled, "Inventions and Patent Laws" and "Patents and Patent Laws" in his book (3). The following quotation from the former attests to his realistic attitude on the subject:

The individual has judged rightly as to his powers of

270

invention, but he has little idea how much remains to be done to make the invention productive of profit; he has probably exhausted his own resources, and the resources and patience of his friends in completing his improvements; he has not the means to conduct the manufacture of his article, and without this he cannot so demonstrate the utility of his improvement, as to derive the advantage from it he expected. He takes the precaution to procure letters patent for his invention, which he counts as property, but which amounts chiefly to this, that the government grants him permission to fight his own battles. Next comes the Herculean task of convincing the public of the advantages of the improvement, and the yet more difficult one of supplying the market with the improvement himself, and of preventing others from doing it by encroaching on his patent. If his object is to derive a profit by disposing of his patents for his inventions, it is well known that patents are so commonly evaded in some way, and that the patent law is so ineffectual for their protection, that the public will not value them highly, if at all; nor can they be expected to do so, for in too many cases the purchase of a patent is only equivalent to the purchase of a law-suit.

A. Graham Bell

Alexander Graham Bell's experience with patents is full of dramatic and unusual episodes. Fortunately Bell was highly skilled in the preparation of patents and their defense. His basic telephone patent was unique in many respects. First, the word *telephone* does not appear in the patent. It describes no apparatus and in fact was allowed before the first successful transmission of the voice over a wire was accomplished. It patented a principle, that of the continuous undulatory electric current, and dominated all subsequent patents on the subject. Bell wrote this patent application and it was filed and allowed substantially as he prepared it.

Bell was quite different from Goodyear in that he prepared his first telephone patent application with a minimum of experimental data. However, his incredible experience with George Brown* delayed filing in this country.

Bell's telephone patents were only two in number and noted for their brevity, but they were the basis for about 600 litigation suits. This can be a lesson to some present day legal staffs which appear to feel that patent coverage is directly proportional to the number of patents dealing with a certain subject and recommend filing on trivial matters primarily to increase patent number. Bell's U.S. Patent 174,465 is considered one of the most important patents of all time.

In order to prevent chaos in the new telephone industry and to recover their development costs and capitalization investment, the Bell Company was forced to bring suit against literally hundreds of small telephone companies which sprang up over the country. Receivers, transmitters, wiring, and primary batteries were readily available or easy to manufacture. Since Bell's two patents disclosed little in the way of "hardware" for telephony, anyone who came out with some change in any part of the telephone apparatus might think that he had a new invention and was free to operate. Most of the cases were settled out of court once the defendants understood the true nature of the Bell

*See Chapter 2.

patents. However, some of the infringers were malicious and six of the court actions went all the way to the Supreme Court.

Bell spent over 10 years involved in legal depositions and court proceedings, with all the mental anguish they cause an inventor. The typical inventor considers legal matters generally a waste of time, detracting from his experimental and other scientific work. However, Bell's superb command of the English language and his great skill in the witness chair were no small factors in the Bell Telephone Company being victorious in all of its suits dealing with the Bell patents.

Among the numerous suits in which Bell was involved, one was extremely unique and should be shocking to every American. This was that in which the Bell Company and Bell himself constituted the defendant with no less than the United States Government being the plaintiff. Bell was accused of perjury and fraud, of collusion, and bribery of Patent Office officials. Mackenzie describes this litigation well (4).

The instigators of this attack, the Pan-Electric Company and its subsidiaries, had been incorporated under the laws of Tennessee to exploit the telephonic and telegraphic inventions of a young gentleman named Harry Rogers, who had been appointed electrician of the House of Representatives some years earlier by the Honorable Casey Young, then member of Congress from Tennessee. The idea of the Pan-Electric venture had originated with Harry's father, Dr. James W. Rogers, who very naturally enlisted the aid of the family patron, Mr. Casey Young, in patenting and developing his son's inventions. Mr. Young had interested a group of his friends, and the company was incorporated with

273

five million dollars capital, of which sum only four dollars and fifty cents was required to be paid in for the use of the State seal. And so, with everything to gain and four dollars and fifty cents to lose, the Pan-Electricians, sitting well in order, embarked on that glittering quest of the eighties, the search for a way to break the Bell patents.

In their application to the Attorney-General, they took their departure from the premise that Reis had invented the electric speaking telephone, and that Bell knew it and concealed his knowledge from the Patent Office — and of course from Joseph Henry, Sir William Thomson, and the judges of the Centennial! This was fraud number one. It was further charged that Bell's attorneys, Messrs. Pollok and Bailey, had connived with the Patent Office officials to obtain dishonest knowledge of Gray's caveat; that they had stolen Bell's specification, re-written it, and returned it to the file; that Bell, then in Boston, came back to Washington the following week, approved of this felony, so becoming party to it, and went to the Patent Office to interlard even more new matter — all derived from Gray's caveat — making the old parts conform to his attorney's interpolations; and that several years later, fearing discovery of the crime, Messrs. Pollok and Bailey had stolen the whole document and substituted an entire new one to conceal all these changes! This last giddy naiveté was designed to anticipate the obvious retort that Bell's original application could be produced from the Patent Office files and shown to have none of these alleged interpolations and changes in it.

All this — charges of the gravest kind — the

office of the Attorney-General passed upon within twenty-four hours, without even the usual formality of referring the papers to the Secretary of the Interior or his Commissioner of Patents, and suit was brought, immediately, with the weight of the United States Government as plaintiff, in an attempt to fasten on Bell 'the infamy of having perpetrated the most gigantic fraud of the century.'

The precipitance of the whole move was the more surprising since the Bell patents had been repeatedly sustained by Circuit Court decisions, and several appealed cases were then awaiting decision in the United States Supreme Court. The value of this speed, to the Pan-Electric Company, was plain, however, when a suit of the Bell Company against a Pan-Electric subsidiary came up for hearing in Baltimore on September 15, and the District Attorney appeared on behalf of the United States, protesting against any hearing of the Bell motion for an injunction until the Government suit could be concluded. In effect, this gave letters of marque to the Pan-Electric to prey upon the Bell interests indefinitely. Further, the Government suit was not brought in the District of Columbia, where Bell lived, nor in Massachusetts, where his company operated, but in Tennessee, where Bell had never been and where his company had never had an office.

The fact that the Bell organization had absorbed the telephone business of Western Union gave the young company an odium of monopoly. Bell, who had already demonstrated to all that knew him to be so honest that he might inconvenience his business associates, now prepared a letter pointing out the absurdity of the charges against him. He planned to submit this to the press but the lawyers of the Bell Company convinced him that he should not do so; *i.e.,* his defense should be made in court! However, the Republican press scented an opportunity to embarrass the Democratic administration and their attack subsequently resulted in the Government dropping the suit. The *New York Tribune* printed a startling story on its front page that Mr. Garland, then attorney general, not only held one million dollars of stock in the Pan-Electric Company but was that company's attorney. The list of stockholders included three United States senators, three ex-members of Congress, and an ex-governor of Tennessee — all Democrats. President Cleveland demanded an explanation from his solicitor-general and the latter announced that he was recommending that the case against the Bell interests be dropped. In 1888 a Supreme Court decision confirmed an injunction against the Pan-Electric Company and the so-called Government case died a natural death. However, the case was not finally abandoned until 1896.

The attacks on Bell from the Democratic press included the charge that he had stolen the telephone invention from Elisha Gray. Still Bell's counsel would not let him retort the charge. This was nearly unbearable to him and likely explains, in part, why his research beginning about 1890 was not the type directed towards patentable inventions. The charges of fraud, widespread against him during the long effort to wrest the telephone patents from him, were completely contradictory to his character. However, ghosts of these charges persisted and during his lifetime Bell was never accepted by all as the undisputed inventor of the telephone. In fact the fabrication persists today that Bell beat Gray to the Patent Office with the telephone invention by only a few hours. The truth is that Bell's invention lay in patent application form for months waiting for George Brown to file a corresponding case in England. Furthermore, Gray did not bring a patent application to the Patent Office, but actually only a caveat. This proposed method for constructing a telephone as outlined in Gray's caveat subsequently proved to be no good and a corresponding application was never filed. There has probably never been a clearer claim of inventorship to a major invention than that of Bell to the telephone.

Thomas Edison

Edison not only obtained more United States patents than any other of our subject inventors, but more than any other individual in history. The total number is 1,093, not 1,097 as is often reported. According to Norwig, this discrepancy is due to the fact that four patents were assigned numbers which were later withdrawn for purposes of interference, subsequently issuing under other numbers (5). Norwig lists all of Edison's patents including the dates of issue and titles. As to subjects, his patents are highly varied; they are classified in 94 of the 300-odd classes used by the Patent Office. Edison obtained one or more patents for each of 65 consecutive years from 1869 to 1933. Four were issued posthumously.

Edison is sometimes pictured as one who failed to recognize creative traits in his employees. Although it is true that he generally insisted that they work on his ideas and projects as outlined, he did obtain 22 patents with others as co-inventors. He had seven joint patents with E. T. Gilliland, a friend from his telegrapher days, who subsequently was employed by him. In addition a number of Edison's employees got patents on their own. Charles Batchelor, Edison's right-hand man for many years, got several and they played a part in Batchelor becoming

277

independently wealthy. When Edison used a patent of an employee in his manufacturing operations, the patentee was paid a royalty.

Edison maintained the same policy in patent matters as he did in all phases of his research, development, and manufacturing. With the exception of directing the research effort, he hired experts to do the job. Beginning at Menlo Park, he always had a patent division. Frank Dyer was head of that division for years, and a very able one. Edison would rough out a patent application and then expect others to do the rest. The most skilled man in his drafting room would sketch the figures, which were part of nearly all of Edison's patents; the best mechanic in the shop would make the necessary models*; and Dyer, or one of his associates, would prepare the final application.

Edison's patents are noted for their conciseness and brevity, both as to specifications and claims. His patents were filed so promptly that he spent little time dating and signing records, and having them witnessed — all time consuming. The electric light patent application was filed within six weeks after the first successful experiment; his phonograph application, within nine days.

The most impressive feature of Edison's inventive career was that within less than two years he obtained two patents which no doubt rank in the 10 most important patents of all time. These are No. 200,521 of February 19, 1878 entitled "Phonograph or Speaking Machine", and No. 223,889 of January 27, 1880 entitled "An Electric Lamp for Giving Light by Incandescence". These and others illustrate that Edison's patent record is not only noted because of quantity, but also because of many outstanding inventions.

*This requirement was discontinued by the Patent Office in 1908.

278

In his early inventive career Edison worked nearly wholly on the telegraph. He made several inventions relating to automatic telegraphy, and his quadruplex for sending four messages over the same wire at the same time was his first famous invention. In 1875 his quadruplex became a matter of litigation between the two arch rivals, Western Union and the Atlantic and Pacific Telegraph Company. In this bitter court battle, the lawyers of Western Union described Edison as a rogue inventor doing business with Atlantic and Pacific when he was under contract to them. Gould's* lawyers described him as a simpleton, who had allowed Western Union to place one of their own men, G. B. Prescott, on Edison's basic quadruplex patent as a co-inventor and thus automatically gain control of 50% of the patent rights. In a few years the two companies merged, with Jay Gould gaining control and operating the monopoly under the name of the larger and older of the two companies, Western Union Telegraph Company. Gould dropped the development of automatic telegraphy and stopped payments to the stockholders of the Automatic Telegraph Company and to Edison for his work on that development. Thus, for his major contributions in the telegraph field, Edison received hardly enough to cover expenses, and, as he said later, he got "nothing for three years of hard work." Edison had received $30,000 as an initial payment on the quadruplex. Considering that the quadruplex saved Western Union $500,000 a year beginning in 1876, one can agree with Edison that he was grossly underpaid.

However, since Edison had no industry when he first began operations in Menlo Park, he had to accept what he could get from those who would buy his services and

*Then president of Atlantic and Pacific.

patents. After Bell's successful demonstration of the telephone at the Philadelphia Centennial in July 1876, Western Union had second thoughts on the telephone and engaged Edison to develop an improved system. He was glad, in spite of his previous ill experiences with Western Union, to receive this retainer of $500 per month.

Edison's important contribution to telephony was, of course, his carbon transmitter. The patent application covering this invention, filed April 27, 1877, was delayed 15 years before issuing. As it so happened, Emile Berliner, a self-taught German-Jewish immigrant, had filed a caveat on a transmitter of the "loose-contact" principle two weeks before Edison's application. The Bell people bought rights to the Berliner transmitter and instigated interference proceedings against the Edison application. The controversy dragged through the Patent Office to the courts. The Edison application finally prevailed, but it did not issue as a patent, No. 474,230, until 1892. This invention by that time was of no value to Edison or Western Union, since in the October 1879 agreement the American Bell Telephone Company received all patent rights on the telephone held by Western Union. There were 85 patents which changed hands as a result of this agreement, of which 41 had been obtained by Edison.

It was the carbon transmitter invention, and it alone, which gave Western Union enough bargaining power to get for 17 years a 20% share of all telephone rentals on the lines it had sold to the Bell Company. It was subsequently estimated that this royalty payment amounted to a total of 3.5 million dollars. In addition to his retainer fees, Edison received $100,000 from Western Union for his telephone inventions. However, since it was paid in 17 annual installations of $6,000 each, the payments amounted to the approximate interest on the principal.

Edison's contract with Western Union dealt only with the American rights of his telephone patents. His carbon-button transmitter was patented in England and his associate, Colonel George Gouraud, proved to be an able negotiator. A telephone company was formed there based on Edison's transmitter and chalk receiver patents. The English Edison and Bell groups subsequently merged and Edison was paid 30,000 pounds sterling for his patent rights in England. Thus he received about a quarter of a million dollars for his venture into telephony which no doubt helped to give him the great confidence which he portrayed in his plunge into incandescent lighting research.

In the fall of 1878 the Edison Electric Light Company was formed to support Edison's work on incandescent lighting. This was a noteworthy event in the annals of American industry. For the first time money was being invested in faith that a research organization would accomplish its objective, and patents on a product not then in existence would allow the stockholders to recover their money and at a profit. The organization might be called the first research and development company. By this time Edison had learned better how to deal with the money-people and his contract with these backers, which included J. P. Morgan, was a shrewd one. The Light Company originally had 3,000 shares valued at $100 per share. Edison received 2,500 shares for his agreeing to sign over all of his patents in the electric lighting field for a five-year period. The others agreed to pay for their 500 shares by advancing Edison $50,000 to help finance his experimental work. He received an initial payment of $30,000.

In order to handle the expanded research program, Edison built a separate building for his shop and one to house the business, patent, and library groups. Before success came his backers advanced another $30,000 and after the open house of December 31, 1879, an additional $57,500. As work towards the central station progressed, Edison and some of his associates financed the setting up of manufacturing facilities. Edison proved to be a tougher operator than his original backers anticipated and soon "Edison men" dominated the board of directors of the Light Company.

Once the new electric light was demonstrated, literally dozens of competitors entered the electric lighting field. Since the Edison companies had more business than they could handle, it was not until 1885 that the president of Edison Electric Light Company considered it necessary to warn infringers. Edison hoped that his head-start would serve to eliminate competitors. "A lawsuit is a suicide of time," he wrote in 1885. He no doubt remembered his trials in the witness chair during the quadruplex suit.

As described in Chapter 4, the Edison group finally brought legal action and chose their principal antagonist, George Westinghouse, for the test case. The suit against the Westinghouse Electrical and Manufacturing Company ran for seven years and was the most expensive patent litigation case up to that time. As Edison feared, he was cross-examined at length in the witness chair. The opposing lawyers attempted to show that he was ignorant of theoretical science. Asked if he understood Ohm's Law in 1878, he replied that he didn't try to figure out things mathematically but experimented instead. Asked why Upton didn't teach him, he said, "The mathematics always seem to come after experiments — not before."

Winning the suit against Westinghouse in July 1891 left the Edison interests in a very dominant position. The electric light patent had six years to run and many auxiliary patents longer. However, with businessmen in control of the Edison General Electric Company, the successor to the Edison Electric Light Company, consolidation looked more promising to them than competition. In April 1892 consolidation with the Thomson-Houston Company to form the General Electric Company became official.

The order of the day was monopoly. Edison opposed monopoly, having seen how it had stifled technical development in the telegraph industry. In a letter to Henry Villard, president of Edison General Electric, Edison made the following significant statement:

If you make the coalition my usefulness as an inventor is gone. My services wouldn't be worth a penny. I can only invent under powerful incentives. No competition means no invention. It's the same with the men I have around me. *It's not money they want but a chance for their ambition to grow.*

Shortly after the consolidation, Edison resigned as director of the new company and sold the stock he had in it.

When the Edison General Electric Company was formed in 1888, Edison realized about one and three-quarter millions in cash and stock. The original Morgan group which had backed Edison's work made an approximate 350% profit on their investment. Although most of Edison's patents dealing with electricity went into the General Electric set up, his electric light venture in less than 10 years had put him into the millionaire class.

Edison's experience with the phonograph was indeed a painful one. In his original patent, U.S. 200,521, the recording surface was claimed, " ... of yielding material — such as metallic foil ..." In the specification of the patent it is stated that over the grooved surface of the cylinder, " ... is placed a sheet of thick metallic foil, paper, or other yielding material."

283

On April 24, 1878 Edison filed an omnibus type of patent in England entitled, "Improvements in Means for Recording Sounds, and in Reproducing Such Sounds from Such Records." It was granted August 6, 1878 as British Patent 1,644. This verbose case, which included 67 figures, was obviously to anticipate others. Edison knew that he was going to be tied up with the electric light for years and wished to make broad enough disclosures that others could not patent rather obvious improvements. The disclosures included a disc, sheet, endless belt, cylinder, roller, or strip as the phonogram to support the medium to be indented. The surface to be indented was any metal foil, paper, paraffin-coated paper, or other hydrocarbons, waxes, gums, or lacs. A corresponding United States case never issued; the British case was cited against it as prior art. Edison's legal staff apparently made the mistake of filing in England first.

As mentioned in Chapter 2, shortly after Bell set up his Volta Laboratory in Washington, his staff, which included Chichester Bell and Charles Tainter, began working on sound recording and reproduction. The Bells and Tainter were granted five patents relating to the phonograph on May 4, 1886. The only one to become important in later patent litigations was 341,214. The inventors utilized a wax-coated cardboard cylinder for the recording surface. Their point of novelty as allowed by the Patent Office was that the recording stylus *incised* the wax surface rather than *indented* as in the case of a metallic foil. Because of physical differences of the two classes of materials, a recording stylus that would only indent tin foil would automatically cut a groove in a wax surface. This was certainly a matter of semantics and not science. Edison was astonished that the patent was allowed, but his lawyers made no strong effort to contest it in the courts.

Although Edison's phonographic business was probably his best source of income over the years, the whole industry was plagued for years with lawsuits and unscrupulous marketing and advertising practices. It is almost unbelievable that the Patent Office and the courts did not consider the original Edison patent as the one to dominate all speaking machines. This would have given Edison overall control of the industry until 1895, subject, of course, to improvement patents by himself and others. Instead, we find his patent restricted to the tin-foil concept and the inventor of one of the most original of all inventions in a secondary patent position during the 1890-1905 period, when this infant industry was being established and giant strides made.

Although Edison got numerous patents over the years relating to the phonograph, he never had a dominant position either patentwise or businesswise. His attitude towards competitors in this field appeared to be that he got patents primarily to allow his own operations. Read and Welch include the patent aspects of the phonograph in their book, *From Tin Foil to Stereo* (6).

Edison's primary invention which led to the motion picture was the camera, by which for the first time pictures could be taken rapidly enough that when reproduced in a continuous manner, apparent motion resulted. Although Edison had many firsts in motion pictures, from a patent standpoint this overall development was very unique for him; he obtained only two patents (7). The motion picture camera today is essentially as developed by Edison. In 1894 motion pictures were first shown to the public by means of his peep-hole kinetoscope (7). In April 1896, in partnership with Thomas Armadt, motion pictures were first shown on a wall screen to a theatre audience.

Edison's venture into motion pictures was also an

unusual one for him in that he realized more from royalties than from profits of his own operations. In the agreement of December 1908 which brought peace to the motion picture industry, Edison was to realize profits up to a million dollars a year in royalties and from his film productions — mostly the former. This patent trust was dissolved in 1917. By this time Edison had largely abdicated the field.

Edison patented several outstanding inventions dealing with his alkaline storage battery, but he could have done as well if he had just kept them as trade secrets. There was no competition during his lifetime or since. The same can be said of his patents relating to his iron ore concentration operations. In this case some of his patents have been used by others later, but not until they had long expired. His patents on cement manufacture allowed him freedom of operations, which became a fairly profitable business. He did reap some royalty from his long-kiln patent, his major contribution of a patentable nature to the cement industry.

Edison took out several foreign patents but only a low percentage of those filed domestically were filed abroad. He handled his foreign operations by means of trusted employees and did not get personally involved as did Goodyear and Acheson. However, some of the actions of foreign patent offices irked him (8):

> I lost the German patent on the carbon telephone through the insertion of a comma which entirely changed the interpretation of the patent. Another foreign patent was lost because the patent office in that country discovered that something similar had been used in Egypt 2000 B.C. — not the exact device, but something which was nearly enough like it, they claimed, to defeat my patent.

Edison had kind words for the United States Patent Office but none for the courts in their handling of patent cases (9):

Some inventors complain of our Patent Office, but my own experience with the Patent Office is that the examiners are fair-minded and intelligent, and when they refuse a patent they are generally right; but I think the whole trouble lies with the system in vogue in the Federal courts for trying patent suits, and in the fact, which cannot be disputed, that the Federal judges, with but few exceptions, do not comprehend complicated scientific questions.

Edison commented further on the courts in *The Literary Digest* article cited above (8):

There is no justice in law. It has resolved itself into technicalities and formulas. A case will be thrown out of one court and carried to another, it will be sent back on writs and advanced on argument, and bandied back and forth more for the exercise of legal practise than for the attainment of justice. Where an important case might be settled in a short time by the use of common sense, it is prolonged for years through the technicality of jurisprudence, the whole course of which defeats the object sought.

In 1930 *The Saturday Evening Post* published an interview with Edison entitled, "Patents, Profits and Pirates". The following is a sample of the various quotations from Edison in this lengthy article (10):

287

I have made very little profit from my inventions in my lifetime. I have taken out 1180 patents*, up to date. Counting the expense of experimentation and fighting for my claims in court, these patents have cost me more than they have returned to me in royalties. I have made money through the introduction and sale of my products as a manufacturer, not as an inventor.

I would not care to go further into this aspect of the matter, for many obvious reasons. But what I have just said is the plain, unvarnished truth. I am not saying it in the humor of complaint. I am far enough along now to make money from manufacturing, but I am speaking for the young fellows just starting out. We have a miserable system in the United States for protecting inventions from infringement. I have known of several inventors who were poor. Their ideas would have made them millionaires, but they were kept poor by the pirates who were allowed through our very faulty system of protection to usurp their rights. The usurpation is particularly apt to obtain in the case of some great epoch-making patent. I deny that I have ever enjoyed a monopoly upon anything that I have ever invented, with this single modification: The producers of motion pictures did pay me royalties until my patents expired. But even in that case I had to fight for a long time in court over my claims.

The pirates can readily get all the money they require — millions, if needed — to carry on their contests. The first step is to hire a sharp lawyer —

*Edison no doubt included his foreign patents in this figure.

one who can make any judge unfamiliar with technology believe that black is white. They set up the claim that they and not the inventor, should be recognized as the originator of certain ideas. They boldly strut into court and enjoin the inventor from manufacturing anything from his own creations and formulas, even though the inventor may hold in his hands a patent issued by the United States Government. In previous years these pirates were thus enabled to hold the rightful inventor back by persisting in litigation sometimes for ten, twelve and fourteen years. Meanwhile, the courts would not infrequently permit the pirates, 'for the good of mankind', to proceed with the manufacture of the same device, pending litigation; so there was, in reality, no such thing as an inventor's monopoly. True enough, a patent is supposed to carry the Government's protection for seventeen years, and I suppose the man in the street, or the man between plow handles, fancies that the inventor's life during these seventeen years of grace is down a primrose path to a pot of gold at the foot of the rainbow.

In the above comments from the *Post*, Edison was likely referring primarily to his experiences relative to his invention of the phonograph. Following a series of lawsuits dealing with patents and business transactions, in February 1896 the court ordered that Edison be prohibited from selling phonographs in the United States for three years. Admittedly this decree along with his other patent and business experiences dealing with the phonograph up to that time were abominable; however, it is a little too much to expect that royalties from patents pay the development costs of a manufacturer's new products. Early in his career

Edison invented with the intent of selling his inventions. When he became a manufacturer, he invented primarily to make possible the introduction of new products. Research and development expenses should then have been considered as operating costs.

George Westinghouse

Although we have little direct information as to methods which George Westinghouse used in inventing, they must have been highly effective. In spite of being a very busy businessman, he found time to get 361 United States patents and to pioneer several major developments. He had the ability to scent a fertile field for technical exploration and then move in, often by the purchase of existing patents held by others. As he proceeded to plow these virgin fields, patents became more or less a by-product. Since Westinghouse kept substantially no records of his work leading to inventions, he must have patented very shortly after each invention was made.

Westinghouse's air brake was his most original invention. He obtained 20 patents on it in the four-year period of 1869-73 at the age of 23-27 years. At that time he had no legal staff in his Air Brake Company so used outside attorneys. Often when he first came to work in the morning he would spend a few hours in the drafting room. Once his drawing was completed it would be turned over to a favorite workman in the shop to make the desired parts for testing. It is likely that he worked out in a preliminary manner many of his ideas in his study at home.

Westinghouse was only one of many in the Pittsburgh area to witness the waste of natural gas as the search for petroleum went forward. However, it was he who conceived that with the proper technology this liability could be converted into an asset. He obtained 38 patents dealing with transporting natural gas through pipes to customers and measuring the quantity used by. each. Unlike manufactured gas, which had been in use for some time in large cities, natural gas was obtained under high pressures and at relatively long distances from customers. Westinghouse obtained patents on the drilling for gas as well as for its distribution and use.

Westinghouse, more than anyone else, recognized the transformer as a means of making possible electricity to be produced at huge, efficient generating plants and then distributed to customers up to hundreds of miles away. The early patents held by others gave him the idea — not basic experimental work of his own. Once he began working on alternating current, patents came easily in such a virgin field. The same was true for the steam turbine, which led in turn to his work on reducing gears so that the turbine could be used for driving ship propellers.

Westinghouse's most productive decade in patents was from 1880-90, when he obtained 125. His electrical company had gotten underway in 1886, he began his natural gas project two years earlier, and this was the period when he was perfecting his quick-action automatic brake for freight cars. Few have been capable of handling so many major projects on a concurrent basis.

In his patent litigations Westinghouse was able to leave most of the unpleasant legal chores to others. However, he was highly aggressive in such matters. Following an early favorable decision as the defendent in the lawsuit over the incandescent light brought against him by the Edison Electric Light Company, Westinghouse instituted a suit against the Edison Company for infringement of the Sawyer-Man lamp patent, which he controlled! It was his defeat as plaintiff in this suit which made way for Edison's final legal victory in 1891. However as pointed out in

Chapter 4, Westinghouse did not compromise his electric light business, but instead developed a non-infringing "stoppered" electric light.

Westinghouse's fabulous patent career extended over a 48-year period. He got his first patent when he was only 19 years of age. He was also introduced to the trials of patent litigation at an early age. Although no railroad man had ever heard of air being used to set brakes when Westinghouse broached the subject to them, competitors turned up a 30-year-old British patent in which air had been disclosed as a means of applying brakes on rail cars. There had been no reduction to practice. Nevertheless this reference forced Westinghouse to bring suit against certain competitors in order to establish the validity of his air brake patents. It was apparently this episode which brought forth the remarks from Westinghouse about patents which have often been quoted. These were that every successful invention passes through three stages:

First, such a thing is absurd or impossible.

Second, the thing is not new.

Third, there is no invention at all.

Edward Acheson

Acheson obtained a total of 70 United States patents. Success came when he began utilizing the high temperatures of the electric furnace to accomplish chemical conversions which were impossible in fuel-fired furnaces. His synthesis of silicon carbide, Carborundum, was the first of the artificial abrasives. Acheson improved the design of the electric furnace resulting in higher temperatures which made possible his invention and development of artificial graphite.

Acheson was a dogged experimenter and determined to become an inventor. He gave up promising salaried positions to work under wretched conditions in attempts to invent on his own. His two major inventions, silicon carbide and graphite, came from keen observations of unusual results followed by experiments designed to prove what actually did happen. One of the favorite pastimes of writers of science for the public is to describe great discoveries or inventions by serendipity; *i.e.*, stumbling on to things one is not looking for. It all started, of course, with Horace Walpole in allusion to a tale, "The Three Princes of Serendip", written in 1754. Goodyear's invention of vulcanization has been called by some an act of serendipity. This would appear to be stretching the definiton too far; Goodyear certainly had been trying to cure rubber for years before he heated a piece of rubber containing sulfur hotter than he had intended. In contrast, Acheson was attempting to prepare diamonds by dissolving carbon in molten clay and hopefully to precipitate it from solution in crystalline form. Although this didn't happen, his keen eyes detected traces of crystals which proved to be silicon carbide. One would hardly call this an accident but it was invention by serendipity; he got a valuable product but not the one he was seeking.

Acheson's great success with his inventions was because he not only manufactured his new products but also determined uses for these products and patented any novel features in use patents. Probably because of this policy he had little patent litigation in the United States. The suit brought by the Cowles brothers was favorable to Acheson on the first court action and the verdict was not appealed.

Acheson's patent problems were primarily in foreign countries. Here he hoped to get considerable royalty income since these patents belonged to him personally and not to The Carborundum Company. He did not file his graphite patents in Europe, which was probably just as well since they were weak*. He did file abroad on the preparation and use of graphite dispersions.

Since several of the countries required a patented product to be prepared within that country by two years after patenting, his patents in the industrial countries of Europe made necessary several trips to that continent. In 1894 he made a hasty trip to France to prepare a few pounds of Carborundum in a crude electric furnace at the Edison lamp works at Ivry-sur-Seine. On the same trip he had preliminary negotiations in Germany and Austria. He returned to Germany in 1897 to manufacture some Carborundum in order to avoid annulment of his German patent and hopefully to license it. Acheson was a tough negotiator and his German counterparts labelled him "the American Bismarck". A possible agreement with Walter Rathenau fell through when this German boasted that Edison never got anything out of his patents in Germany and indicated that the same thing might happen to Acheson. It ended by Acheson establishing a small plant in Deuben, Germany with Jim Hipple, an employee of his American plant, in charge.

While in Germany on this trip a letter from Weissberger of Austria ended with the following (11):

. . .I can only give you the advice to act fairly because my directors have a grudge against you on account of the Russian patent, and will, of course, endeavor to retaliate using (every) all means in their power.

This is a serious matter. You better think twice before doing anything that might not suit our interests. We would — I know — prefer peace. If

*See Chapter 5.

you want war, you will get it with a vengeance.

Let me hear from you very soon!

While on the 1897 trip Acheson did not go to Vienna in fear of being arrested in connection with the misunderstanding about the sale of his Russian patent. Although he made some money from his European patents and operations, it appeared hardly worth his trials there.

Although Acheson utilized the electric furnace in developing several products, it is somewhat surprising that he did not attempt to prepare other carbides after his synthesis of silicon carbide in 1891. Calcium carbide was synthesized in an electric furnace one year later by T. L. Willson while attempting to prepare metallic calcium by heating lime and pine tar using surplus hydroelectric power at a cotton mill operated by J. Turner Morehead at Spray, North Carolina, It was soon found that contact of this product with water gave off an ill-smelling gas. William R. Kenan, Jr., of nearby University of North Carolina, identified the gas as acetylene. Industrial production of calcium carbide began in 1895.

Alfred Nobel

Although Nobel obtained certain patents prior to those dealing with explosives, only the latter were commercially important. These were not only important but highly original in nature. His inventions appear to have resulted from critical needs in his father's or his own business which arose. Once such a need was satisfied, he tended largely to business matters until the next one. As an internationalist he was in competition with explosive scientists and engineers worldwide, which included those of the Du Pont Company in the United States, the world's largest manufacturer of black powder. Whereas he had a monopoly in most countries, the free-wheeling Americans gave him plenty of competition.

Nobel's blasting oil reached the United States in July 1865 in the luggage of Colonel Burstenbinder, who had offered to promote its manufacture and sale in America. Nobel's first U.S. patent issued in October of that year*. In the fall of 1865 a Nobel & Company sales office was set up in California and shipments of nitroglycerin began from the factory in Krümmel, Germany. On hearing of the successful use of the oil as an industrial explosive, Preston Shaffner, a soldier of fortune who had seen a sample of nitroglycerin in the Nobel foundry in Russia, whipped up a patent application for interference with Nobel's pending application. Testimony obtained from Nobel and others in January 1866 resulted in Shaffners's case being rejected.

In early 1866 Nobel became concerned about Burstenbinder's grandiose idea of a million-dollar stock company and came to New York. He arrived to find the country in an uproar over the explosions attributed to the new "glonoin oil", as the early nitroglycerin was called. Nobel still had a sublime faith that nitroglycerin was safe if properly handled. Furthermore, the ship explosion in a Panama port was attributed by some to gunpowder being shipped to South American revolutionaries, rather than the glonoin oil aboard. Nobel put on a demonstration in a quarry near New York showing its apparent safety and when exploded by a detonator, its terrific shattering power.

In the end the effectiveness of the liquid explosive outweighed the fear of it. The west coast agency continued to market the product for use in mining. Burstenbinder's promotion resulted in the formation of the United States Blasting Oil Company, capitalized with 10,000 shares of

*See Reference 1 of Chapter 6.

stock. For his two patents, Nobel received $10,000 in cash and 2,500 shares of the stock. The plant manager from Krümmel came to America to supervise the building of a plant at Little Ferry, New Jersey. The project went poorly. Burstenbinder was primarily a promoter and he was being sued for damages from the explosion at the Wells Fargo warehouse earlier in the year. Others began manufacturing the oil ignoring Nobel's patents*. It was publicized that Sebrero and not Nobel was the first to prepare and explode nitroglycerin, and Nobel's detonator was considered of no moment since black powder, an old explosive, could be used for the purpose.

Thus Nobel's invention of dynamite not only alleviated the hazards of handling liquid nitroglycerin but served to improve a deteriorating patent situation in the United States as well. Due to what Nobel considered dishonest business practices, he ignored the United States Blasting Oil Company**and set up the Giant Powder Company near San Francisco to manufacture and sell dynamite. His dynamite patent*** was assigned only to the latter company. This well-managed company soon had a thriving business. Dynamite was hailed in America as the greatest boon to progress since the invention of the printing press. Dynamite at $1.75 per pound was considered cheaper for blasting in underground mines than black powder at 20 cents.

The California Powder Company at Santa Cruz, the large west coast supplier of black powder, soon felt the

---

*See Reference 1, Chapter 6.

**The primary asset of this company became its rights to Nobel's detonator patent. The company went into receivership following a serious explosion at its Little Ferry plant in 1870.

***See Reference 2, Chapter 6.

competition. This company proceeded to develop so-called "active-dope dynamites". Their Black Hercules was nitroglycerin adsorbed on black powder and their White Hercules, a mixture of 75% nitroglycerin with sugar, magnesium carbonate, and potassium nitrate. Although Nobel had not restricted his patent to the use of inert adsorbents such as kieselguhr, he had not pointed out the advantage of solids which would add to, rather than dilute, the effectiveness of nitroglycerin. Nobel refused to support Giant Powder in a court action against the active-dope manufacturers since, as sole patentee of his dynamite patent, he would be required to swear that he alone made such active-base dynamites. He would not deny the part that his father and his brother Emil had in the early development work on black powder-nitroglycerin mixtures.

As his detonator had provided an effective way for exploding nitroglycerin, and dynamite had made possible the safe handling of the liquid explosive, Nobel now proceeded to put the profligators of his dynamite invention at rest. He did it with his invention of blasting gelatin; nitroglycerin, a low molecular weight liquid, was thickened by dissolving therein 7 to 8% of low-nitrogen nitrocellulose, a polymeric solid. The rigid gel could be used as such or used in dynamite form. The nitroglycerin-nitrocellulose blend was not only more effective than any of the active-base dynamites, but had the advantage that it was highly waterproof.

By the time Nobel's U.S. patent on his gelatin explosive had been issued*, the trend towards consolidation in the explosives industry was underway. In 1870 the du Ponts, who formerly had ridiculed the use of nitroglycerin in any form, bought California Powder and soon they were making

---

*U.S. Patent 175,735 (April 4, 1876).

Atlas dynamite in Delaware, using wood pulp as base. Nobel's affiliate, the Giant Powder Company, had built plants in the eastern part of the country as a separate company, the Atlantic Giant Powder Company. Lammot du Pont considered Nobel's gelatin patent so valuable that in order to license it he agreed to pay the Giant Powder Company 45% of the combined profits on dynamites of all types sold by the Du Pont companies! This must have been a sweet victory indeed for Nobel.

Lammot du Pont and several other high Du Pont officials were killed in an accident in 1884 due to a nitroglycerin explosion in an experimental unit. The Atlantic Giant Powder Company, after a prosperous history, came under the control of the du Ponts by their purchase of stock. By 1895 the country's high explosives industry was largely under the control of the Du Pont Company. It remained so until 1912 when, as the result of action brought by the Justice Department, the so-called powder trust was broken up with the formation of the two new independent companies, the Hercules Powder Company and the Atlas Powder Company.

Although his American operations were a good source of income for many years, Nobel did not cross the Atlantic after 1866. He remained a silent stockholder in the two Giant Companies until 1885, but never exchanged as much as a letter with them. His opinion of American businessmen was not high.

Nobel's invention of an explosive for weaponry, his three-component ballistite, was the first of the successful "smokeless powders". For a high explosive it was unique in that instead of exploding instantly, it decomposed or "burned" in a uniform manner with great rapidity. Thus, it was excellent as a propellant where a shattering type explosive is not desired. Early in his work on ballistite,

Nobel began giving full details to Frederick Abel and Professor Dewar, who were members of a British Government commission to investigate new explosives for military use. Unknown to Nobel, the two filed a patent of their own using Nobel's formulation, but modified in that a nitrocellulose of higher nitrogen content was used. They called their product cordite.

Nobel brought court action in an attempt to annul the cordite patent since the patentees had obtained confidential information from him. Although Nobel lost, the judge added the following satirical comment in his verdict: "It is quite natural that a dwarf on the shoulders of a giant should see further than the giant." Obviously, Nobel was the giant. Nobel considered that his English confidentians had double-crossed him. He commented, "You refer to numerous friends. Where are they? They are stuck fast in the morass of lost illusions, or in the bags of money making."

In 1895 Nobel wrote "The Patent Bacillus", a satirical comedy based on his unfortunate patent experiences in England. This was never published due to his death shortly after. As a whole Nobel had little patent litigation and he swept all before him. One reason for this was that his patents introduced radically new products and he manufactured them worldwide. However, Nobel tended to be an intolerant man, and his problems in the United States and the late one in England left him bitter towards those involved. His ballistite litigation made him so antagonistic towards lawyers that he never used their services again.

It is impossible to say how many patents Nobel obtained since he filed differently in one country than in another. His patents as a whole were poorly written, often requiring re-issues and continuations-in-part to plug loopholes and broaden claims. One can conclude that for such an

300

important inventor, he obtained relatively few patents within a given country. A reason for this was that his major patents were so basic that he did not need supplementary patents to serve as a "second line of defense". In the 19th century, the explosives field did not attract learned inventors to the degree that those of electricity and mechanics did.

Nobel appears to have had no grandiose ambitions to become a world-renowed inventor. Until late in life, he invented as his business conditions required it, and it was a matter of need followed by hard thinking and experimentation. He never commented on any theories which he had as to how certain explosives behaved. G. E. Johannsson, a medical student who had worked with Nobel in Paris for a time, later recalled that Nobel had often "indicated that he thought medical theory might be a hindrance, and that a person who was free from it would more readily get at the root of a problem. . ." (12).

Starting in 1894 Nobel undertook in his "retirement" a broader research program. It was too late; the desire was there but not the strength. More inventions were unnecessary to qualify him as one of the world's great inventors. In an age and on a continent where only those of aristocratic background could hope to become distinguished, Nobel of humble background not only became one of the most wealthy, but his reign as the "Dynamite King" made him one of the most famous persons in Europe.

All six subject inventors extensively used the United States Patent Office. None appears to have embarked on any new subject without getting all the patent protection he could. Most took an active part in the preparation of their patent applications, particularly early in their careers. None strove for patents *per se* but rather in achieving a specific objective, the getting of patents was a part of a successful research and development program.

All followed up a basic patent with supplementary ones if they felt it necessary. Westinghouse got a series of patents on his air brake since he found that he was not the first to suggest compressed air for setting train brakes. Others had used both carbon and an evacuated receptacle in electric lighting so Edison not only patented his improved light bulb but many features of the production, transportation, and utilization of electricity. On the other hand, if their patent position was basic they wasted no time on trivial patents; Bell had only two patents on the telephone, Edison two on the motion picture, and Nobel only one on blasting gelatin.

However, our six did not always set up their patent structures properly. This usually happened when a given patent was not a part of the primary objective being pursued. Edison's invention of the phonograph was a by-product of his work on the telephone and telegraph. At that time he was committed to work on the telephone and shortly on the incandescent light. Both of these projects were providing him with income, and at that time Edison often had problems in meeting his payroll on schedule. The phonograph offered no immediate income other than as a gadget to show the public. It was neglected with dire results. Similarly when Nobel invented dynamite he was desperately seeking a form of nitroglycerin which could be marketed and used safely. A type of dynamite which was slightly more effective than his guhr type appeared of no moment at the time, especially if it meant some sacrifice in safety. At it turned out, his guhr dynamite had safety to

302

spare and soon competitors were marketing active-base dynamites, which were not covered by Nobel's patents, even though they were known to him before filing his patent.

If one wishes to pick a 10-year age period when our inventors were most creative, it is the approximate 25-35 age bracket. It should be recognized that during this age period our inventors were all striving to make their mark and as they became successful inventors, they spent a higher percentage of their time with business matters. It is safe to say that our six never lost their inventive traits as they became older but as physical deterioration took its toll with age, each became less productive.

The patent experiences of our inventors illustrate the desirability of utilizing a continuing staff of good lawyers. Bell's patent applications were handled by a private Washington, D. C. law firm, closely associated with Gardiner Hubbard. If Edison had had to spend as much time in the filing of each of his patents as does the typical present-day inventor, he would have had time for little else. A competent and experienced internal law-technical group took care of everything once the invention had been made and recorded. On the other hand, Goodyear's and Nobel's patent applications were often prepared in a helter-skelter fashion and they suffered because of it.

All six patented abroad, but the pitfalls of foreign filing took their toll. Nobel had no problems in his native Sweden but did in the United States and Britain. Goodyear lost out in England because he sent samples of vulcanized rubber there and also was slow to patent. In France he lost his basic patent coverage because the patented process was not used there within the specified time. Bell gave Sir William Thomson duplicates of his membrane transmitter and iron-box receiver which he had demonstrated at the

303

Philadelphia Centennial. Later in 1876 Thomson published an article in a British journal, which not only described Bell's telephone but showed a sketch of the instruments. This early introduction of the telephone into Britain threatened to bar Bell's subsequent patent application, until it was proved by the sketch of the receiver that it had been damaged in transit! Edison lost out on his phonograph in the States because of the timing of filing a British application. Thus red tape, and not inventorship, decided many crucial decisions.

A successful invention usually brought infringement. It was relatively easy in case of the telephone, the electric light, or the sulfur vulcanization process to set up competitive operations if one chose to ignore patents, since it took little investment to do so. Where an electric furnace or a large crushing mill or kiln was required, infringement was less likely. Patent lawsuits were more bitterly fought in the 19th century than at present. An individual is obviously more emotional than a corporation. Edison would likely have never admitted by court action that he was not the inventor of the incandescent light even if it had meant financial ruin. As history shows Westinghouse did not give in either but proceeded to manufacture and use an inferior light bulb at great cost rather than be humiliated by licensing the Edison light.

It should not be concluded that all patents are justified nor that a patent cannot be a deterrent to the country. One of the most famous patent suits of all time was that dealing with George B. Selden's U.S. Patent 549,160 covering every type of "road-locomotive" in existence. Selden was a patent lawyer located in Rochester, New York. His patent was a "paper invention" and he never built an automobile. In 1879 Selden filed for a patent covering a composite of all the known parts of a road vehicle including an engine, a power shaft, a steering mechanism, a clutch, axles and wheels, a device for varying speed, a braking mechanism, a receptacle for fuel, and a body for passengers. Selden nursed the application along in the Patent Office and it did not issue until November 1895 at which time the auto was showing signs of becoming commercial. A group of New York financiers gained control of the patent, formed the Association of Licensed Automobile Manufacturers, and attempted to prohibit all non-members from manufacturing automobiles. Over 90% of the industry signed up, each paying approximately one percent of its gross sales to the association.

Henry Ford was one of the few who refused to sign. He was sued by the Selden backers and the suit dragged on for eight years. The association attempted to destroy Ford's business by advertising that all who bought his cars were liable to prosecution for infringement. Evidence was taken from all pertinent witnesses for presentation to the judge. The exhibits and briefs amounted to more than 14,000 pages and five million words. Ford's lawyers relied primarily on the prior art. The case came before Judge Hough who was unversed in patent law and admitted that he didn't know what a "gas-engine" was. After studying the deposits for several months, his verdict in September 1909 held the Selden patent valid although admitting that, "Selden has contributed little to motor car advancement in the United States, and nothing at all abroad."

Ford vowed to go to the Supreme Court if necessary and appealed the case to the circuit court. However, most of the independents besides Ford now signed up with the association. Fortunately Ford's Model-T was now a commercial success so he had the money to carry on alone. The size of the suit is exemplified by the fact that on the first day of the appeal proceedings, 40 attorneys gathered in the old Post Office Building in New York to present their written briefs and oral arguments. This time there were three judges on the panel of which one, Walter Noyes, was a recognized authority on patent law. This court ruled that Selden held a restricted patent covering a vehicle with a modified Brayton engine, the predecessor to the Otto type used by Ford and others. Thus on January 9, 1911, Ford won a decision which released all auto manufactures from a patent which had never been reduced to practice and whose inventor had contributed nothing to that new industry. The inventor of this restricted patent had already been paid $1,600,000 in royalties and the amount paid into the Association of Licensed Automobile Manufacturers had approached six million (13).

Selden's patent is an excellent example that a "paper patent" is likely, if the subject of an important product or process, to become involved in litigation, and very likely the opposition will win if sufficiently resolute. Although Bell's famous telephone patent, U.S. 174,465, was largely based on a new scientific principle, he continued to experiment and soon reduced his theory of undulatory electric current to practice. This and subsequent work led to his U.S. Patent 186,787, which was largely of the hardware type. Selden, who was no mechanic, chose to sit back and attempt to profit from his mental concepts rather than participating in the physical development of his "invention."

In more recent times the legal battle over the granting of United States Patent 2,964,083 of December 13, 1960 to the General Tire and Rubber Company approached the Selden case in costs and potential financial burden to an industry. An extended suit in the circuit court resulted in forcing the Patent Office to grant a patent which had been on file for over 10 years, having been turned down by a

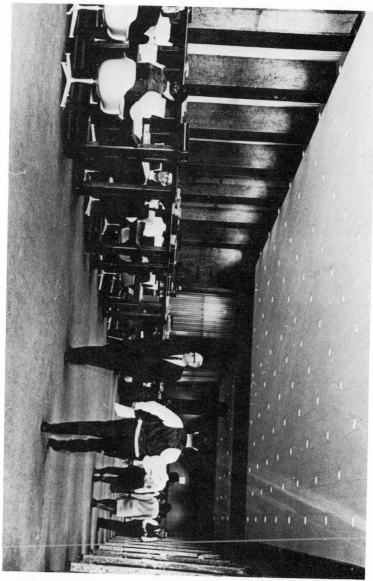

Courtesy of Patent Office, U.S. Department of Commerce, Washington, D.C.

Public Search Room of the Patent Office at its present quarters, Arlington, Virginia

Reproduced from the October 1964 issue of *Rubber World*; permission granted by
Bill Brothers Publications

This cartoon shows in an exaggerated humorous manner the trials and pitfalls
of the optimistic young inventor.

patent Examiner and the Board of Appeals of the Patent Office. This application for patent dealt with the use of a high proportion of a mineral oil as a softener-extender in a tire compound containing a tough grade of styrene-butadiene rubber (SBR). Use of oils in such rubber compounds was old. However, the court was convinced that General Tire had used more oil than anyone previously and that the results were unexpected. An article published by *Rubber World* on this patent suit included the humorous cartoon shown here (14).

The rest of the rubber industry was flabbergasted at the issuance of this patent and united in a common front in refusal to pay royalty. General Tire has apparently made no serious effort to enforce its controversial patent.

Although most inventors have been unhappy with certain aspects of the United States patent laws, there is general agreement that a patent system is necessary and that of the United States is likely the best. Like any organization, it needs to be modified and modernized as defects become apparent. In the Patent Modernization and Reform Act of 1973 being considered by Congress, it is proposed to publish each patent application before granting so that any member of the public may challenge it before issuance. This should help to avoid costly and lengthy court battles. Another proposal is to make the life of a patent 20 years from date of filing rather than 17 years from date of issue.

Unfortunately the battles in Congress dealing with changes in our patent laws appear to be between politicians, who worry about "patent monopoly" and so-called "public interest", and patent lawyers, who do not necessarily represent the viewpoint of inventors. Changes which the inventor would like to see include means of decreasing paperwork and red tape in obtaining patents, patent litigations to be handled by tribunals composed of technically trained as well as legally trained members, and that an infringer of a patent be required to pay all court costs if judgment is against him. The inventor would also like to see the patenting process simplified so that legal costs would not be such a burden on new product development. For example, the Polaroid Corporation, a relatively small company, had 25 patent attorneys in 1972 (15).

All of our inventors dreaded the witness chair. This was certainly a factor in certain decisions in Bell's and Edison's careers. In reading some of the testimony in the telephone litigations, where Bell had to answer the same questions time after time, one is appalled at the amount of time a great scientist had to spend with such trivia.

The basic principle of all patents is that the inventor, in return for his short-term monopoly, discloses his invention so that others can use the information in further research and development and thus benefit mankind. This principle is certainly sound. It is hoped that those who modify our patent system from time to time do not overlook that the short-term monopoly is essential. If an inventor and his sponsor do not stand a reasonable chance of recovering their development costs, they will not commercialize an invention. Otherwise companies will find it advantageous to be second rather than first in a new industry; *i.e.*, hopefully to let their competitor have the high costs, headaches, and perhaps failure of commercializing a new product.

Chapter 9

Invention: Past, Present, Future

How do our conclusions on inventing, based on the experiences of the six great inventors who worked primarily in the 19th century, compare with what is being said, written, and done about inventing in more recent times?

Let us first consider what is coming from the applied psychologists. Surprisingly they have become the spokesmen for the methodology of inventing rather than the inventors themselves. Perhaps this is inevitable. The typical scientist or engineer engaged in research and development is so busy and so interested in what he is doing, he is little interested in the science of his behavior or even the history of his profession. In this respect he has abdicated largely to the status of a guinea pig for the psychologists but on the whole is an uncooperative one. He hates to fill out questionnaires and he shows little interest in psychologists who volunteer to teach him how to be more creative.

Webster defines psychology as the science of the mind. A psychologist has told me that the science of the individual might be a better definition. Psychology began as a part of philosophy and did not become a separate science until about the turn of the century. Thus it developed after our subject inventors had done most of their work; it was such a young science that it is doubtful if any of the six knew much about it.

The work of psychologists as related to invention has largely been a part of their broad interest in creativity. Starting in August 1955 a series of biannual conferences were sponsored by the University of Utah on "The Identification of Creative Scientific Talent" (1), a topic certainly related to invention. Some of the conclusions which came from these conferences on this and closely related subjects include the following:

(a) Everyone has some creative potential, but in this respect people vary greatly.

(b) Creative people have broad interests at an early age.

(c) A straight-A record may not be a good criterion for creative abilities.

(d) The creative person is basically an introvert whereas society glorifies the extrovert.

(e) Speeding up the educational process is desired so that potential inventors have a chance to begin inventing at an earlier age.

(f) Serendipity is a factor in invention. The longer a person works in a given field, the less probable he will come up with a creative idea.

(g) Ingenuity is different from reasoning or memory. Possibly it can be tested by problem solving.

(h) Literally dozens of tests have been designed to predict creative traits. However most psychologists contend that creativity is so nebulous that it is impossible to predict or even to evaluate it.

The above cited conclusions are not in conflict with those which I have made based on the careers of our six master inventors. However, some writings of psychologists dealing with scientific creativity, and particularly those dealing with creativity generally, are not in accordance with the history of invention. Some of these questionable statements are as follows:

310

(a) One author feels that creativity and neurotic processes are intertwined. He cites that Beethoven had a lifelong inner struggle of love, hate, suspicion, jealousy, and rage.

(b) Creativity may be the way a schizoid personality expresses himself.

(c) Much is made of the subconscious mind as originally postulated by Freud. A preconscious mind has also been postulated which serves to bring ideas and answers from the subconscious to the active mind; after a long period of toil the subconscious mind comes up with a sudden revelation.

(d) Drugs have been tested as a means of improving the creativity of an individual.

(e) Dreams have been cited as a source of scientific discoveries. The favorite example is that of Kekulé's concept of the benzene ring. Kekulé, an organic chemist, discovered that carbon has a valence of four and this effectively explained the structures of many organic compounds with carbon atoms attached in a linear manner. However, there was one class of compounds, now known as the aromatics, which did not fit into his noncyclic pattern. The story goes that one night as Kekulé sat sleeping in front of his fireplace, in a dream "dancing serpents seized their tails in their mouths". This supposedly revealed to him the ring structure of benzene and allied compounds! Kekulé was an architect by early training and it is not surprising that he thought of numerous configurations for organic compounds including the closed ring type. The important thing was that a six-member ring structure for benzene fitted all the facts of its chemical behavior. Compared to a simple statement of chemical behavior, the dream story no doubt brought more attention to Kekulé's theories of molecular structure. At that time there was considerable rivalry between Kekulé and the Scottish chemist, A. S. Couper, as to their respective theories of the molecular structures of organic compounds.

(f) In discussing genius, many carry the definition to an extreme. Some psychologists consider a genius as different from the average man as the latter is different from an ape. Some consider genius biologically linked with insanity. A genius is born and not made; he may result from psychological mutation.

None of these exotic ideas appears to have had any bearing on how our subject inventors created new things. However, before commenting on them further let us consider certain other publications dealing more specifically with invention and some of the more recent outstanding inventors.

Joseph Rossman obtained a bachelor degree in chemical engineering from the University of Pennsylvania in 1922 and shortly thereafter became an Examiner at the Patent Office. By night school he earned a L.L.B. degree and a Ph.D. in patent law. He subsequently worked for a time in industry and then in private patent law practice. He was active in a number of scientific and professional societies. Rossman published a series of articles in the *Journal of the Patent Office Society* on inventors and invention. Later much of the information from these articles as well as from others was published as a book entitled, *Industrial Creativity* (2).

In his book Rossman utilized information from questionnaires directed to inventors, patent attorneys, and research directors. He supplemented these data with comments based on his background as a chemical engineer and as an experienced Patent Examiner, plus information from an extensive bibliography. Although the first edition of his book was published in 1931, he brought the 1963 edition up to date by means of a 13-page introduction.

Rossman's criterion for an inventor is that he has obtained numerous United States patents. The 710 patentees from whom he received replies had an average of 39.3 patents. On the surface this is impressive, but when one considers that the majority of patents are worth little or nothing, patents based on number alone are no quantitative measure of an inventor. However, it is probably the best measuring stick available when making a survey of literally hundreds of inventors. Not unexpectedly its use resulted in an array of different philosophies as to how to invent.

Although Rossman's book should be read by everyone interested in invention, it may be overwhelming to the beginner. In the chapter dealing with characteristics of the inventor, Rossman states: "To accomplish what he desires the inventor must have originality, vision, perseverance, and logic... But in additon he must be ingenious, versatile, and resourceful." This may be the ideal inventor, but it is unlikely that most inventors meet all these criteria.

The comments of 78 directors of research relative to the frequency of characteristics of successful inventors are likely the most accurate information reported by Rossman. Some inventors may not be able to see "the forest for the trees". Although obviously restricted to inventors in companies, the observations by research directors are no doubt based on hundreds of inventors and those who have made the most important inventions in their respective laboratories.

The frequency of mental characteristics of effective research workers and inventors as reported by the research directors were:

		% of Total*
Analysis	48 }	44
Perseverance	41 }	
Originality	37 }	36
Imagination	35 }	
Training and Education	20 }	20
Reasoning and Intelligence	20 }	

The last two characteristics, which represent education, experience, and traits which can be measured by intelligence and I.Q. tests, are the only impersonal evaluations an employer can use in hiring. Yet they represent minor factors in the ultimate success of the future researcher. The first two factors, analysis and perseverance, represent roughly how hard and how efficient the researcher works, and are important in all vocations. The big unknowns, originality and imagination, represent over a third of the favorable characteristics cited, yet are traits which cannot be measured in the prospective employee.

Rossman doesn't hesitate to tackle such difficult questions as the mental processes of inventors, their motives, the psychological theories of inventions, and the training of inventors. It is pointed out that once an idea is conceived, it should be put through a mental trial and error process based on reasoning. There is no use to go into experimentation if the potential invention would not have a practical use and be superior in one or more ways to competitive products or processes. As to motives, Rossman found that financial gain was not the paramount one, but rather the love of inventing. Obviously this varies depending upon the financial status of the inventor. Rossman

*The three groupings and the percent column added by author.

examines the various theories of invention as proposed by the 710 patentees but finds little to substantiate anything mystical about them. As to training, he concludes that although it is unlikely that a useful course of study can be laid out for potential inventors, they should avoid specialization, they should know the scientific principles of the fields in which they plan to work, they should be familiar with patent law, and they would benefit from a study of the methods used by successful inventors.

Since Rossman gathered the material for his book from many sources, it is not surprising that there are errors. On page 42 it is stated that Miller Reese Hutchison "has approximately one thousand patents. . . ." Hutchison was apparently answering a questionnaire for Edison, his employer. If Hutchison obtained any patents, they were very few. On page 142 it is stated that Bell and Gray invented the telephone the same year, 1876. Gray never came close to inventing the telephone. On page 150 there is an unfortunate statement if true: "Many patent attorneys often invent for their clients in order to help them to avoid the infringement of outstanding patents." This certainly should not be the function of a patent attorney. Such a patent would no doubt be purely the "paper" variety, backed up with no experimental reduction to practice. If a client infringes a patent, the attorney should arrange for licensing and payment of royalty.

Although Rossman's book has much valuable information, it is also an example of the difficulties of drawing conclusions from questionnaires on a subject as complicated as invention. As mentioned previously, the number of patents one has is not a true indication of his inventive ability. One of the most prolific inventors of all time was John F. O'Connor of Chicago, who obtained 949 U.S. patents. However, they were the "nut-and-bolt variety", and few people have heard of John O'Connor in spite of his impressive patent record. If an inventor works for a company which is anxious to break into a given field, the company will sponsor filing on numerous marginal inventions in order to build up their total number of patents. A patent application rejected by the Patent Examiner after several Office actions can usually be issued if its claims are made sufficiently narrow. The scope covered by the claims may be of little or no value, but it *is* another patent. On the other hand, an inventor may work for a company which will not sponsor the filing of a patent unless there is about a 90% chance that the company will use it in its manufacturing. This is often the practice of small companies.

A book which might appear to be helpful in picking potential inventors based on their backgrounds is *Cradles of Eminence* by Goertzel and Goertzel (4). This book is based on a study of over 400 famous 20th-century men and women. Unfortunately the "famous" is defined as follows in the "Foreword" of the book:

> Include each person who has at least two books about him in the biography section of the Montclair, New Jersey, Public Library if he was born in the United States and all persons who have at least one book about them if they were born outside the United States. Include only those who lived into the twentieth century and are described in a standard reference work.

This is indeed a remarkable criterion to use and then proceed to make sweeping conclusions about eminent people generally. Westinghouse and Acheson were not included in the study even though both lived well into the 20th century. The conclusions made by the authors of this book may be meaningful for movie actors and politicians but since scientists, engineers, and inventors make up such a small proportion of the 400, the conclusions are meaningless for inventors, whether eminent or otherwise.

The book *The Sources of Invention* by Jewkes, Sawers, and Stillerman (5) is an extensive study on that subject. The authors, who are lawyers, seek with the zeal of a Perry Mason these sources by studying the literature and, when possible, by interviews with inventors or their associates. The first edition appeared in 1958 and the second in 1968. The former is revised and the case histories brought up to date in the later edition. The authors also review and revise their earlier conclusions in the 1968 book.

Although all of the case histories described by Jewkes *et al* concern inventions made in the 20th century, and most of them during the past few decades, one chapter does deal with 19th-century inventions. The authors conclude that although the inventors of that period were largely self taught, they did have scientific knowledge in their fields of choice. These authors close their chapter on the 19th century with the following conclusions:

> Distinctions between the present and the past, therefore, must not be drawn sharply. History is not simple and cannot be made to seem so without distortion of facts. The modern view about invention in the nineteenth century seems to have arisen out of a misunderstanding. It is based on the assumption that science and the spread of formal scientific education have transformed the methods of invention, whereas they have only modified them; and that, in consequence, no previous inventors can have worked in the same manner as modern inventors, whereas they could and did.

317

This quotation is in accordance with my own conclusions that methods of the six subject inventors may appear more empirical than those of present-day inventors, but only because consideration is not given to the fact that less scientific information was available at that time. Let us compare examples of methods used in the two periods under roughly comparable circumstances.

After Edison had concluded that a carbon filament in vacuum made the best incandescent light, he prepared such filaments from hundreds of different organic materials. He baked various kinds of finely divided carbon and graphite dispersed in tars, asphalts and molasses, rolled into worm-like shapes; reeds cut from cardboard, various woods, and hides; and all kinds of fibers used in weaving. His goal was to prepare the best carbon filament of not over one sixty-fourth of an inch in diameter and about six inches in length. Once it was demonstrated that reeds cut from the wall of bamboo between joints were best, envoys were sent to the Orient, to the West Indies, and to South America seeking the best bamboo. Why didn't Edison come to the mental conclusion without experimentation that the continuous cellulose fibers of the bamboo, which we now know function in the bamboo stalk as do glass fibers in reinforced pastics, would be best for making strong carbon filaments? This is certainly too much to have expected. Carbon fibers did not exist, in fact Edison was the first to make them. His choice of raw material was a good one; today pure cellulose in the form of rayon is the best raw material for making carbon and graphite fibers for the space program. Furthermore, chemists as exemplified by Jean Dumas, the noted French chemist specializing in analytical organic chemistry, predicted that fragile carbon would not withstand incandescent temperatures without disintegrating. Edison was betting that it would, but he didn't know what physical form would hold up best so he tested all possible raw materials.

Selman Waksman (1888-1973) was an authority on soil microbiology at the time it was discovered that penicillin had amazing chemotherapeutic properties. Waksman and his students examined about 10,000 soil cultures in the search for other molds that would yield similar antibiotics (a term that Waksman coined). They employed soil samples from all possible sources including dirt that they scraped from vegetables in the supermarkets. The principal result from this highly empirical study was streptomycin, an antibiotic which was the first specific agent effective against human tuberculosis. Although the search for antibiotics goes on, it is still a matter of preparing and testing many samples. Waksman's work won him the Nobel Prize in medicine in 1952. Waksman's approach was actually more empirical than that of Edison since he had infinite possibilities to examine, whereas materials potentially suitable for making carbon filaments were limited.

Bell, following up the well-known telegraphic technique of sending dots and dashes by the making and breaking of current to an electromagnet, discovered that a continuous undulatory current produced by the voice, or other sounds of different pitches, on a suitable transmitter could reproduce that sound at a receiving device connected to the transmitter by a wire. Bell's research equipment was simple, his first basic studies were carried out using a human ear obtained from the school of medicine, Boston University. Sir William Thomson, as a member of the committee of judges at the Centennial in Philadelphia, marveled that Bell's telephone was "the most wonderful thing I have seen in America" in spite of the fact that the instruments were crude and the overall setup simple. Bell's principle of sound transmission via a varying electrical current through a wire is still the basis of all telephony.

Shortly after the turn of the century semi-conductors, such as silicon, were used as so-called crystal detectors in radio. However, de Forest's vacuum tube became the standard electronic amplifying device in radio, television, hearing-aids, etc. It held reign as the only feasible electronic amplifier for over 30 years. Following World War II and as a result of fundamental studies, Shockley, Bardeen, and Brattain of the Bell Telephone Laboratories learned how to make semi-conductors amplify as well as to detect microwaves. The resultant product, called a transistor, went through the electrolyte type, the point-contact type, and finally to the practical junction type. The three Bell Laboratory scientists used very simple apparatus in their studies and their starting materials were such well-known elements as germanium and silicon, which they modified by purification, crystallization, and the use of additives. Thus as Bell modified the dot-and-dash telegraph to produce the speaking telegraph, Shockley, Bardeen, and Brattain modified the well-known semi-conductors for a new and more important use. The inventors of the transistor received the Nobel Prize for physics in 1956.

As one may note from Goodyear's struggle to cure rubber, there was no scientific information available to help him. The process nearest to what he sought was the curing of hides to leather. However, this was an animal product whereas Goodyear was working with a product from a tree. If he did try the effect of oak bark, sumac, and hemlock on rubber, it simply added to his many failures. After Goodyear recognized the highly favorable effect of heat on a piece of rubber containing sulfur having been brought "carelessly in contact with a hot stove," he systematically investigated all variables. The proportion of sulfur and cure temperatures used today are close to those worked out by

Goodyear over 130 years ago.

Karl Ziegler (1898-1973) made one of the most important inventions of the 20th century. During World War II literally hundreds of chemists carried out research with the objective of making a polyisoprene of the same configuration as that of natural rubber. The general purpose synthetic rubber made in government plants was a butadiene-styrene copolymer, and although usable as a replacement for natural rubber in most cases, for certain strategic uses it was not. Vast expenditures did not produce the desired "synthetic natural rubber", and it was left to one on a small research budget to make possible this objective. As in the case of Goodyear's epic development, a happy "accident" led Karl Ziegler to this long-sought goal.

In 1953 while director of the Max Planck Institute for Coal Research at Mülheim, Germany, Ziegler was studying the growth reaction of aluminum triethyl and ethylene in bombs. When by chance he used a bomb contaminated with colloidal nickel from a previous experiment, instead of getting the growth reaction, all of the ethylene was converted to its dimer, 1-butene, and higher alpha olefins. He then went through a series of experiments in which aluminum triethyl was suspended in an inert hydrocarbon in a flask, freed of air, and ethylene bubbled through the mixture. Various metal additives were studied. When titanium tetrachloride was added to the mixture, a flask full of high molecular weight polyethylene resulted.

Subsequent studies with this highly active aluminum-titanium catalyst, as well as other aluminum triethyl-heavy metal halides, showed that it was not only highly effective for polymerizing ethylene but also the higher alpha olefins such as propylene. Subsequently the Ziegler catalyst was shown to be capable of polymerizing isoprene to *cis*-polyisoprene, a duplication of natural rubber. The catalyst was widely licensed in the United States, Germany, Italy, and Great Britain to make a variety of plastics and elastomers. In 1963 Ziegler shared the Nobel Prize in chemistry with Giulio Natta of Italy, who had further developed the Ziegler catalyst to prepare stereoisomers of polypropylene and a rubbery copolymer of propylene and ethylene.

I have cited three inventions of the post World War II era in which inventors used methods substantially as those employed by our subject inventors. Let us review briefly methods of some other outstanding inventors from the late 19th century to the present time.

An inventor who was close to our subject six in eminence was Elihu Thomson. He was weak as a child and the school principal recommended that the lad of 11 stay out of school for a while to build up his physique, which he did for two years. He received a high school education but his training in science was largely self acquired. Most of Thomson's 696 patents are in the electrical field. His most important invention was electric welding which he conceived when two wires shorted and stuck together. Although involved in industry most of his life, he preferred the laboratory.

Charles Steinmetz arrived in the United States in 1889, penniless and unable to speak English. He spent most of his working life with the General Electric Company. With company permission Steinmetz set up a laboratory in a barn on the property where he was living. He continued to work at times in his private laboratory even after General Electric had established a research laboratory at the Schenectady plant where he was employed. Steinmetz made improvements in arc lighting, was the first to produce artificial lightning, developed the law of hysteresis, and reduced to quantitative terms many phenomena of the alternating current. As a prolific writer and lecturer, he contributed much to the teaching and understanding of electricity. He obtained about 200 patents. Although he was a hunchback, he never complained that his physical condition was any handicap to him.

Louis Pasteur was much like Edison in his attitude and the way he worked. He considered a scientific discovery of little value unless it had practical applications. He was of poor health as a youth, and his eyes were very nearsighted. He was noted for his keen observation. He discovered anaerobic fermentation by observing by microscope that in a drop of sugar solution, the microorganisms were most active in the interior. One of the famous quotations from Pasteur is: "In the field of observation, chance favors only the minds which are prepared." His greatest contributions were the development of the germ theory and the pasteurization process. Pasteur contended that, "science is not the product of lofty meditations and genteel behavior; it is fertilized by heartbreaking toil and long vigils."

Orville and Wilbur Wright attended grade and high schools but liked neither. At early ages they worked with mechanical devices and in 1892 they set up a shop in Dayton, Ohio to repair, and later to manufacture, bicycles. In 1896 they became interested in the possibility of heavier-than-air craft and read everything they could find on the subject. By use of a wind tunnel, a large biplane kite, and later with gliders, they designed an aircraft which made the first manned flight in December 1903. They built their own internal combustion engine, their propellers were of their own design, and they were the first to use wing devices and a rudder to balance and control a plane in flight.

By 1905 the Wright brothers had built a plane which travelled twenty-one miles in 35 minutes. They offered to sell their patents and know-how to the United States

Government, and to guarantee a plane which could fly at least 100 miles nonstop. They got a form letter in return! Whereas the United States could have had a monopoly on early aircraft, the government's lack of interest forced the Wrights to seek help in Europe. A highly successful series of flights was made in France in 1908 and in Germany in 1909. All planes flown by American aviators in World War I were of either French or English design and manufacture.

Thus the Wright brothers, expert mechanics, chose a field where their abilities and manufacturing facilities offered very favorable opportunities for invention and the founding of a new industry. Their limited financial resources slowed the development beyond their first successful machine. Their tenacious efforts finally brought success in spite of discouragement by certain noted scientists and engineers and failure of the United States' armed forces to recognize the potential of the airplane. Wilbur died in 1912 of typhoid fever and Orville sold out his interests in the aircraft industry in 1915. Orville made several minor inventions after 1915.

It has been said that Carleton Ellis' primary ambition, once he became a successful inventor, was to get more patents than Thomas Edison, his neighbor. Ellis had a laboratory and an interest in a small plant in Montclair, New Jersey. Although Ellis died in 1941 without achieving his goal, he did get about 750 U.S. patents. He was particularly apt in patenting and licensing simple things such as a paint remover consisting of paraffin wax dissolved in benzene, a dog biscuit in the shape of a bone, and a rat poison in the form of corn kernels. He never manufactured except on a small scale and was an example that it is possible to successfully invent for licensing only. His more sophisticated inventions included the first practical process for making isopropyl alcohol from cracked petroleum gases

324

and an improved liquid-phase operation for cracking petroleum, known as the "tube-and-tank process".

Charles Kettering was plagued with poor eyesight as a child and youth which interrupted his schooling; he did not graduate from college, as an electrical engineer, until age 28. His major inventions included an electric starter for gasoline automobiles, the determination of the cause of knock in internal combustion engines and its remedy, quick-drying lacquer finishes for auto bodies, and various improvements of the diesel engine. He scoffed, usually in a humorous way, at the traditional thinking of most engineers and businessmen and was a great advocate of the experimental method: "In research, after all scientific methods have been tried, I prefer the cut-and-dry method of groping in the dark, with the possibility of bumping into something, to just sitting still and philosophizing." He contended that it was as important that the experimenter have economic horse sense as knowledge of science. He maintained that hard work and clear thinking could solve any technical problem. Kettering demonstrated that an inventor could also function effectively as an executive of a large corporation.

Since the turn of the century, the petroleum industry had been interested in catalytic cracking to replace the less selective thermal cracking. Many effective catalysts were found, but on use they soon lost their activity. It was obvious that for a catalyst to be commercially practical, it must be capable of being regenerated by burning off carbonaceous deposits. Eugene Houdry, son of a French steel manufacturer and an engineer by training, became interested in the problem because he found that the quality of fuel used in his racing car greatly affected its performance. He set up laboratory facilities and tested over 1,000 catalysts before he found one that could be regenerated without loss of activity. It proved to be a special kind of clay, a material which had already been used by the petroleum industry for purifying lubricating oil. Houdry had great difficulty in selling his process to the industry but was finally successful with the Sun Oil Company. His work spurred others, including the engineers at the Standard Oil Company of New Jersey who developed fluid catalytic cracking. However, it was an individual outside the oil industry who solved the critical problem of catalyst regeneration, which made possible the major advance of replacing liquid phase thermal cracking with gaseous catalytic cracking.

In spite of the fact that DDT must be used with certain precautions because of its persistency in the environment, the invention of this synthetic insecticide is one of the milestones of applied technology. Its introduction opened the way for a large number of new insecticides and fungicides which made possible vast increases in the production of foodstuffs and the saving of millions of lives by the control of disease-bearing insects. (Americans tend to forget that even today the mosquito is still man's worst enemy; more people will die in 1974 from mosquito-borne disease than from any other single cause.)

As part of a general program of the Swiss firm of J. R. Geigy on moth-proofing agents and insecticides generally, their chemist, Paul Müller, prepared l,l-bis-*para*-chlorophenyl-2,2,2-trichloroethane, now known as DDT. As it turned out DDT was an old compound, having been prepared by Othmar Zeidler, a student, in 1874; thus Müller's invention was not DDT as a new composition, but rather as an insecticide. In 1948 Müller was awarded the Nobel Prize for medicine. The award was in this category rather than chemistry since DDT had become so important in the prevention of diseases such as malaria. The use of DDT was expanded very rapidly during World War II because of its importance in tropical areas. Thus, DDT came from a systematic synthesis and test program in a field lucrative for invention since organic insecticides had previously been restricted largely to the two natural materials, pyrethrum and rotenone.

Once it was learned that DDT had been "sitting on the shelf" for more than 60 years before its insecticidal properties were discovered, there was a broad program in industry and agriculture laboratories to test available organic compounds. The research affiliate of the Standard Oil Company (N.J.), then called Esso Research and Engineering Company, set up a joint program with the New Jersey Agricultural Experimental Station of Rutgers University to test various chemicals which had previously been prepared for testing as lube oil additives and the like. Several hundred such compounds were tested as insecticides, fungicides, and herbicides without success. A synthesis program was then initiated. Allen Kittleson, one of the chemists working at Esso Research, noted in the patent literature that N-butyl tetrahydrophthalimide had been used in a fly spray. He then proceeded to carry out a program in which various other groups were substituted for the butyl in such compounds. When perchloromethyl mercaptan was used as an intermediate in such a synthesis, an outstanding fungicide resulted. Twenty-five years later, N-trichloromethyl thiotetrahydrophthalimide, originally named Captan, is still the most widely used fungicide for crops, orchards, and gardens. Its invention and ultimate success resulted from the recognition of the need for improved agriculture chemicals plus outstanding synthesis and development work by Kittleson.

Teflon was truly an invention by the serendipity route. In 1938 Dr. Ray Plunkett was working in Du Pont's

Jackson Laboratory with tetrafluoroethylene (TFE) as a possible refrigerant or intermediate for a refrigerant. Based on experience with tetrachloro and tetrabromo ethylenes, the tetrafluoro derivative was believed to be incapable of being polymerized. Plunkett stored his TFE, a gas at ordinary pressure, in pressure cylinders. One day he began removing some of it from a cylinder but found very little pressure and a white solid had fouled the valve. The cylinder was cut open and found to be full of nontacky white polymer. Du Pont gave it the trademark name, Teflon. It is insoluble in nearly all liquids and is very thermally stable. The housewife is familiar with Teflon as a lining for cooking utensils.

The overall development of the various synthetic elastomers in the approximate period of 1925-1965 represents a series of outstanding inventions which revolutionized an industry. Thomas Midgley's early work using isoprene resulted in products of low quality and illustrates the fact that in attempting to replace a natural product, the best approach may not be that of trying to duplicate it chemically. In the mid-1920's the Germans made a major advance when they turned to butadiene instead of isoprene as raw material. However, whether it was mass polymerized using sodium catalysis or polymerized in emulsion using a peroxide, the rubber obtained was of poor quality due to 1,2-type polymerization rather than the desired 1,4. E. Tschunkur and co-workers of the I. G. Farbenindustrie greatly improved elastomer quality when they went to butadiene-styrene and butadiene-acrylonitrile copolymers by emulsion polymerization (6). This was an amazing development at the time since homopolymers of styrene and acrylonitrile are hard and brittle. The styrene copolymer became the widely used replacement for natural rubber.

328

However, the Americans were the first to market synthetic elastomers although they were specialty types. Thiokol, a rubbery polysulfide prepared by the reaction of ethylene dichloride with sodium polysulfide, was introduced in 1930. It has outstanding resistance to weathering and oils, but is no substitute for high strength rubber.

In the 1920's the Du Pont Company began a program directed towards converting acetylene to diacetylene and then by hydrogenation to butadiene. About this time Father J. A. Nieuwland of Notre Dame University reported on the conversion of acetylene to divinyl acetylene using ammonium chloride as catalyst. Du Pont followed up Nieuwland's work and found that low quality rubbery polymers could be made from divinyl acetylene. However, the break came when Arnold Collins, in the process of purifying divinyl acetylene by fractional distillation, obtained a small low-boiling fraction which on standing solidified to a rubbery material. It proved to be 2-chlorobutadiene, a by-product in the trimerization of acetylene using ammonium chloride. Thus monovinyl acetylene became the desired product, which was found to easily undergo an addition reaction with hydrogen chloride to give the easily polymerizable 2-chlorobutadiene. The polymer so obtained can be vulcanized to products of high extensibility having many outstanding properties. This elastomer, now named neoprene, continues to be an important commercial product. In a recent address at the time of receiving the Goodyear Medal (7), Collins attributed imagination, thoroughness, and common sense as having led to the invention and success of neoprene. Du Pont research brought forth an important synthetic rubber but not the type they originally sought.

A very unique synthetic rubber, known as Butyl, was

329

invented in the late 1930's by Robert Thomas and William Sparks of the Standard Oil Development Company (now Exxon Research and Engineering Company). The Germans had shown that isobutylene, cooled well below its boiling point, could be polymerized with gaseous boron trifluoride to give a molasses-type polymer. Exxon continued the study with the objective of developing viscosity index improvers for lubricating oils. It was subsequently found that if isobutylene was polymerized at dry ice temperature, a solid rubbery polymer resulted. It was then attempted to copolymerize isobutylene with other monomers including the conjugated diolefins. However, when butadiene or isoprene was used with the isobutylene, the reaction was severely poisoned. Success came by the use of the more active aluminum chloride dissolved in ethyl chloride as catalyst, reaction temperatures as low as -100°C., and reactants of higher purity. It was possible to copolymerize several percent of isoprene with isobutylene and maintain a highly rubbery polymer. Unexpectedly it was found that this elastomer could be vulcanized with sulfur. Because of its excellent air-holding properties, Butyl rubber took over the entire inner tube market. Thus this project, which was originally directed towards preparing lubricating oil additives, not only resulted in a new synthetic rubber but two new basic facts of rubber chemistry as well. First, a conjugated diolefin is not necessary to produce a rubbery polymer; and secondly, a mere one percent of the double bonds in natural rubber is sufficient in a synthetic rubber for vulcanization. Both Sparks and Thomas were awarded the Goodyear Medal for their invention of Butyl rubber.

It has already been pointed out that a dual catalyst invented by Karl Ziegler for polymerizing alpha olefins was the key to converting isoprene to *cis*-polyisoprene, the truly synthetic rubber. Highly linear polybutadiene can be

330

similarly prepared. The Ziegler catalyst also made possible ethylene-propylene rubber (EPR), an elastomer with no double bonds but which can be crosslinked by means of an organic peroxide and thus achieve "vulcanization". The ethylene serves to break up the crystalline nature of the combined propylene and provides methylene groups which are suitable for crosslinking with peroxides. It was inevitable that once EPR was developed, chemists would make tripolymers by means of a small proportion of a third monomer to impart enough unsaturation for sulfur vulcanization. The best polyolefinic monomers for this purpose are dicyclopentadiene, ethylidene norbornene, and 1,4-hexadiene. Thus the new catalyst system of Ziegler proved to be the key to several new types of elastomers.

Fifty years ago manufacturers of rubber products had one elastomeric raw material. Natural rubber is the same chemically whether it comes from the *Hevea* tree, guayule, or goldenrod leaves. Today, because of numerous inventors working in many laboratories, the manufacturer has literally dozens of different elastomers* to choose from, each having certain properties or price advantage which makes it more suitable for given end uses than any other. For example, a tire manufacturer uses one type of elastomer in the tread, a different one in the sidewall where flexing is severe, and still another of low air permeability as liner. The experimentation, which created this revolution in raw materials, also greatly increased our scientific knowledge relating to the structure and behavior of elastic materials generally.

A success story of the 20th century which approaches

---

*Other synthetic rubbers of less importance include silicone rubber which contains high proportions of silicon and oxygen, modified polyethylenes known as Hypalon rubber, and polyacrylate rubber.

that of Goodyear in personal tenacity, in failures to interest others in his invention, and overall economic hardship is that of Chester D. Carlson (1906-1968). At age 14 Chester, the only child, had a father who had been ill for some time with tuberculosis and arthritis and now his mother contracted tuberculosis. She died three years later. The father lived for another 10 years, but he never regained his health.

Young Carlson attended Riverside Junior College, Riverside, California, for three years spending alternate six-week periods attending school and working. He transferred to the California Institute of Technology in his junior year and graduated with a degree in physics in the depression year of 1930. He obtained a job with the Bell Telephone Laboratories in New York but was subsequently laid off. He then worked for a private law firm and with P. R. Mallory & Co., an electrical equipment company. He studied law at nights from 1936-39 and obtained a L.L.B. degree. In 1942 he became head of Mallory's patent division.

In his patent work Carlson noted how laborious it was to reproduce documents. He also had strong ambitions to better his economic position in life: "I was greatly influenced by the success stories of Edison and others." In 1935 Carlson decided to try to invent a copying machine.

He followed up his idea, as time permitted, reading technical literature in the New York Public Library. He rejected chemical methods as used in photography since he felt that Eastman Kodak and others had studied such possibilities thoroughly. He read that an investigator had used a powder to develop an electrostatic image. He decided that his approach would be to form such an image on a light sensitive plate, adhere powder to the charge, and then transfer and fix the powder to a piece of ordinary paper.

332

Carlson filed a patent application in late 1937 to cover his basic concept of what is now known as xerography. He unsuccessfully carried out some experiments in his small apartment. He decided he was inadequate as an experimenter to reduce his invention to practice so he rented some additional space and hired an unemployed physicist, Otto Kornei, to do experimental work. By October 1938 they had succeeded in preparing the first xerographic images using sulfur coated plates. More patent applications were filed.

During the next six years Carlson unsuccessfully tried to interest some 20 firms in his invention. The National Inventor's Council rejected his process as being impractical. Finally by assigning exclusive patent rights to the Battelle Memorial Institute, Carlson was able to get the development division of that organization to undertake development and possible commercialization of his invention. Carlson was to receive 40% of the subsequent royalty income if he could pay a certain proportion of Battelle's development expense, otherwise it would decrease to 25%. During the subsequent development period, Carlson put in all the money he could possibly spare from his salary, used up his small savings, and had to borrow from relatives and friends to retain his higher share in the development.

Battelle had only one man on the project the first year, but then increased their effort. The Haloid Company, a small photographic supply firm located in Rochester, New York, gave financial support beginning in 1947. This company, with only about $100,000 profit in 1946, spent about 4.3 million on the development of xerography. The first xerox copier was introduced in 1950 and the first profits came in 1953, 18 years after Carlson had begun his search for a quick copying process. However, his long struggle paid off financially; Carlson became a multimillionaire.

The Haloid Company became the Xerox Company in 1961*. The phenomenal growth of this company is well known. The development and success of xerography is an example that even in this day of industrial giants with large research laboratories, it is possible for a lone inventor to go from "rags to riches". However, as it was for Goodyear a hundred years earlier, Carlson, a man of relatively limited scientific training and whose invention had been rejected by the "experts", maintained his faith in himself and his product for many trying years before success was achieved. In accepting the Inventor of the Year Award for 1964, sponsored by The George Washington University Patent, Trademark, and Copyright Research Institute, Carlson ended with the following comments:

> The time scale of invention is a long one. Results do not come quickly. Inventive developments have to be measured in decades rather than years. It takes patience to stay with an idea through such a long period. In my case I am sure I would not have done so if it were not for the hope for eventual reward through the incentives offered by the Patent System.

If it were possible to accurately rate all contemporary inventors, Dr. Edwin H. Land of the Polaroid Corporation would likely come out No. 1. In many ways Land's career is much like Edison's. He is largely self educated; although Land attended Harvard, he did not graduate, apparently

---

*The 3M Company developed their Thermofax copying process about the same time — Carl Miller, inventor.

Edison and Charles Steinmetz, friends and mutual admirers, examine experimental equipment in the latter's laboratory.

Henry Ford and Harvey Firestone visit Edison at his Fort Myers home. Ford and Firestone were successful inventors but this was overshadowed by their phenomenal successes in pioneering new businesses.

Chester Carlson examines the mechanism of his first copying machine at the time it was donated to the Smithsonian Institution in 1965.

Edwin H. Land, founder, president, and research director of the Polaroid Corporation

feeling that he could not spare the time to take certain required courses. As Edison, Land has made at least two outstanding inventions. Edison revolutionized methods of his time for doing industrial research; Land has introduced several new innovations in methods for doing industrial research. He is completely sold on broad patenting with detailed disclosures and then allowing patentees to publish their scientific results. This makes it possible for a scientist at Polaroid to publish nearly as freely as if he were doing research in an academic institution. Like Edison, Land spends practically nothing on market research but instead operates on the basis that a new product will find a market if it fills a need and is technically sound.

While a 17-year-old Harvard freshman in 1926, Land reputedly was struck by the glare of auto headlights while walking along New York's Broadway and visualized the equipping of cars with light-polarizing windshields and headlights to cut glare. However, he soon found that his idea was not novel. Others had tried using large crystals of herapathite, a synthetic iodoquinine sulfate hydrate of light-polarizing properties, and failed. Land conceived the idea of using many microscopic crystals oriented in a like manner imbedded in a transparent matrix. He took leave from Harvard and worked in an improvised laboratory in his rented room on Manhattan's West 55th Street, the New York Public Library, and occasionally, with the cooperation of a friend, in a physics laboratory of Columbia University.

He returned to Harvard in 1929, now married, and the physics department was so impressed with his work that the university allowed him a private laboratory for his research. His wife served as his laboratory assistant. Late in 1932, still short a few courses for his bachelor degree, Land again left the university, and with G. Wheelwright, a former physics instructor at Harvard, set up the Land-Wheelwright

Laboratories. A practical process was worked out for orienting minute herapathite crystals in plates of cellulose acetate using a combination of extrusion and stretching. Success came in the mid-1930's, not for the intended uses in automobiles, but in photographic filters, sunglasses, and for optical instruments. By 1936 Land-Wheelwright employed some 50 physicists and other laboratory personnel.

Land was able to interest a number of financiers in the prospect of his mass produced synthetic light polarizers for automobiles, and Polaroid Corporation was formed in 1937. However, the idea was not sold to the auto makers before the war and has not been since. Because of the shortage of quinine during the war, it became necessary to find a substitute for herapathite. This was accomplished by staining certain plastics in a stretched, oriented state. During World War II the company was kept busy producing goggles, glasses, and filters, but sales sagged after the war ended. With the failure of the anticipated business with the auto companies to materialize, Polaroid Corporation lost $2,000,000 in 1947.

Only the introduction of the Land camera saved the company. Responding to a chance remark made by his three-year-old daughter as to why she had to wait so long for pictures he had taken of her, in 1943 Land began thinking of how photos might be developed and printed inside the camera. By 1947 he was able to announce "instant photography" and the first Polaroid Land camera was put on sale in late 1948. Whereas the photography professionals had written off Land's camera as an expensive toy, Polaroid's sales in 1949 reached $6,700,000 of which over five million was from the camera and film. Continuing improvements including the replacement of the original sepia prints with black-and-white film, introduction of color film in 1963, and a series of improvements in camera design and operation culminating in the SX-70 model in 1972 have made Polaroid one of the top "glamour stocks" of the world. This company sells more cameras in the $50-and-over class than all other companies in the world combined.*

Land has not only broken the pattern that an outstanding inventor is a poor businessman − probably a false premise from the start, but he has also demonstated that the laboratory can be more attractive than the front office even in a highly profitable organization. Again we see the resemblance to Edison, but unlike Edison, Land has surrounded himself with highly competent technical and business staffs. He attributes the overall success of Polaroid to a top management imbued in science, the policy of carrying out research on a broad basis, and concentration on a few products. Polaroid apparently spends a much higher percent of gross income on research and development than the average company. Land is probably the most daring exploiter of new technology since Edison. A quarter-billion dollars were committed to the development and manufacture of the SX-70 before it was known whether the camera would work.

Land has a private laboratory next to his office where he may disappear for weeks to work 18 hours a day. One of his theories of successful research is that once a solution to a problem is in sight, interruptions are bad; it is hard to get going again. He attributes his success to "sound perceptions drawn from a thousand groping approaches." Land feels the ability to create and invent is not rare, but is generally uncultivated. Although he continues to be the most prolific inventor in the company, well over half of the

*As of June 1972.

337

patents assigned to Polaroid have been obtained by others. Land's patent record does not fit the pattern, advocated by some, that inventors become less creative after about age 35. Land's patent record, which totals 437 United States patents as of September 1973 of which he is inventor or co-inventor, includes the following:

Ten-Year Period	Number Patents Issued	Age Range
1933-1942	63	24-33
1943-1952	101	34-43
1953-1962	109	44-53
1963-1972	155	54-63

From these data a statistician would likely predict that during ages 64-73, Land will invent at an even higher level! Edwin Land has received many awards including an honorary doctor of science degree from Harvard in 1957.

In 1973 I sent a questionnaire to 15 of my fellow chemists and chemical engineers whom I knew had made one or more inventions which were in commercial use. Although this questionnaire was quite informal, it did specificially ask if the inventor considered he had a subconscious mind and if so, did it help him in making inventions. The questionnaire dealt in some detail with his methods for making inventions, effect of age, motives, etc.

These contemporary inventors had an average of 86 patents each. Of the 14 who answered the question dealing with the subconscious, nine believed they had a subconscious mind but only four felt it had any part in their inventing. All felt that hard thinking followed by experimentation, or vice versa, was a major source of inventions — an average of over 50% for all patents obtained — and the next most important source was unexpected experimental results which were followed up.

Not a single invention arose from dreams. As to motives, most mentioned the desire to help their employer who was paying their salary — all but one of the 15 were or had been corporate employees. Another major motive was the desire to achieve, both in respect to their peers within the company and professional associates broadly. Most mentioned that they went into research because they liked it and that patents were a by-product, and at times a nuisance due to the time spent with the legal staff in preparing and prosecuting such patents, in their search for new knowledge and new products.

The methods of inventors discussed in this chapter, plus those reported by Rossman and Jewkes *et al*, result in the fact that methods used by our six master inventors are still those largely used by inventors today. Results from studies relating to creativity, carried out by psychologists, are not entirely in accordance with the record. Some psychologists have placed too much emphasis on the subconscious mind and its feeding long-sought solutions to the conscious. Even among psychologists, and certainly among inventors, the subconscious mind is a nebulous thing and what it means to one may be quite different from another's conception of the term. Perhaps the new science of electroencephalography will ultimately be able to determine if a so-called "flash of genius" from the brain is a signal highly different in pulsations than the usual rhythms.

Certainly the inventor does not fit the pattern of the neurotic individual pictured by some as a typical creative person. As Roger Williams, an eminent biochemist, points out (8), each person has a unique brain structure. Although each human brain consists of approximately the same number of cells, their arrangement may be quite different.

An individual who becomes an outstanding musician may have less practical sense than the average. One of the necessary characteristics of the inventor must be common sense, and if one's brain structure makes it possible that he is very gifted in a given field, he may very well lack the desired overall balance.

The same reasoning would appear to hold for geniuses. If we accept Webster's definition that a genius is "a person endowed with transcendent mental superiority, inventiveness, and ability", certainly all of our six subject inventors were geniuses. Each invented one or more things which continue to be of paramount importance some 100 years later. As pointed out by Williams (8):

> Genius is not a unitary trait; it can arise from almost any set of parents; every child may possess some genius-like characteristics and if given the proper environment may become an exceptionally effective individual.

Genius is a relative term and as long as it is part of the world's languages it should be used to describe inventors as well as artists, painters, poets, and others. However, it should be considered a strictly relative term, some have more genius, or of a different type, than do others.

All who have studied invention appear to agree that motivation, imagination, and originality are characteristics the successful inventor must have. Motivation is so basic that it is essential for success in any activity; however, the experimenter needs it more than most since he encounters far more failures than successes. Creative imagination is certainly a very profound mental process. Although some psychologists may attribute it to cortical activity at the subconscious level (9), it is more likely an attitude plus the

340

willingness and ability to engage in hard thinking. One of Edison's choice remarks was that people will do most anything to avoid the hard work of thinking. In my personal survey, one engineer-inventor stated that he found engineers either basically inventive or not inventive, the differences being due largely to attitudes. Originality means little unless properly directed. The first of the younger generation who bought a pair of jeans, cut a hole in the seat, and then sewed a highly colored patch thereon showed originality. Creativity is not necessarily good and the definition of what is good varies from country to country, from generation to generation, and even among individuals under similar circumstances.

As mentioned previously, the choice of research project may be more critical to success than the subsequent mental and physical labor to achieve success. If Edison had chosen to improve the arc light rather than pioneer incandescent lighting, he would have become less famous. Acheson had failure after failure until he abandoned thermoelectricity and went to chemical conversions at electric furnace temperatures. At one stage Bell was pursuing both harmonic telegraphy and the telephone. If he had not made the decision to abandon the first and concentrate on the second, he would likely be unknown to posterity. Land's concept of instantaneous photography opened up a fertile field for research and development. Carlson's decision to pursue the rapid copier was probably his most important contribution to xerography.

Surprisingly little has been written about the science of choosing the best field for research and development. Governmental and company priorities no doubt play their part and may be overall controlling in many situations. In a truly exploratory situation, some feel that applied research in a field where there has been a recent advance in pure

341

science offers the best opportunity. However, applied research may lead to advances in pure science as well as vice versa. Market research is unlikely the answer since a new product may create the market. There was no demand for the phonograph until it was invented. The reading of the broad technical literature, plus observation of the world about one, and hard thinking on the ideas obtained therefrom likely constitute the best approach. Certainly the choice of problem is particularly important to the lone inventor who literally has the "whole world" to choose from.

Although prospective employers often advertise that they are seeking innovative* scientists and engineers, most colleges make no attempt to improve this trait of their students or to evaluate it by testing. The concensus appears to be that everyone has some innovative ability but that it varies greatly. It is also generally agreed that anyone can improve his ability to invent if placed in the proper environment. It is my opinion that this can best be done by close working arrangements of potential inventors with successful inventors. Initially the former should function as an assistant to the "beck and call" of the inventor. After a year or two, the beginner should be put on his own but with a liaison arrangement with his former boss or equivalent.

It is not surprising that companies have been organized whose business is to teach others how to be more creative. One such organization is Synectics, Inc. founded in 1960 by W.J.J. Gordon and G. M. Prince, both formerly of A. D. Little, Inc. of Cambridge, Massachusetts. The objective of

---

*Innovation is a broader term than invention, denoting anything new and useful. Invention is innovation which results in something which did not exist before.

the new company was to do research and teaching on the innovative process. Both Gordon and Prince have written books on the subject (10). Their original approach was to use analogies, but now they use what they call mental excursion. Each approach emphasizes the subconscious mind. No attempt is made here to evaluate the effectiveness of their methods in the field of invention. The fact that Synectics, Inc. is still in business is certainly a plus factor in their favor.

Another venture which was not so successful was The Innovation Group, whose purpose was "to advance the art of managing technology". Their major activity was the publication of the magazine, *Innovation*, beginning in May 1969. This publication was designed to appeal primarily to the management of research and development organizations. The publication of *Innovation* ceased after about three years. The magazine was very expensive to produce with many photographs and sketches which had little to do with technology. However, its demise was probably due to the basic fact that innovation cannot be managed.

A modest periodical which deals primarily with invention is *The Creativity Review*, published by L. C. Repucci of Midland, Michigan. In spite of the broad name of the journal, it deals primarily with invention. Editor Repucci has the philosophy that people can become more creative.

In 1972 the National Science Foundation set up a project to develop new methods for fostering research and development, with a budget of about 20 million dollars. Part of this program deals with "incentives in stimulating the innovation process". Thus the government through the National Science Foundation is concerned about the poor return in recent years on research dollars. In 1973 it is estimated that $30.1 billion will be spent on research and development in the United States, representing 2.4% of the gross national product. This far exceeds in total money, and is also higher on a percentage basis, that of any other country. The magnitude of this annual expenditure can be appreciated when one considers that it is greater than all similar expenditures the first 150 years of this nation.,*i.e.*, from 1790 to 1940. The period cited covers the birth of steam power, electric power and lighting, the automobile, the airplane, and in fact the entire period of what is known as the industrial revolution.

As a part of the Science Foundation's research on how to do research was a project financed at the Battelle Columbus Laboratories (11). This study dealt with eight technical developments with emphasis on the factors which led to decisive events. The two most important factors found were "recognition of technical opportunity" and "recognition of need". The first factor emphasizes again the importance of choice of field in which to carry out research. This study had little to do with the traits and methods of individual inventors.

The biggest change in the source of inventions since the days of the six inventors covered in Chapters 1-6 is the rise of the corporate laboratories. The majority of present day inventors are employees of large companies. Some writers speak glibly of large corporations amassing patents by using teams to invent. No corporation or any other organization can apply for a patent in the United States.* It is still the individual who makes inventions, usually singly but occasionally with a co-inventor, but seldom more than one for a given patent. If employed by a company, he is usually under contract to assign all patents to his employer.

*A bill before Congress (October 1973) would allow the owners of patentable material, under certain circumstances, to file for a patent.

The fact that the majority of those working in research and development are today employees of large companies is offered by some as the reason why our expenditures in these fields are less productive than in the past. This is a question too complex to discuss here. Irrespective of what the record may or may not show, should it be more effective to spend X dollars on research in a large company, a small company, a research institute, government laboratories, or by lone inventors? Theoretically the large company should be best. Here the inventor has the most extensive support services — analytical, physical testing, shops, electronics, computers, library, and, not least, associates knowledgeable in many technologies which the inventor may call on for information and advice. The inventor is assured of a salary whether he successfully invents or not, and he is likely building a pension equity under the umbrella of his company's benefit plans. Thus he is able to work in an atmosphere where dire financial problems are no distraction. Furthermore, once a promising invention is made the company theoretically has ample funds to exploit it.

Although large corporate laboratories would appear to be the best route by means of which inventions can originate and the fruit therefrom carried to the marketplace, there are problems. Some are briefly discussed below:

(a) Some feel that the organization of a typical large company makes it practically impossible to come out with a radically new product (12). In a small company new products of limited sales volume are attractive. The president, who is usually also manager of manufacturing and director of research, is largely responsible only to himself. In a large corporation the president, in order to please the stockholders, is looking for a higher return on investment; since each manager wants his division to be more profitable than when under his predecessor, he wants no losses from the introduction of new products; and the philosophy is to do what the company can do best. Thus research becomes improving and lowering the cost of making present products rather than looking for new products or radically new processes. The lower echelon of executives who are seeking advancement follow the adage: "You never lose a battle if you never fight one."

(b) There tends to be too much emphasis on research management, with the experimenter having to spend too much of his time preparing reports and attending meetings in order to keep this pyramid of management informed. Also the directorship of the research laboratory may be used as part of a training program for executives. This is very bad. The director of research should be the best inventor in the company and he should continue to invent, leaving routine operations to others.

The senior research people should have laboratories without telephones. It is just as important not to disturb an inventor in the laboratory as an executive in conference. The same patent attorney should be assigned to a given inventor on a continuing basis so that the former can prepare patents for filing with a minimum of help from the inventor.

(c) Companies tend to be too departmentalized with different laboratory, engineering, and manufacturing divisions working largely independently. Thus when an invention comes from the exploratory division, the inventor cannot follow "his baby" through the pilot plant and manufacturing stages but must turn it over to others.

(d) With so many services and assistants available, research personnel tend to desert the laboratory and concentrate on desk work.

346

As we have seen, there continue to be other sources of inventions besides the large research laboratories. Jewkes *et al* summarize the situation well (13):

> It cannot be disputed that inventions and discoveries have had, and continue to have, many sources. It may be tempting to argue that one or other of these sources is more fruitful than others and should be stimulated even at the expense of the rest. Our impressions are that, given the present state of knowledge, it is safer to strive to keep all the sources open since competition strengthens the total flow of new ideas.

Although the lone inventor is certainly one of the sources of invention which must be kept open and our six major case histories are those of lone inventors, the facts of life are that today most potential inventors seek the security of company affiliation — and most are large companies. Are not there other factors which are more important in research productivity than size of company or company affiliation *vs.* no company affiliation?

Our education system has become more regimented with many required courses and specified periods of study before the student can become a graduate with the various privileges resulting therefrom. These requirements are no doubt necessary for practitioners such as teachers, doctors, dentists, and lawyers, but for the creative scientist they are largely nonsense. Since educators admit that they do not know how to train inventors, why should restrictive curricula be required? More complex mathematics than high school algebra is a waste of time for most organic chemists, and even more so for biochemists. Foreign language requirements for the scientist are as far out-of-date as the

Model-T. There is always more pertinent literature in English than the researcher has time to read. I propose that students interested in science and engineering be allowed to take whatever courses they wish and after completing satisfactorily the specified number of semester hours, they be granted bachelor degrees. If, for example, one has taken all of his courses in the sciences, it is up to his subsequent employer to decide whether he is qualified for a particular job. Certainly for the potential inventor, the student himself is likely to be a better judge of what knowledge he needs to succeed than is a university administrator.

All of our six subject inventors were well educated even though they had little formal education. Bell, the only one of the six who had any college training, had no training in the field where he ultimately made his greatest invention, *i.e.*, electricity. The six were largely self educated, a phenomenon most educators fail to give due attention. Why shouldn't reading a book written by an authority be more educational than listening to one who knows much less expound on the same subject? Instead of a curriculum to produce a "well-rounded" graduate, why not assume that he can correct by self education where he may find he is seriously deficient? For the scientist, and most other professions, college training is only the start of his education. After 10 to 15 years in industry it is difficult to tell what type of training a particular technical man had; he picks up several unofficial degrees on the job and by self education in his fields of major interest.

Industry apparently has learned that their recent technical employees may be too narrowly trained. The recent trend for colleges to emphasize theory rather than descriptive matter further tends to keep the student away from inventive-rich facts of science. Those with bachelor degrees are finding it easier to find employment in industry than those with Ph.D. or post-doctorate training. Some have interpreted this to mean that industry is trying to save money. This is hardly the explanation. The bachelor man is certainly more flexible in finding a suitable place in an organization than is the specialist and according to the record, he may be more inventive. The industrial employer should make it clear to potential members of their technical staff that except for starting salaries, a higher degree has no significance salarywise. Also we must get away from the illusion that scientists and engineers who take employment after bachelor or M.S. degrees do so because they are not qualified to seek Ph.D. status. The graduate who is able to enter industry at age 22 as compared to 26, makes possible an approximate 10% longer productive career. Westinghouse invented the air brake at age 22 and one year later was the president of a company to manufacture it. By age 24 Edison had made several important inventions, including the stock ticker, and was employing 50 men in its manufacture.

Industry should allow their technical employees more flexibility as to nature of their work. In many companies if a new employee is hired by the research department, it is difficult to get transferred to development, manufacturing, or sales if research is not to his liking. Employment at a relatively early age should make such transfers easier since the employee would know what he wants to do before he gets up to a salary range that makes such transfers even more difficult. Also the benefit plans of all companies should be such that if an inventor-employee makes an invention which the employer is not interested in carrying to manufacture, the inventor can leave his company to go with a licensee or manufacture on his own without loss of accumulated benefits.

There appears to be enough evidence to indicate that the

trend to centralize research facilities has gone too far. De-centralization may very well be in order. Whether this means a geographical separation is probably immaterial, but a separation of an exploratory or new product division from those primarily oriented to help the company in short-term profit making appears essential. To set up a division with the advantages of a small company within the framework of a large company is not easy, but certain large corporations appear to be able to do it. In such a "small company" setup, the inventor is more market oriented and should take an active part in the development of his invention from the bench to manufacturing and early marketing.

However, let's not conclude that company organization is basically bad for research. Edison had a very substantial research organization at Menlo Park and a more elaborate one at West Orange. The services which he had available were a major factor in his getting so many important patents. He could not have done it working alone. Edison accepted a certain amount of company regimentation; he came to work on time, he punched a time clock, and he met deadlines.

Unless independently wealthy, the lone inventor can best get started with inventing as a sideline to his regular job. Carlson worked as a patent attorney as he spent nights and weekends working on his rapid copier idea. Bell appears to have set the best pattern for today's potential lone inventor; he taught school while he worked on the telephone during his spare time and summer vacations. Teaching is a well paid profession today and if the teacher wishes he can have his summer vacation free for other things. Many universities encourage members of their staffs to follow up any practical applications from their research by setting up foundations to assist in the getting and licensing of patents arising therefrom. The researcher in an industrial laboratory should not expect to work on personal research at any time, since it is impossible to separate his two categories of interest. However, industry should favorably consider a leave of absence for any employee who wishes to try the lone inventor route for a trial period, on the same basis as educational leaves are granted.

Some may feel that inventiveness has fallen off in America because the "picking is getting thin", particularly for the lone inventor who cannot afford elaborate equipment. History shows that most inventions are accomplished using inexpensive equipment. Ziegler revolutionized polymer syntheses when he mixed two cheap well-known chemicals together and bubbled ethylene through a suspension of them in a glass flask — total cost of materials and equipment, a few dollars. The inventors of the transistor used only cheap materials and ran simple tests. Carlson reduced his invention to practice in a "garret" using materials purchased from a meager budget. Important research of the future is certain to include energy from solar radiation, recovery of minerals from sea water, and new and improved methods for producing food. Low cost research is possible in all three of these fields as well as in others.

Inventivesness is not new; the ancients practiced it to glorify their gods, their royalty, and to make war. The great Pyramid of Cheops at Giza, which was built some 4,500 years ago, was made with more than two million stone blocks, each weighing over two tons. The Greeks had huge battering rams up to 120 feet long, made of wood and sheathed with iron; and towers up to 180 feet high mounted on wheels, which could be moved to fortified walls in order to hurdle stones and other missiles on the enemy. New materials were developed for statues, paintings, and weapons but little thought was given to improving the health of the populace, providing more food and better shelter, and to devise labor-saving devices for decreasing human drudgery and help to end slavery.

In our research and development today some inventive talents continue to be devoted to useless things. As Bell was forced to do, an inventor may have to spend hundreds of hours preparing legal briefs and testifying at patent litigation court proceedings. When an inventor makes a good invention instead of acknowledging a job well done and paying a reasonable royalty for its use, some companies will have members of their technical staff spend months combing the literature in an attempt to find some obscure reference which will nullify the new invention. Research, which is purely for image-forming purposes, should also be condemned.

There are those who deplore invention and science generally as creating more problems than are solved and yearn for the "good old days". They forget the trials of those days. Goodyear lost six of his 12 children before they were one year of age. The mother of Morse, of telegraph fame, lost eight of her 11 children in infancy. After being shot in 1881, President Garfield, who certainly had the best medical care available, lay suffering in the White House in the torrid summer heat and high humidity. The only relief was to move him to the seashore. He probably did not die from the bullet wound but rather from infection from unclean hands of physicians who probed his wound. A charity patient today receives far better care than did President Garfield.

Greek scholars had time to gather in the square and discuss philosophy because slaves toiled for them. Joel Hildebrand adds (14):

352

Modern philosophers owe their leisure to meditate and write to a different kind of slave — electric power — as they sit in the midst of comforts made possible by work of scientists and engineers. But for these they might be wielding hoes instead of pens or they might have died in infancy. Despite all this, some, as they write, regret that society had not long ago seen fit to starve out science!

Science and technology offer the greatest promise for world peace. Most of the wars of the past were to steal treasures from others, to get slaves, and to seize territory to provide raw materials and living space for growing populations. The inventor has made it possible that nations skilled in technology can be prosperous even though short in raw materials and space. Switzerland has been a long time example of this. Japan is the emerging excellent example. Furthermore, because of scientists creating the atomic bomb, perhaps Alfred Nobel's prediction has been realized; a weapon so terrible that nations will refrain from war.

Inventors have probably played a greater role in the development of the United States than have statesmen. Shortly after the Louisiana Purchase in 1803, President Jefferson lamented that it would take 1,000 years to develop the country west of the Mississippi. He was thinking in terms of the stagecoach and the wagon. Steam power and the telegraph cut his projected time tenfold. Slavery existed in the South in 1860 because it was economical, not because southerners were more wicked than their northern countrymen who had found slavery uneconomical in their more industrialized economy. If there had been an "Edison" several decades earlier, it is possible that there would have been no Civil War. The

353

electric motor and electric light, which greatly spurred industrialization, particularly of the small shop variety, and resultant labor-saving devices could have emancipated the slave rather than the tragedy of war. Shortly after the turn of the century, Woodrow Wilson, president of Princeton University, expressed the fear that the new automobile would usher socialism into this country. The masses would see the rich travelling rapidly around the countryside in their luxurious vehicles, whereas they would continue to travel by means of the plodding horse. Henry Ford, the inventor who subsequently obtained a total of 161 U.S. patents, solved the problem by building an auto so inexpensive that the ordinary citizen could also own one.

Does an interest in invention help an individual do a better job at other things? Abraham Lincoln, who had only six months of formal education, had a great interest in inventions and new things generally. As a Congressman, Lincoln loved to roam the exhibit room of the Patent Office examining models. On May 22, 1849 he obtained U.S. Patent 6,469 for "Buoying Vessels over Shoals". A number of expansible buoyant chambers are placed at the sides of a vessel. Upon lowering the chambers into the water and filling with air, the ship is buoyed and thus passes over a sand bar or the like. Although this invention appears quite practical, it has never been put into commerical use.

Lincoln served as patent counsel in a number of lawsuits. He saw the advantages of the railroad to the state of Illinois and he fought in the courts to remove impediments to its progress. In 1860 Lincoln gave a speech in Springfield, Illinois on the subject of inventions (15). This was apparently an attempt to raise additional funds for his political aspirations.

Did Lincoln make a better war-time President because he

354

had an interest in and some knowledge of inventions? The answer would appear to be yes. As commander in chief of the armed forces he felt no inventor of a supposedly superior weapon should be dismissed without a fair hearing. He often met with them after they had been turned down by ordnance officials. Although he found many inventors "not infrequently carried to eccentricity", Lincoln helped in the development of balloons for observation purposes, the repeating rifle, the machine gun, and it was only because of his pressure on the Union Admiralty that Ericsson's *Monitor* was built.

Lincoln felt that the desire to invent is ingrained in the human soul and in his speech on invention, he cited many Biblical references. In spite of his trials of war, he helped promote and signed an act of 1862 which set up our land-grant colleges and universities. He saw the need for experiment stations to improve farming methods. The setting up of these educational centers for specialization in agriculture and the mechanical arts was a part of Lincoln's greatness.

Innovation can be of great value if not of the patentable variety. P. T. Barnum developed techniques for assembling, disassembling, and transporting his circus with a precision whereby thousands of things, animals, and people ended up at the right places at the right times, and quickly. The German General Staff was so impressed by the mobility of Barnum's circus that when it performed in Germany, a detailed study was made of its transportation methods. Lawrence Welk adopted a certain musical style and type of program whereas his band stayed in business while most of the other large bands were disbanding. Welk's ability to innovate and his self education in music resulted in a farm boy of little formal education becoming one of national reputation.

Although some have criticized the methods of Edison as being grossly empirical (16), it is fortunate for humanity that inventors have not waited until theoreticians could explain their results. Chemists still do not know the chemical reactions which rubber and sulfur undergo in vulcanization as carried out by Goodyear well over a hundred years ago. Although hundreds of billions of aspirin tablets have been taken internally since 1893, when it was first introduced as a medicine, no one has been able to explain how aspirin functions as a pain killer. I read recently where the science of the boomerang has now been solved by the use of computers! All this goes to prove that inventions can be made by people who cannot explain why they get the results they do.

In the biographical chapters the author has given more detailed information than was necessary to substantiate the conclusions made in the later chapters. Perhaps the reader can make additional deductions from these life histories and from reference material which he may choose to read. Hopefully these biographies have added something to the reader's knowledge of history over that which he was taught during his formal education. Most history courses in our schools and colleges contain little relative to the part that technology and invention have played in the development of our country and the world.

REFERENCES AND APPENDICES

Chapter 1

1) Goodyear's original book was entitled *Gum-Elastic and Its Varieties*, published in 1853 by Yale College. Another printing was issued in 1855. This book, in two volumes with a total of 624 pages, has been the source of most of the information on Goodyear's life for biographers. Volume I deals with a great variety of subjects relating to rubber including his own experiments, claims, and future plans. The second volume lists hundreds of uses for his vulcanized rubber and some information as to methods of preparation. Both of these editions were published while Goodyear was out of the country. Actually the manuscript was incomplete with many blank spaces in the text.

Only a few copies of the original publication remain. However, fortunately for posterity, in 1937 Maclaren and Sons, Ltd. of London issued a photostatic reproduction of the original in one-volume form entitled *Gum Elastic*.

2) Benjamin Silliman (1779-1864) taught chemistry, mineralogy, geology, and pharmacy at Yale College. Among his various books he published "Elements of Chemistry" in 1830. Although Silliman was apparently quite interested in Goodyear's work, having commented favorably both on his acid-gas process and later on sulfur vulcanization, there is no evidence that he contributed any suggestion which helped Goodyear in his experimental work.

Silliman's son (1816-1885), also named Benjamin but who apparently never used the suffix junior with his name, followed in his father's footsteps. After teaching at the University of Louisville, Kentucky from 1849-1854, he returned to Yale to succeed his father on retirement in the chair of chemistry. The younger Silliman is most noted for his work with the young petroleum industry which brought in the first producing oil well near Titusville, Pennsylvania in 1859.

3) Barker, P. W., *Charles Goodyear*, p. 39, Godfrey L. Cabot Inc., Boston, Massachusetts, 1940.

4) Helpful to the nonchemist, the process of vulcanization can be likened to that of making a ladder or net starting with individual ropes. A mass of ropes has no overall strength. If two long ropes are coupled together with short splices to make a ladder, the composite has strength in all directions. If two or more of the ladders are spliced together, the composite becomes a net and the overall rigidity increases. Just like a mass of ropes can be coupled together to make one net, the thousands of molecules making up a piece of rubber can be spliced together by sulfur atoms to make molecules so huge that they will not dissolve in solvents.

5) Wolf, Ralph, *India Rubber Man*, pp. 103-04, Caxton Printers, Ltd., Caldwell, Idaho, 1939.

(6) Goodyear, Charles, U.S. Patent 3,633 (June 15, 1844). The broadest claim covered "the process of exposing the India Rubber fabric to the action of a high degree of heat ... " Although the title of this patent is "Improvement in India-Rubber Fabrics", it is stated that the rubber compound may be used without fabric. White lead or some other lead salt or oxide is employed along with the rubber and sulfur. The temperature of cure is cited as 212-350°F with 270° preferred. This shows evidence of good experimental data.

On the surface it may appear that coverage by this patent was narrow since it dealt only with ternary mixtures containing a lead compound. However, binary mixtures of rubber and sulfur were adequately covered by Nathaniel Hayward's U.S. Patent 1,090 (Feb. 24, 1839), which was assigned to Goodyear. This patent's one claim reads as follows: "The combination of sulfur with gum-elastic, either in solution or in substance, either in modes above pointed out or in any other which is substantially the same." In his U.S. Patent 3,633 Goodyear states, "...I do not now claim the combining of sulfur with caoutchouc...this combination having been the subject of a patent granted to me on the 24th of February, 1839." Actually No, 1,090 was not granted to him but rather to Nathaniel Hayward and assigned to him.

The chemical reaction of sulfur with rubber is very slow but can be speeded up by a third ingredient which does not actually enter into the vulcanization reaction. Goodyear covered " ... the carbonate of lead, other salts of lead or the oxides of that metal ... " as such agents. Litharge (lead monoxide) was the most widely used vulcanization accelerator for over 50 years. However it was soon found that other inorganic materials such as lime, magnesia, and antimony sulfide could be used as vulcanization accelerators. Hence from the standpoint of patent infringement, it was fortunate that Goodyear's earlier caveat had disclosed the third ingredient more broadly.

(7) Goodyear, Charles, *Gum-Elastic*, pp. 225-27, Maclaren and Sons, London, 1937.

(8) Barker, P. W., p. 74.

(9) Wolf, Ralph, *India Rubber Man*, pp. 192-95, Caxton Printers, Ltd., Caldwell, Idaho, 1939.

(10) Barker, P. W., pp. 88-89.

(11) Regli, Adolph, *Rubber's Goodyear*, pp. 204-06, Julian Messner, Inc., New York, 1941.

(12) Goodyear, William, *Architectural Record* (1905) *17*, 433-35.

This article by William Henry Goodyear was an editorial in connection with the statue of Charles Goodyear by F. M. L. Tonetti, designed for the St. Louis World's Fair of 1904. At the time of writing this article, William was Curator of Fine Arts at the Brooklyn Museum. As pointed out by his son in this article, following 1844 Charles Goodyear had a very good income. However, he

358

excessive spending on developing uses for rubber often left him without adequate funds. Besides his heavy expenses at the two fairs in Europe, plus that of living abroad for six years, several of his research projects cost several thousand dollars each. For example he spent $5,000 in developing rubberized sails for boats and an approximately equal amount attempting to rust-proof steel by means of rubber coatings. The subsequent income to the estate was likely the relatively high royalty income during the Civil War period when the demand for rubber goods was much above pre-war level.

3) Barker, P. W., p. 96.

Chapter 2

1) Bell, Alexander, U.S. Patent 161,739 (April 6, 1875).

This was the first of the so-called harmonic telegraphy patents. Signals are transmitted simultaneously by instruments, each of which creates a succession of electrical impulses differing in rate from the others. Each receiver is tuned to a pitch at which it is put into vibration to produce its fundamental note by one, and only one, of the transmitters.

) Bell, Alexander, U.S. Patent 174,465 (March 7, 1876).

The title of this patent is "Improvement in Telegraphy", and although it is the basic telephone patent, the word *telephone* does not occur. Its originality is the use of a continuous undulatory electric current to transmit and receive telegraphic messages in contrast to the intermittent or pulsatory current previously used. Claim 5 is the most illustrative of the invention: "The method of, and apparatus for, transmitting vocal or other sounds telegraphically, as herein described, by causing electrical undulations, similar in form to the vibrations of the air accompanying the said vocal or other sounds, substantially as set forth."

) Bell, Alexander, U.S. Patent 186,787 (January 30, 1877).

This patent is a followup of 174,465 in which there is more emphasis on apparatus. In the earlier patent a stretched membrane with a disc of iron or magnet attached thereto was used for creating an undulatory current in insulated wires wrapped around an electro or permanent magnet. An important feature of this patent is the substitution of "a plate of iron or steel capable of being thrown into vibration by sounds" for the membrane and attached armature. In this patent the words *telephone* and *telephony* are freely used.

) *The Bell Telephone – Deposition of Alexander Graham Bell*, printed by the American Bell Telephone Company, Boston, 1908.

This book is available in many of the larger libraries in United States. Besides the depositions for the earlier suits, it includes that for the suit by the United States to annul the Bell patents. Although this suit never came to court, because of its unique nature, it is discussed in some detail in Chapter 8.

As well as the depositions, this reference book reproduces in full the two patents of References (2) and (3). Although Bell was granted a total of 30 United States patents, these two constitute the so-called Bell patents.

Another good source of history of the telephone: Rhodes, Frederick, *Beginnings of Telephony*, Harper and Brothers, New York, 1929.

(5) Bell, Alexander, U.S. Patents:
    235,199 – December 7, 1880
    235,496 – December 14, 1880
    235,497 – December 14, 1880
    235,616 – December 21, 1880

(6) Read, Oliver and Welch, Walter, *From Tin Foil to Stereo*, Howard W. Sams, Indianapolis, 1959.

(7) Catherine Mackenzie's book, *Alexander Graham Bell*, Grosset & Dunlap, New York, 1928, has a very good section on Bell's work on aircraft. Since the author states in the "Preface" that F. W. Baldwin checked over this section of her manuscript, the account should be highly authentic.

The pamphlet made available by the Canadian Department of Indian Affairs and Northern Development entitled "Alexander Graham Bell Museum, Baddeck, Nova Scotia", has an excellent but brief summary of Bell's work as an "Aeronautical Scientist".

(8) Bell, Alexander, *Proceedings Amer. Assoc. Adv. Science*, 31st meeting (August 1882) pp. 151-206.

(9) Osborne, Harold S., "Biographical Memoir of Alexander Graham Bell," *Biographical Memoirs, National Academy of Sciences* (1945) *23*, 1-29. This biography includes a list of 61 of Bell's major writings and addresses. It also includes a list of Bell's U.S. patents by number, date of issue, and subject. He was a co-inventor in case of six of his 30 patents.

(10) Bruce, Robert, *Alexander Graham Bell and The Conquest of Solitude*, Little Brown and Company, Boston, 1973. It is surprising that the official biography of Bell was not published until 51 years after his death. He wanted and expected a biography to be written and went to great pains to preserve material for it. Mabel Bell spoke often of it during the few months following her husband's death. The long delay removed such pertinent witnesses as his daughters and David Fairchild. Author Bruce reports one luncheon date with son-in-law Gilbert Grosvenor in 1965, one year before the latter's death at the age of 90.

Chapter 3

(1) Greenfield Village at Dearborn, Michigan was built by Henry Ford to preserve many features of American life of the late 19th century. An important part of

this restoration is Edison's Menlo Park laboratory and auxiliary buildings, as well as the Jordan Boarding House across the street and Edison's small laboratory from Fort Myers. Adjacent to the Village is the vast Henry Ford Museum, housed in an enlarged replica of Independence Hall of Philadelphia. Literally thousands of exhibits portray the accomplishments of American industry and invention. The corporate title of Greenfield Village and the Henry Ford Museum is The Edison Institute.

2) There have been numerous books written about Thomas Edison and most public libraries have copies of some of them. Although many are out of print, the latest and most complete biography is still available as a paperback: Josephson, Matthew, *Edison*, McGraw-Hill, New York, 1959.

A recent book, Frost, L. A., *The Thomas A. Edison Album*, Superior Publishing Co. Seattle, Washington, 1969, has the most complete set of photographs dealing with Edison of any publication. Unfortunately there are very few pictures from his winter home at Fort Myers. The book, in addition to the pictorial material, is a fairly complete biography.

Other current books which cover more specific phases of Edison's career include the following:

(a) Silverberg, Robert, *Light for the World*, Van Nostrand, Princeton, New Jersey, 1967.

(b) Vanderbilt, B. M., *Thomas Edison, Chemist*, American Chemical Society, Washington, D. C., 1971.

(c) Welch, W. L., *Charles Batchelor, Edison's Chief Partner*, Syracuse University, Syracuse, New York, 1972.

3) Jewett, F. B., "Edison's Contributions to Science and Industry", *Science* (January 15, 1932) *75*, 67.

4) Vanderbilt, B. M., *Thomas Edison, Chemist*, American Chemical Society, Washington, D. C., 1971. Chapter 5, pp. 138-77, entitled "Iron Ore Concentration", describes this project in detail.

5) "The Edison Concentrating Works", *Iron Age* (October 28, 1897), p. 1.

6) Dickson, Antonia, Dickson, W. K. L., *The Century Magazine* (June 1894) *48*, 206.

7) Hendricks, Gordon, *The Edison Motion Picture Myth*, University of California Press, Berkeley, 1961.

Dickson, an Englishman, began work with Edison in 1883. Beginning in 1887 Dickson was assigned nearly full time work on photography, which included duties as the official laboratory photographer. As Edison became embroiled in his iron ore project, Dickson had considerable freedom of operation. He was very active in the Orange Camera Club, gave talks before groups on photography, and published. Besides the article in *Century Magazine* (Reference 6), he again collaborated with his sister, Antonia, to write the book:

The Life and Inventions of Thomas Alva Edison.

In 1893 Charles Batchelor, now a wealthy man, left Edison's employ although he continued to carry out certain special assignments for him. Batchelor was replaced as laboratory manager by W. E. Gilmore. Edison' finances were in sore array as expenditures at the Ogdensburg ore plant continued to mount with little income from the phonograph and other inventions. The discipline at the laboratories suddenly became more rigid as the bustling Gilmore strove to put the laboratories on a more businesslike basis. Dickson no longer had the freedom as he did under Batchelor. Dickson's heart and soul were in photography, and when Edison showed little interest in developing a projector for motion pictures, Dickson became friendly with the Lathams, a father and sons group who were trying to develop such a projector. Gilmore became aware of this and Dickson was asked to resign. He then worked for a time with the Lathams and later joined the American Mutoscope and Biograph Company. The latter company soon put out a peep-show machine in competition with the Kinetoscope. Dickson shortly thereafter returned to his native England.

That the motion picture industry was highly skeptical of Hendricks conclusions is indicated by Raymond Fielding's review of *The Edison Motion Picture Myth* appearing in *Flims in Review*. Following is a paragraph taken from that book review:

> But far more important is the fact that because Mr. Hendricks is so obviously partisan the professional scholar and critical reader is led to wonder to what extent accuracy may have been compromised by his pre-commitments. Many readers will suspect that Mr. Hendricks reached his conclusions long before he began his research.

Although Dickson outlived Edison, he apparently never made a derogatory remark about Edison. Hendricks explains this apparent tranquility because Edison continued to pay Dickson his $30/week salary after leaving Edison's employment and thus Dickson was "afraid to talk". I find no evidence that Edison continued these salary payments although he sent Dickson some money later in his life when the latter appealed for financial aid.

(8) Scott, L. N., "Naval Consulting Board of the United States", Government Printing Office, Washington, D. C., 1920.

(9) Polhamus, L. G., "Plants Collected and Tested by Thomas A. Edison as Possible Sources of Domestic Rubber", Agricultural Research Service ARS 34-74, July 1967.

Chapter 4

(1) Leupp, Francis, *George Westinghouse, His Life and Achievements*, Little, Brown and Company, Boston, 1918.

(2) Prout, Henry, *A Life of George Westinghouse*, Charles Scribner's and Sons, New York, 1922. This book was sponsored by the American Society of Mechanical Engineers.

(3) Westinghouse, George, U.S. Patent 50,759 (October 31, 1865).

(4) Westinghouse, George, U.S. Patent 61,967 (February 12, 1867).

(5) Westinghouse, George, U.S. Patent 245,591 (August 9, 1881).

(6) Edison, Thomas, U.S. Patent 223,898 (January 27, 1880).

(7) Prout, Reference 2, lists Westinghouse's total patents beginning on p. 332 of his treatise. In addition on pages 341-67 are listed short summaries of the patents which Prout considered most important.

(8)   Westinghouse, George, U.S. Patents 1,031,759 (July 9, 1912) and 1,036,043 (August 20, 1912). The spring consisted of two telescoping tubes arranged in a near vertical position with the lower, smaller-diameter tube projecting into the upper tube. The upper tube contained air and the lower one a liquid, such as glycerin. The upper tube had a check valve which opened when compressed and partially closed on the extension movement. The only fluid to escape at the packing was the liquid and there was a device, actuated by movement of the spring, to return this small amount of liquid to the lower chamber.

     Westinghouse's telescopic, pneumatic cylinder spring was the first commercial device to improve the riding comfort of automobiles over the old steel leaf spring which had previously been used in carriages.

(9) One of the most recent books on American inventors is *Those Inventive Americans*, published by the National Geographic Society in 1971. The book contains no article on George Westinghouse even though inventors from Benjamin Franklin to Charles Townes are discussed. There are 12 pages dealing with Cyrus McCormick. Admittedly McCormick made an important contribution to world agriculture, but it is difficult to classify him as a great inventor; and certainly he should not be rated as highly as George Westinghouse. We apparently need a better yardstick for the evaluation of inventors and their inventions.

(10) The Hall of Fame for Great Americans, which honors U.S. citizens who have achieved lasting distinction, stands at the summit of University Heights on the uptown campus of New York University. It was established in 1900. Any man or woman who was a citizen of the United States, who made his home in the United States, and who has been deceased 25 years or more is eligible for election. The choices are entirely in the hands of its electoral college, made up of approximately 100 men and women from every state of the Union, and from every field of endeavor.

     Bronze portrait busts of those who have been elected are placed, facing one

363

another, in the open-air colonnade. Below each bust is a recessed tablet which commemorates the person honored.

Chapter 5

(1) Fifty-one pages of this book are Acheson's own words. This is a factual story of Acheson's failures as well as his successes told with a minimum of rhetoric.

(2) Szymanowitz, Raymond, *Edward Goodrich Acheson*, Vantage Press, New York, 1971. Mr. Szymanowitz knew Edward Acheson and many of the latter's close associates. Acheson's personal and business papers were made available to him. This is an excellent reference book and much of it makes highly interesting reading as well. I wish to acknowledge this biography as a major source of material for Chapter 5.

(3) *A Pathfinder*, Acheson Industries, Inc., Port Huron, Michigan, 1965, pp. 15-16.

(4) As Reference 3, p. 18.

(5) Although Acheson was getting a low salary, during the early development of the carbon filament light, many ambitious young men worked at Menlo Park for their meals and lodging. As jobs opened up in manufacturing and the setting up of the first central electric generating plant, the better ones were put on the payroll. Edison didn't worry about contracts with his employees and security rules were lax. Once the light was a commercial success, several of his employees took jobs with competitive companies.

(6) As Reference 3, p. 32.

(7) Acheson, E. G., U.S. Patents 342,892 and 343,099 (June 1, 1886).
   The first is a product patent and the second a process one covering a preferred method for preparing the composition covered in 342,892. The cable consisted of a primary conductor such as a copper wire, insulation such as cotton fibers impregnated with asphalt, and a flexible metal sheath deposited on the insulation by an electrolytic process. In the last mentioned step the insulation was first coated with a graphite powder to make the surface conductive and then a film of copper deposited by electrolysis. The composite was then coated with coal tar or the like.
   This was an ingenious invention. The copper sheath could be deposited in a continuous operation. In practice the sheath could be grounded and thus serve as a magnetic shield to protect the primary conductor from neighboring electrical circuits, or it could be used as the return conductor.

(8) Acheson obtained six patents on what he called thermoelectric or calelectric generators. His improved techniques were covered in three patents issuing July 30, 1889: 407,761-62-63. Acheson had two approaches to the construction of such electric generators. One was to heat the junctions of two different metals

at different temperatures, and the other was heating the iron core of a transformer.

The generation of an electric current at the junction of two dissimilar metals is the principle used with thermocouples for measuring temperatures. Copper and iron wires are often used for this purpose. However, the current generated is very small. Acheson apparently hoped to find a combination of metals which would give a much stronger current and a higher electrical potential. In patents U.S. 407,761 and 407,763 he subjected such thermocouple junctions to the action of a transformer as well. He states that he got more electrical energy than just from the dynamo, which furnished alternating current to the transformer, plus that from the thermocouple used singly.

U.S. Patent 407,762 deals with a transformer in the form of an iron ring which was heated by an external source. This patent is obviously of the "paper" variety; no experimental data are given.

Acheson's results from his attempts to convert thermal energy directly to electrical energy never approached commercial reality. His patents filed on the subject were speculative with the apparent hope that he or someone else would subsequently make major improvements within the scope of his patents.

(9) Acheson's patents dealing with the preparation of synthetic graphite include the following:

U.S. 568,323 . . . . September 29, 1896
617,979 . . . . January 17, 1899
645,285 . . . . March 13, 1900
711,031 . . . . October 14, 1902
836,355 . . . . November 20, 1906

Although Acheson's patents on preparing graphite were filed over a period of over 10 years, he never got away from the concept that graphite was formed as a two-step process; i. e., a carbide is first formed and this decomposes to its elements liberating the carbon as graphite. Acheson's first patent of this series, 568,323, uses only 50 percent of ground coke in the reaction mixture and differs from his basic Carborundum patent, 492,767, only that a higher temperature is used.

By the time Acheson filed his patent application which resulted in U.S. 645,285, he apparently was beginning to see "the light". In this patent he covered natural carbon materials containing inorganic impurities, such as anthracite coal, as the sole raw material for making graphite. His patentability dealt with the use of less than the stoichiometric proportion of silica or the like to form carbides and postulated that such inorganic oxides functioned as "a catalytic or progressive action". He attributed the high yields of graphite from non-coking coals, containing up to 95 percent carbon, to the uniform distribution of impurities in such natural products. If Acheson ever realized that carbide formation is not a significant factor in the manufacture of synthetic graphite, he never admitted it publicly.

Petroleum coke is the primary raw material used today in the manufacture of graphite. Acheson covered this raw material in U.S. 836,355, which was directed to making finely divided graphite suitable for use as a lubricant.

Petroleum coke is relatively free of non-carbon materials which may lead to the formation of stable carbides which do not decompose at the synthesis temperature. Since carbides are highly abrasive, their presence in a lubricant is, of course, highly objectionable.

(10) Acheson, E. G., U.S. Patents 560,291 (May 19, 1896) and 718,892 (January 20, 1903).

(11) Acheson, E. G., U.S. 693,482 (February 18, 1902).

(12) Although graphite dispersions did not become the "universal lubricant" as visualized by Acheson, such products continue to have special uses. With the advent of oil-soluble chemical additives for lubricants in the early 1930's, work with dispersed solids in liquid lubricants largely ceased. Solid additives, such as graphite, now find major uses in greases. Acheson Industries, Inc. – originally named the Acheson Oildag Company – is a robust company with headquarters in Port Huron, Michigan and manufacturing facilities in England, Holland, and Japan as well as in United States. Coatings, additives, and process lubricants are marketed world-wide. Two grandsons, Howard, Jr., and James Acheson, are active in the business which Edward Acheson founded in 1908.

Chapter 6

(1) The corresponding U.S. patent is 50,617 (Oct. 24, 1865). In order to get more specific patent coverage Nobel subsequently broke down this patent into four reissued patents 3,377; 3,378; 3,379; and 3,380, all of April 13, 1869. These not only dealt with means of exploding nitroglycerin but also a continuous process for preparing it.

Nobel's U.S. Patent 57,175 (Aug. 14, 1866) covered an improved grade of nitroglycerin as compared to that of Sebrero. He claimed a more stable product because of a higher melting point and one free of "hyponitric acid". He was probably dealing with nitrous acid, not the highly unstable hyponitric acid. By this patent Nobel attempted to cover nitroglycerin as a new commercial explosive even though it was an old compound and known to have explosive properties.

(2) Nobel's basic dynamite patents include the following:
England, Patent No. 1,345 (May 7, 1867)
Sweden, Patent No. 102 (September 19, 1867)
United States, Patent No. 78,317 (May 26, 1868)

This United States patent was also reissued as several patents in order to get more extensive claims. Nobel's dynamite patents covered the combination of nitroglycerin with any inert adsorbent solid. An additional advantage over liquid nitroglycerin was that of not permeating into seams of the rock from the drill hole. Also the percussion cap was conveniently pressed into the solid dynamite.

366

) The list was actually drawn up by Nobel and left in his personal records; Bergengren, Erik, *Alfred Nobel* p. 67, Thomas Nelson and Sons Ltd., New York, 1962.

4) U. S. Patent 175,735 (April 4, 1876).

5) Bergengren, Erik *Alfred Nobel* pp. 111-12, Thomas Nelson and Sons Ltd., New York 1962.

6) The only evidence of this episode in Nobel's life is the following poem, found among his personal papers after his death:

> A young girl who, good and beautiful,
> Looked up to me, to me alone, for love.
> No selfish motive drew the link between us,
> No parents whispered of a proper match.
> Why then loved she? Because it was her nature
> As fragrance is the nature of the rose.
>
> . . . .
>
> My life, till then a dreary desert like,
> Revived to bliss and hope. I had an aim,
> A heavenly aim – to win that lovely girl
> And to be worthy her . . .
>
>   . . . I felt
> Supremely happy, and we met again,
> And oft again till we had grown to be
> A heaven to one another; and I learned
> The sweet compassion of her love and sealed
> It with a kiss, the chaste and hallowed kiss
> Of pure affection though no eye was there
> Save the Almighty's to keep watch o'er us.
> This might have ended in the usual manner
> And brought the joys and griefs of wedded life;
> But 'twas not so ordained, another bridegroom
> Had stronger claims – she's wedded to her grave.

7) Since 1926 the Foundation has had its offices in its own building in Stockholm: Nobel House, Sturegatan 14. The Nobel funds have been invested primarily in Sweden and Norway, but to some degree in other countries. Beginning in 1946 the Foundation has been exempted from taxation on its holdings as well as on the revenue therefrom, except the local real estate tax.

8) William K. Stuckey in a recent article, *Saturday Review Science* (Sept. 2, 1972) 55 (36), 33-39, entitled "The Prize", cites as one of the rules for the potential Nobel prize awardee, "Work with certain people in certain laboratories in certain countries."

Chapter 7

(1) Tate, A. O., *Edison's Open Door*, p. 145, E. P. Dutton, New York, 1938.

(2) Warren, W. P., *The Century Magazine* (July 1911) *82*, 415-19.

(3) Rosanoff, M. A., *Harper's Monthly Magazine* (1932) *165*, 402-17.

Chapter 8

(1) A booklet entitled "General Information Concerning Patents" may be obtained free on request to the Patent Office. Many other aids for the potential inventor may be purchased from the Superintendent of Documents, Washington, D. C. 20402. These include:
    (a) Patents and Inventions, An Information Aid for Inventors
    (b) Roster of Attorneys and Agents Registered to Practice Before the United States Patent Office
    (c)Directory of Registered Patent Attorneys and Agents Arranged by States and Cities
    (d) The Story of the United States Patent Office
    The *Official Gazette of the United States Patent Office* is published each Tuesday simultaneously with the weekly issue of patents. It contains the number, a claim, and a selected drawing (if any) of each patent granted that day. Copies of the *Gazette* may be found in large public libraries, many university libraries, as well as in offices of most large law firms and research laboratories. The present cost of an annual subscription, domestic, is $50, available from the Superintendent of Documents. Individual patents, regardless of the date of issue, may be ordered directly from the Patent Office at a cost of 50 cents each.

(2) Vanderbilt, B. M., *Thomas Edison, Chemist*, pp. 320-44, American Chemical Society, Washington, D.C., 1971.

(3) Goodyear, Charles, *Gum-Elastic and Its Varieties*, pp. 235-46, Yale College, New Haven, Connecticut, 1855.

(4) Mackenzie, Catherine, *Alexander Graham Bell*, pp. 258-60, Grosset & Dunlap, New York, 1928.

(5) Norwig, E. A., "The Patents of Thomas A. Edison", *J. Patent Office Soc.* (1954) *36*, 213-32 and 275-96.
    This article, published in the March and April 1954 issues, is highly authentic. Norwig was a member of the Patent Office for many years and served as Administrative Assistant to the Commissioner prior to his retirement.
    Edison's patents are also listed by Dyer and Martin in their two-volume *Edison, His Life and Inventions*. The list is, of course, incomplete in both the 1910 and the 1929 editions. However, this source may be of special interest to some since the dates of execution are given rather than the dates of issue.

6) Read, Oliver, Welch, W. L., *From Tin Foil to Stereo*, Howard W. Sams, Indianapolis, 1959.

7) Edison, T. A., U.S. Patent 493,426 (March 14, 1893).

Edison, T. A., U.S. Patent 589,168 (August 31, 1897).

The latter patent was reissued in 1902 as 12,037 and 12,038, and again in January 1904 as 12,192.

Both of the original patents were applied for at the same time, August 24, 1891. The first covered Edison's peep-hole Kinetoscope in which a continuous film of positive pictures was passed before the eye. A shutter successively exposed and covered the pictures.

The second patent dealt with the camera, one of Edison's most important patents. The film was moved intermittently, being held at rest 90% of the time. It was capable of taking up to 46 photographs a second.

Another Edison patent, U.S. 1,178,062 of April 4, 1916, was a forerunner of the talkie motion picture. As the film moved through a projector it actuated various sound devices of a phonographic nature at appropriate times. It also disclosed the use of colored light for projecting the pictures. Although this patent was never of commercial importance, it is another example of Edison pointing the way to future developments.

"Mr. Edison's Forty Years of Litigation", *The Literary Digest* (September 13, 1913) *47*, 449-50.

Dyer, F. L., Martin T. C., *Edison, His Life and Inventions I*, p. 188, Harper, New York, 1910.

Crawford, Remsen, "Patents, Profits and Pirates", *The Saturday Evening Post* (September 27, 1930) *203*, 3. Excerpt reprinted with permission of The Curtis Publishing Company.

Syzmanowitz, Raymond, *Edward Goodrich Acheson*, p. 288, Vantage Press, New York, 1971.

Pauli, H. E., *Alfred Nobel*, p. 198, Nicholson & Watson, London, 1947.

Nevins, Allan, *Ford, the Times, the Man, the Company*, Charles Scribner's Sons, New York, 1954.

Scott, O. J., "The Great General Tire Patent Suit", *Rubber World* (October 1964) 33-39.

Time, the Weekly Newsmagazine, (June 26, 1972) *99*, No. 26, 80-88.

Chapter 9

(1) Taylor, C. W., Barron, Frank, *Scientific Creativity: Its Recognition and Development*, John Wiley & Sons, Inc. New York, 1963.
This book is made up of selected papers from the first three University of Utah Conferences. Papers from the fourth conference were published in 1964 (McGraw-Hill Book Co.) and those from the 5th conference also in 1964 (John Wiley & Sons). Numerous other books on the general subject of creativity were published during this period, most of the authors having been active in these conferences.

(2) Rossman, Joseph, *Industrial Creativity, the Psychology of the Inventor* University Books, New Hyde Park, New-York, 1963.

(3) Kent, A. P. "Current Patent Office Procedures", *Chem. Tech.* (October 1972) 599-605.

(4) Goertzel, Victor and Goertzel, Mildred, *Cradles of Eminence*, Little Brown & Co., Boston, 1962.

(5) Jewkes, John; Sawers, David; Stillerman, Richard, *The Sources of Invention*, W. W. Norton & Co., New York, 1968.

(6) Tschunkur, E., Bock, E., U.S. Patent 1,938,730 (1933) and Konrad, E. Tschunkur, E., U.S. Patent 1,973,000 (1934).

(7) Collins, A. M., *Rubber Chem. and Tech.* (June 1973) *46*, G48-52.

(8) Williams, R. J., *Nutrition Against Disease*, p. 26, Pitman Publishing Corp., New York, 1973.

(9) Eccles, J. C., "The Physiology of Imagination", *Scien. Amer.* (September 1958) *199*, 135.

(10) Gordon, W. J. J., *Synectics*, Harper and Brothers, New York, 1961.
Prince, G. M., *The Practice of Creativity*, Harper and Row, New York, 1970.

(11) "Interactions of Science and Technology in the Innovative Process: Some Case Studies", a final report prepared by the Battelle Columbus Laboratories for the National Science Foundation (March 19, 1973). There is an abridged version of this report entitled "Science, Technology, and Innovation". Both reports are available from the National Science Foundation, Washington, D.C. 20550.

(12) Clark, R. D., "Can the Chemical Industry Afford Research?" *Chem. Tech.* (November 1972) 656-59.

(13) As Reference 5, p. 228.

Wohlauer, G.,"Scholar on Skis – Hildebrand at 90", *Chem. Tech.* (April 1972) 216-19.

Joel H. Hildebrand, long time professor of chemistry at the University of California, Berkeley, has described science in the making as follows:

> . . . starting with hunches, making guesses (most of which prove to be wild), making many mistakes, going off on blind roads before hitting on one which seems to be going in the right direction.

Smith, A. M., "A. Lincoln, Inventor", *Jour. Patent Office Soc.* (July 1959) *41*, 447-57.

Chem. Eng. News (September 16, 1968) *46*, 62-63.

This staff article reports an interview with Dr. Roald Hoffmann, Cornell University, in connection with his receiving the 1963 ACS Award in Pure Chemistry. Hoffmann is quoted as saying:

> . . . chemists work without much help from theory, and parts of the chemical industry chug along on Edisonian research . . .

Since Webster defines "to chug" as "to proceed or operate as with a laboring engine", Hoffmann's description of Edisonian research is certainly not complimentary. Other scientists, mostly of the academic world, have also used the term, Edison approach, to describe research carried out by endless random testing. One of the incomprehensible aspects of Edison's career is that his name should be used to describe an unscientific approach to research when, in reality, he was the first to carry out applied research using the best scientific methods of his time.

In contrast we have the remarks of Charles Steinmetz, who was a theoretician as well as an engineer, at the time of the 35th anniversary of the electric light (1915):

> It is true that Edison never went to college, but he knows more about the subjects taught in college than most college men. He is essentially a practical man in the sense that whatever he undertakes, he wishes to know whether, and how, it would be of use and benefit to mankind, but at the same time he is apparently interested and familiar with almost any field of human knowledge. Whether you talk with him about electrical engineering or other engineering, organic chemistry or anthropology or any other subject, you always find him fully familiar with the subject and able to give you valuable hints solving your difficulties as I have found more than once during the various times I have had the pleasure to meet him, and that even in the highly theoretical aspects of the subject. . . . From my experience I consider Edison today as the man best informed in all fields of human knowledge.

INDEX

373